RESOURCE MASTER BOOK

MERRILL

living systems

RAYMOND F. ORAM
The Peddie School
Hightstown, NJ

ALBERT KASKEL
Evanston Township High School
Evanston, IL

MERRILL
PUBLISHING COMPANY
A Bell & Howell Information Company
Columbus, Ohio
Toronto • London • Sydney

MERRILL SCIENCE PROGRAM

BIOLOGY: Living Systems, Student Edition
BIOLOGY: Living Systems, Teacher Annotated Edition
BIOLOGY: Living Systems, Teacher Resource Package
Evaluation Program
Reading and Study Guide, Teacher Edition
Resource Master Book
BIOLOGY: Living Systems, Reading and Study Guide, Student Edition
Laboratory Biology: Investigating Living Systems, Student Edition and Teacher Annotated Edition
Probing Levels of Life: A Laboratory Manual, Student Edition and Teacher Annotated Edition
BIOLOGY: Living Systems, Transparency Package
BIOLOGY: Living Systems, Computer Test Bank

To The Teacher

The ***Resource Master Book for BIOLOGY: Living Systems*** is a unique, time-saving device designed to aid you in all phases of biology instruction. It provides effective tools for reinforcing science skills, developing laboratory skills, teaching content, and evaluating student performance.

The loose-leaf binder format of the *Resource Master Book* offers flexibility and convenient access to all material. The teacher guide provides many resources for planning and teaching the material found in the *Resource Master Book.* A comprehensive program planning guide correlates, chapter-by-chapter, all components of the ***BIOLOGY: Living Systems*** program. Ideas and suggestions are provided for using the student masters, investigation worksheet masters, and teaching masters.

The remainder of the *Resource Master Book* is organized and tabbed to follow the text chapter by chapter. Each chapter includes a planning guide that correlates all program components for that chapter. Also included for each chapter are student masters, investigation worksheet masters, and teaching masters. Answers for these pages are provided at the end of the book.

Project Editor: Carla J. Weiland; *Editor:* Linda Biggs Thornhill; *Cover Design:* Barton D. Hawkinberry; *Illustrators:* Nancy A. Heim, Jeanine S. Means, Don Robison; *Production Editors:* Kimberly Munsie, Janet B. Arledge

ISBN 0-675-06492-9

Published by
Merrill Publishing Company
A Bell & Howell Company
Columbus, Ohio 43216

Printed in the United States of America

Table of Contents

Teacher Guide

Chapter Resource Masters

Planning Guides

BIOLOGY: Living Systems is organized to present the study of biology from simple levels of organization to complex levels. Basic chemistry, cell biology, and genetics precede information about organisms, populations, communities, and ecosystems. This logical organization also is flexible to meet your planning requirements. You are in the best position to design a biology course that satisfies your students' needs. The planning guides provided in this *Resource Master Book* can assist you with both long-range and daily planning and with designing the best possible biology program.

Planning the Program

The ***BIOLOGY: Living Systems*** program provides a total package of student materials and teacher aids. Student materials in various formats incorporate a wide variety of learning experiences including laboratory activities and review and reinforcement exercises. Time-saving teacher aids help you to (1) plan and implement the learning options you have chosen, (2) evaluate student performance, and (3) diagnose student weaknesses.

The ***BIOLOGY: Living Systems*** program is also highly adaptable to meet the needs of students with different performance abilities. There are often many levels of performance within a single class or among several classes. The *Teacher Annotated Edition* and supplementary materials offer many alternatives to you in planning for several ability levels.

In addition to the student's text and the *Teacher Annotated Edition*, the following supplementary materials are available.

The Teacher Resource Package for ***Biology: Living Systems*** contains three unique, time-saving ancillaries designed to aid you in all phases of biology instruction. The *Reading and Study Guide, Teacher Edition* has over 210 pages of masters to develop text concepts and vocabulary. The *Resource Master Book* includes teaching masters and investigation worksheets that reproduce the text investigation data chart and questions. Also included for each chapter are two student masters to reinforce critical thinking, science skills, and concept development and application. The third component of the package, the *Evaluation Program* is a complete testing program designed to be a teaching as well as an evaluating tool in the classroom. The program is composed of one four-page test to go with each chapter of ***Biology: Living Systems.*** The questions and problems are of varying difficulty to focus on different levels of learning. An alternate test for part B of each chapter test is included so that you can construct alternate forms of each test.

A *Reading and Study Guide* provides students with six worksheets for each chapter. The worksheets reinforce vocabulary, develop and apply concepts, and analyze data.

Laboratory Biology: Investigating Living Systems combines basic biological processes and concepts with successful laboratory experiences. You can select from over 80 laboratory investigations (2 or 3 per text chapter) to best meet your classroom needs.

Laboratory Biology: Investigating Living Systems is a completely self-contained laboratory manual. All observations, data, and answers are recorded in the spaces provided in the manual. No extra laboratory notebook is required.

Among the features that make this laboratory program a useful tool are the following.

1. The investigations are readable. Procedural steps are short and simple.

2. The self-pacing format facilitates individualized learning.

3. Many illustrations are used, accurately showing procedural steps.

4. Many investigations use models and simulations.

5. Behavioral objectives are included in each investigation.

6. Three aspects of scientific literacy are developed.

Most of the investigations require simple, inexpensive equipment. Only about one-third require living or preserved specimens. All paper models needed for investigations are included in the teacher edition for reproduction in proper quantities.

Probing Levels of Life: A Laboratory Manual includes over 80 investigations (2 or 3 per text chapter) in a teacher-directed, student-involved format.

While using *Probing Levels of Life: A Laboratory Manual,* students learn firsthand the value of making accurate observations and of recording data to arrive at valid conclusions. All laboratory records—observations, data graphs, diagrams, answers, conclusions—are to be kept in a separate, student-supplied notebook. With some assistance and supervision, students can become actively involved in understanding biological principles and concepts.

Among the teaching and learning features of this laboratory manual are the following.

1. Clear and concise step-by-step directions are in paragraph form.

2. Collection of data is stressed.

3. Illustrations are used extensively, showing procedural steps and specimens.

4. Some investigations use models and simulations. Living organisms are used extensively.

5. Behavioral objectives are included in each investigation.

6. Three aspects of scientific literacy are developed.

The time needed to complete most of the investigations is one laboratory period. Some investigations, however, involve daily or weekly observations. Also, some investigations have been designed to take students outside the school to investigate organisms in their environments.

Planning the Chapter

For your convenience, a Chapter Planning Guide is located at the front of each chapter in this *Resource Master Book*. The chart locates and identifies the activities, exercises, and teacher aids that are available for each chapter. The Chapter Planning Guides will aid you in determining exactly which activities and exercises will best meet your classroom needs.

Using The Masters

Three different types of masters for each chapter of ***BIOLOGY: Living Systems*** are provided in this *Resource Master Book.* Each master may be reproduced by photocopying or by producing a spirit-duplicating master. In addition, the teaching masters are designed to be reproduced as transparencies. In this section, each type of master is described so you will be better able to choose those that meet your classroom needs.

Student Masters

Included for each chapter are two student masters to reinforce critical thinking, science skills, or concept development and application. These masters can be used as adjuncts to the text in several ways. Students who desire an additional challenge can read and report on various topics covered in the student masters. These projects can be assigned individually or to small groups. Many of the student masters present topics that lend themselves to open discussions, while some masters are designed to reinforce basic concepts. Each master begins with a presentation of a topic, which is followed by a set of questions. The questions may be used for reinforcement or as springboards for class discussion. Many of the questions have no right or wrong answers, but encourage students to think about certain ideas. The three types of student masters—skills, essay, and critical thinking—are discussed below.

The skills masters are designed to reinforce concepts presented in the text. For example, student master 9–1, *The Genetic Code,* discusses the structure of DNA in further detail and tests students' understanding of protein synthesis. Other masters cover ideas such as atomic structure (student master 3–1) and the use of keys to identify unknown organisms (student master 12–1).

The essay masters cover recent trends in biological research and are designed to enhance a student's appreciation of some of the exciting discoveries being made in biology. The essay masters offer a balance between current events in theoretical biology and those in applied biology. For example, student master 26–1, *Cyclosporine and Transplants,* discusses some of the recent research into how cyclosporine suppresses the immune system and the application of that research in transplant surgery. Student master 33–1, *Living Together—Amensalism,* talks about a subject that promises to unlock some of the mysteries surrounding biological communities.

The critical thinking masters extend concepts presented in the text, sometimes concentrating on questions with difficult answers. These masters may be used to enhance students' awareness of some of the puzzling questions facing biologists, and, in many cases, people like themselves. For example, student master 17–2, *Polio Vaccine—Dead or Alive?* discusses the pros and cons of the Salk and Sabin polio vaccines. The reintroduction of wolves into Yellowstone National Park and the possible consequences to other park wildlife, park visitors, local ranchers, and to the wolves themselves are highlighted in student master 32–2.

Investigation Worksheets

The investigation worksheets in this *Resource Master Book* reproduce the data and observations and questions and conclusion sections in the text investigations. The worksheets can be reproduced and handed out for students to fill in as they complete the investigations. Filling in the data charts gives students practice in organizing information. Answering the questions and conclusion reinforces concepts learned during the investigation.

Teaching Masters

Teaching masters are provided for each chapter. For an example, see page 1–4. These masters may be reproduced as transparencies for use with an overhead projector or as student study guides. You may wish to reproduce each master as both transparency and study sheet for in-class use. The use of each master in relation to the text section it accompanies is described below. Teaching tips, explanatory notes, and extensions for the masters are included in these paragraphs.

CHAPTER 1: Teaching Masters 1–1 and 1–2, *Movement of Materials* and *Movement of Energy Through a Community,* may be used together to illustrate the material presented in text Section 1:4. Students should understand that the movement of energy and materials influences the number of organisms present in a community as well as the complexity of the community. As energy and materials flow through a community simultaneously in organic matter, materials are recycled. However, energy is not recycled as it moves through the community. Students might think of energy "paying" for the continuous "round trip" of materials through a community.

CHAPTER 2: Teaching Master 2–1, *Parts of the Microscope,* provides diagrams of two widely-used student microscopes. If the microscopes available to you are different, you will need to modify the master. Teaching Master 2–2, *Measuring Mass,* reproduces some typical scales found on a balance. It can be used for drill by having students read measurements that you mark on the transparency. You may also want to use this master as a quick review for laboratory activities that require mass measurements.

CHAPTER 3: Teaching Master 3–1, *Formulas of Organic Compounds,* can be used to illustrate the material in Section 3:11. Relate the properties of organic compounds to the number and types of atoms in the compound and the pattern or structure in which the atoms are bonded. Teaching Master 3–1 will aid students in understanding how these compounds are named and what the names mean.

CHAPTER 4: Teaching Masters 4–1, *Plant Cell,* and 4–2, *Animal Cell,* present idealized diagrams of plant and animal cell structures. You may want to caution students that they are unlikely to see all of these structures at one time with a light microscope. Some students may find it helpful to construct a table of cell parts and their functions on a separate sheet of paper.

CHAPTER 5: For your convenience, the reactions involved as the energy of glucose is changed to ATP during aerobic respiration are reproduced on Teaching Master 5–1, *Aerobic Respiration Cycle.* Refer students to Appendix C on page 769. Relate the details of aerobic respiration, which occurs in four major stages, to the general purpose of ATP production.

CHAPTER 6: For your convenience, text Figure 6–12, *Stages of Mitosis,* has been reproduced as Teaching Master 6–1. Remind students that mitosis is a process that guarantees genetic continuity. Be sure that students can name the stages and follow the movement of chromosomes through each stage. Use Teaching Master 6–2, *Stages of Meiosis,* to illustrate the information in text Sections 6:7 through 6:9. Have students compare and contrast meiosis in males and females. Be sure that students understand the importance of meiosis in the life cycles of organisms.

CHAPTER 7: The Teaching Masters 7–1 and 7–2, *Punnett Squares I* and *Punnett Squares II,* may be used to illustrate simple genetic crosses. You may wish to begin by demonstrating the genetic crosses of peas, guinea pigs, and flowers described in Chapter 7. Be sure students understand that Punnett squares show the possible ways genes combine when passed from parents to offspring. Each box of a Punnett square shows a possible gene combination that an offspring might receive. Remind students that percentages shown by a Punnett square hold true only when there are large numbers of offspring. With very small numbers of offspring, any proportion could occur.

CHAPTER 8: Teaching Master 8–1, *Sex-linked Traits,* is designed to aid students in understanding and working with the concept of sex-linkage. Be sure that students understand that the traits represented by the genes have nothing to do with maleness or femaleness, but that these genes just happen to be located on sex chromosomes. Students should note that a male can have only one gene for each trait, and therefore, can never be heterozygous for a sex-linked trait. If necessary, review material from Chapter 7 to refresh students on genetic crosses, hybrids, and the use of Punnett squares.

CHAPTER 9: Use Teaching Master 9–1, *Replication of DNA,* to illustrate the material in text Section 9:3. Emphasize that exact duplication of a DNA molecule involves specific base pairing. Adenine always pairs with thymine, guanine always pairs with cytosine. The result of this replication process is two DNA molecules exactly like the original molecule.

CHAPTER 10: By using fossils, radiometric dating, and other techniques, scientists have been able to divide Earth's history into units called the *Geologic Time Scale.* This time scale has been reproduced as Teaching Master 10–1. All geologic time up to 500 million years before the present is called Precambrian. Few fossils of this age have been found. The time between the Precambrian and the present has been divided into three eras. These eras have been subdivided into periods and epochs based on fossil evidence. As an extension, some students may be interested in researching the life of past geologic periods, or the changes that occurred over time to a single organism such as the horse.

CHAPTER 11: Teaching Master 11–1, *Human Origins,* illustrates and ties together Sections 11:10–11:12. Comparison of skull shapes of human ancestors and the times at which each was a dominant species may be easily made.

CHAPTER 12: Teaching Master 12–1, *Classification of Organisms,* demonstrates the format of the biological classification system. Note that as you move from left to right, the organism classified in each successive column differs from the previous one by one more level of classification. Emphasize that if two animals are closely related, they will be classified the same at almost all levels. Remind students that the scientific name of an organism consists of both genus and species names. As an extension, some students may be interested in researching the Latin words used in classifying a particular organism to see how they build into a description of that organism.

CHAPTER 13: Teaching Master 13–1, *Comparing Fungi,* may be used as either an introduction to Sections 13:13, 13:14, and 13:15, or as a review of these sections. If possible, display this master while specimens of the fungi are available for student examination. Emphasize the actual difference in size of these organisms. The bread mold is shown magnified at about 100×, the yeasts at about 1000×.

CHAPTER 14: The external structures of two major angiosperm organs are illustrated on Teaching Master 14–1, *Physical Features of Leaves.* Used in conjunction with Teaching Master 14–2, *External Structures of Stems and Leaves,* students can become familiar with the major structures and features used to identify angiosperms in the field. You may wish to have a collection of leaves and stems available for students to compare. Field references such as *Trees of North America* by Frank Brockman may also be helpful.

CHAPTER 15: Representative organisms from phyla Coelenterata, Mollusca, and Annelida are shown on Teaching Masters 15–1, 15–2, and 15–3. *Annelid Anatomy: Earthworm, Mollusk Anatomy: Clam and Snail* and *Coelenterate Anatomy: Hydra* may be used as general diagrams for identification and comparison of structures or as guides for dissection. With some modification, each master could be used for student evaluation by having students identify structures under testing conditions.

CHAPTER 16: The five teaching masters included in this chapter may be used as general diagrams for identification and comparison of structures among phyla or as guides for dissection. Representative organisms from the phyla presented in Chapter 16 are included on Teaching Masters 16–1, *Arthropod Anatomy: Crayfish;* 16–2, *Vertebrate Anatomy: Fish;* 16–3, *Arthropod Anatomy: Grasshopper;* 16–4, *Echinoderm Anatomy: Starfish;* and 16–5, *Vertebrate Anatomy: Rat.* These masters may also be used for student evaluation with some modification.

CHAPTER 17: For your convenience, text Figure 17–9 has been reproduced on Teaching Master 17–1, *Bacteriophage Life Cycles.* Project this master as you discuss Section 17:7. Be sure students can differentiate between the lysogenic cycle and the lytic cycle.

CHAPTER 18: The structure of an *Euglena* is provided for you on Teaching Master 18–1, *Structures of Euglena.* Use this master to illustrate the structures discussed throughout Chapter 18. This master may also be useful during laboratory activities in which this organism is observed or discussed.

CHAPTER 19: Teaching Master 19–1, *Life Cycle of Plasmodium malariae,* illustrates an example of the parasitic lifestyle of a protist that can cause human disease.

CHAPTER 20: Teaching Master 20–1, *Parts of a Flower,* can be used with Section 20:6 to illustrate flower structures. When used in conjunction with Teaching Master 20–2, *Life Cycle of Flowering Plants,* the master should aid students in identifying and differentiating between male and female organs and the structures produced in these organs. Teaching Master 20–2 also can be used to summarize the information in text Sections 20:7 and 20:8.

CHAPTER 21: Teaching Master 21–1, *Leaf Structure,* provides both surface and cross-sectional views of a typical leaf. You may want to set up microscopes with wet mounts of leaf sections or pieces of epidermis so students can view the actual structures being discussed. Point out the guard cells and discuss how they open and close the stomate. Discuss the conditions that cause the stomate to be open or closed. You may wish to add information from Section 21:1 to the master describing the materials that pass into and out of leaves during photosynthesis and respiration.

CHAPTER 22: For your convenience, cross sections of monocot and dicot roots and stems have been reproduced as Teaching Masters 22–1, *Roots,* and 22–2, *Stems.* Students should compare and contrast monocot and dicot structures and should be able to differentiate between the two types of plants. Students should also be able to identify all structures on monocot and dicot stems and roots. It may be helpful to have cross sections available for microscopic examination while discussing these organs.

CHAPTER 23: Figures 23–9 and 23–10 of the text have been reproduced as Teaching Master 23–1, *Human Reproductive Systems.* The master is designed as a summary of Section 23:6 of the text. Students should be able to locate and identify the various organs involved in the reproductive system. The location of the testes, an adaptation for temperature control, may be discussed. Students should note the relationship of the reproductive and excretory organs of both males and females.

CHAPTER 24: Teaching Master 24–1, *Insect Metamorphosis,* shows examples of both incomplete metamorphosis and complete metamorphosis. Students should be able to compare the stages that occur in each type.

Teaching Master 24–2, *Frog Egg Development,* may be used to illustrate the early stages of the development of a frog zygote. Development begins with a series of cell divisions called cleavage. Students should note that the cells in the animal pole divide more rapidly than those in the vegetal pole. These cell divisions result in the formation of the hollow blastula. Rearrangement of the cells of the blastula is called gastrulation. This series of changes results in the formation of three tissue layers. After gastrulation is complete, changes that result in the formation of different body parts begin. These changes are called differentiation. Formation of the neural tube, one of the earliest events of differentiation, is illustrated on Teaching Master 24–2.

CHAPTER 25: Teaching Master 25–1, *Digestion of Carbohydrates,* illustrates the steps involved in this process. This master may be used as a general overview of text Sections 25:8–25:12. Students should be able to identify the organs involved in the digestive system as well as glands that secrete digestive juices and hormones. Students should also understand the importance and function of enzymes in digestion.

CHAPTER 26: Use Teaching Master 26–1, *Comparing Circulatory Systems,* to compare the circulatory systems of different types of animals. Compare the hearts of these animals to the human heart on Teaching Master 26–2, *Circulation of the Blood.* Students should be able to trace the flow of blood through the heart and circulatory system. Review the names and functions of all structures in the heart and circulatory system.

CHAPTER 27: Teaching Master 27–1 shows the major organs of the *Human Respiratory System.* Have students compare this system with tracheal and gill systems of other animals. Emphasize that all systems provide a moist area where gas exchange may be accomplished.

Human excretory organs are diagrammed on Teaching Master 27–2, *Excretory Organs.* Students should be able to identify each structure as well as describe its function. Use the chart at the bottom of the master to summarize the information in Section 27:10.

CHAPTER 28: Teaching Master 28–1, *The Endocrine System,* can be used to best advantage as a review of Chapter 28. Students should be able to locate and identify each gland, as well as describe its function. Discuss the location and function of the male testes as well as the female ovaries.

CHAPTER 29: Use Teaching Master 29–1, *The Nervous System,* as a review or as a study guide. Students should be able to describe the function of each structure of the nervous system and trace the path of a nerve impulse.

CHAPTER 30: Use Teaching Master 30–1, *Bone and Joint Structure,* as a review of text Sections 30:4 and 30:5. Have students identify the structures and functions of both bones and joints.

CHAPTER 31: The honeybee is one type of animal that communicates with others of its kind. In the round dance, one bee communicates the presence of a food source within 100 meters of the hive. A waggle dance describes the direction of a food source as well as its distance from the hive. These dances are illustrated on Teaching Master 31–1, *Honeybee Communication.* Have students discuss how bees learn these dances, and the methods other animals use to communicate.

Teaching Master 31–2, *Routes of Long-Distance Migrants,* illustrates the thousands of miles over which some organisms travel. Emphasize to students that migrating birds are joined by other animals such as caribou, salmon, monarch butterflies, whales, and green turtles. The general path of each animal shown on the master is represented by a symbol. Blackpoll warblers begin their trek in Alaska and travel across the Atlantic Ocean to South America. European eels make a 2½-year journey from North America to Europe. Golden plovers fly over both the Atlantic and the Pacific Oceans. Some Atlantic subspecies of the plover may fly a 25 000 kilometer loop. White storks travel from middle Europe to South Africa. Green turtles migrate from Brazil to breeding grounds on a tiny island 2400 kilometers to the east. Humpback whales in both the Arctic and Antarctic swim to breeding grounds in equatorial areas and then return to the original feeding grounds.

CHAPTER 32: Teaching Master 32–1, *Population Growth,* is designed to allow students to see past trends in population growth and explore implications of continuing the present growth rate. You may want to ask students to suggest reasons for the growth curve beginning about 1930. For dramatic effect, extend the curve to the year 2050. You will need to add an extension to the graph. Students might consider that, given current trends in life expectancy, most of them will be alive in the year 2050.

CHAPTER 33: Teaching Master 33–1, *Food Chains,* is designed to clarify the food and energy relationships found in communities and ecosystems. Be sure students can identify producers and consumers. Reinforce the idea that all producers are plants or plantlike organisms. Food chains must always start with photosynthetic organisms. Use the bottom part of the master to reinforce the concept of energy transfer through a food chain.

CHAPTER 34: Use Teaching Master 34–1, *Mean Annual Precipitation,* in conjunction with the sections describing biomes. Have students compare the precipitation map with Figure 34–5. Students should see a definite correlation between the amount of rainfall and the type of biome.

CHAPTER 35: Teaching Master 35–1, *Acid Rain,* is designed to supplement the information given in text Section 35:6. Have students speculate as to why the acidity of rain is more severe in some areas of the country than in others. Discuss possible solutions to the acid rain problem.

Teaching Master 35–2, *Major Energy Resources,* summarizes the major sources of energy available to humans now and in the near future. Discuss energy conservation and alternative energy resources.

INVESTIGATION 10. RNA NITROGEN BASE SEQUENCES

COMPARISON OF RNA NITROGEN BASE SEQUENCES AMONG FIFTEEN ORGANISMS

RNA NITROGEN BASE SEQUENCE	ORGANISMS WITH THIS BASE SEQUENCE	RNA NITROGEN BASE SEQUENCE	ORGANISMS WITH THIS BASE SEQUENCE
CCCCAG	7,8,9,10	UCCUAG	1,2,3
CCCAAG	8,10,15	UUCCAG	1,2,3,4,5,6,7,8
CAACCG	12,13	CCUAUG	4,10
ACCACG	11,12,13	CUACUG	1,2,3,4,8,9
ACACCG	8,11,12,13,15	UCACUG	4,10,11,12,13,14
AAACCG	12,13,15	CUAUCG	11,12,13,14,15
CCACAG	14	UCAUCG	11,13
AAAACG	14	CAUCUG	11
CCCACG	9,10	ACUCUG	11,12
CCCUCG	5,6,12,15	ACCUUG	5,6,7,8,9,10,14
CCUCAG	5,6	AUCCUG	1,2,3,4,5,6,7,8,11,12,13,14,15
CUCCAG	5,6	UCUAAG	11,12,14
UCCCAG	3,11,12,13,14,15	UUACAG	12
CCACUG	5,6,7,13	UAUCAG	13
ACCUCG	13	UAUACG	11
CCUAAG	1,2,3,4,5,6,15	UAAUCG	1,2,3,4,5,6,7,8,9,10,11,12,13,14,15
CUCAAG	5,6,7,8	AUACUG	4,9,10,11,12,14,15
CCAUAG	7,14	ACAUUG	1,2
CAUACG	1,2	AACUUG	4
ACACUG	5,6,7,11,12,13,14	AAUCUG	5,6,8,11,12,13,14
AACCUG	1,2,3,4,5,6,7,8,9,10,15	UAAAUG	7
AAUCCG	9,10,11,13,14,15	AUUAAG	1,2,3,4,5,6,7,8,11,12,14
CUAAAG	11,12,13,14	AAUAUG	13
UAAACG	1,2,3,4,5,6,7,8,12,13,15	UUACCG	14
ACUAAG	9,10,13	CUCAUG	9
ACAAUG	1,2,3,4,5,6,7,8,9,10,11,12,13,14,15	CACUUG	9,10
AUAACG	15	CAUAUG	9,10
AAUACG	1,2,3,4,5,6,7,8,15	CCUUCG	10
AACAUG	15	CCUUUG	1,2,3,5,6,9
AAACUG	1,2,3,4,5,6,7,8,9,10,11,12,13,14,15	CUUUCG	15
AAAUCG	1,2,3,4,11	UCUCUG	1,2,3,5,6,7,8
AAUAAG	1,2,3,5,6,7,8,9,10,14	UUCCUG	5,6
CCCUAG	2	UCUUAG	5,6
UACACG	14	CUAUUG	1,2,3,4,7,8,9,10
CCUACG	9,10	UUACUG	15
CCAUCG	9,10	UAUUCG	4
AUCCCG	9,10	AUUCUG	3,12,13,15
AACUAG	9,10	ACUUUG	3
CCCUUG	8,15	UAUAUG	12
CCUCUG	11,12,13,14	UCCUUG	10
UCCCUG	1,2,3,4,5,6,7,8,9,10,11,12,13,14,15	UCUAUG	10
CCUUAG	7,11,12	CUUUUG	1,2,3,4,5,6,7
CUCUAG	1,2,3,4	UCUUUG	2,7
CUUCAG	13	UUUUUG	11

INVESTIGATION 11. DIAGRAM A

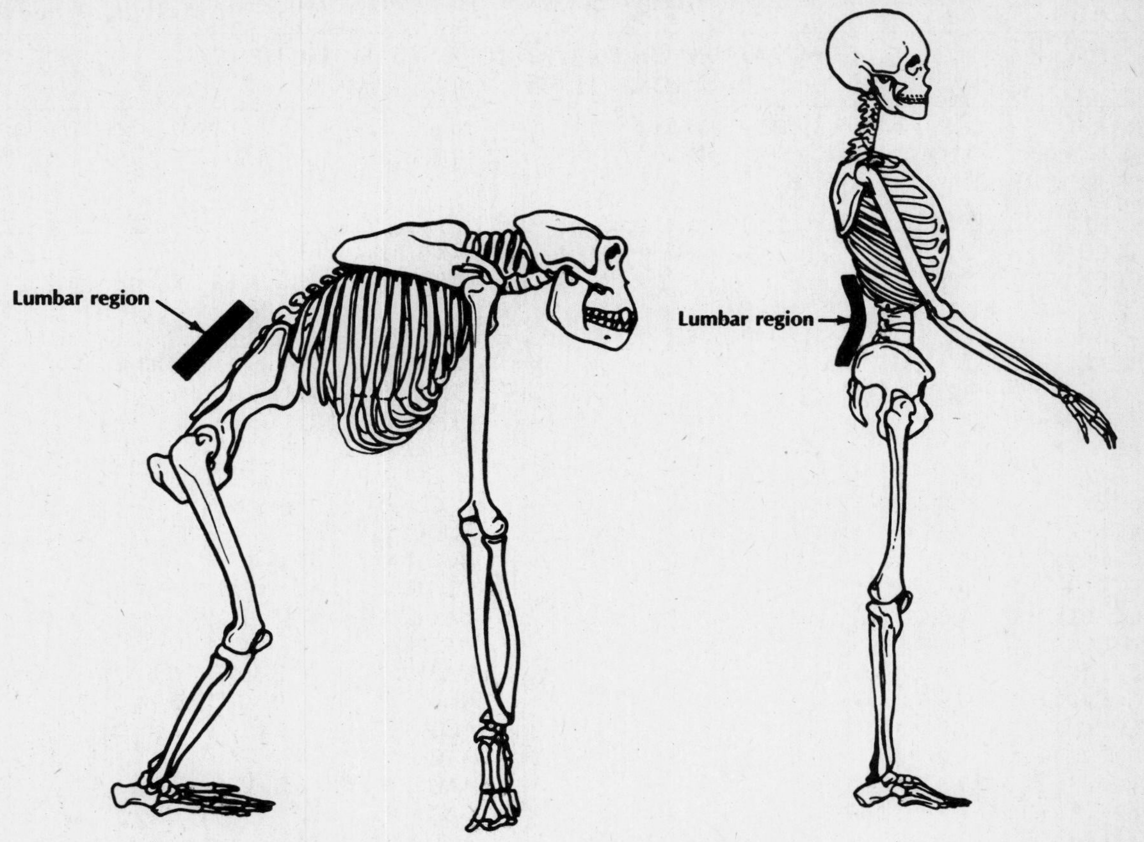

INVESTIGATION 11. DIAGRAM C

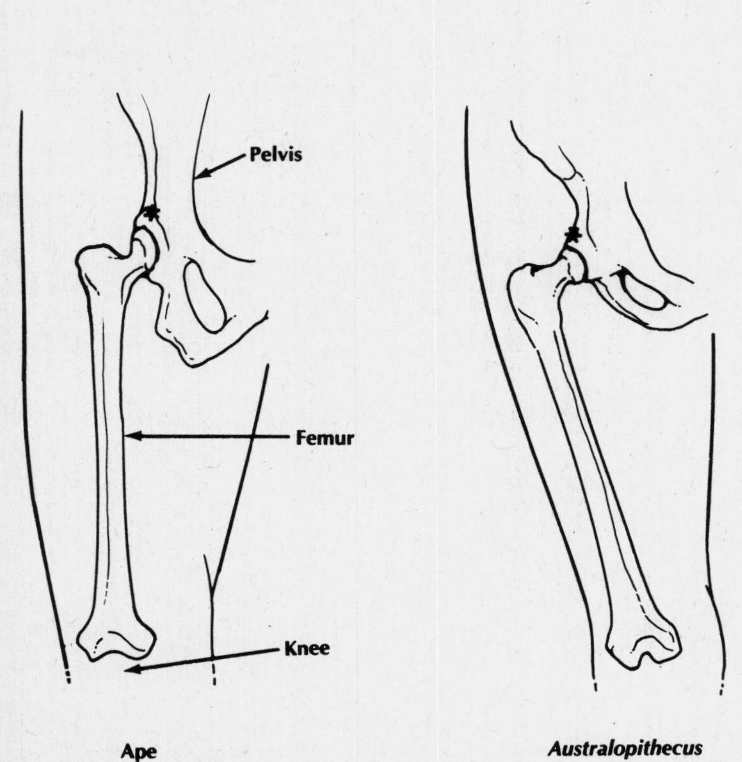

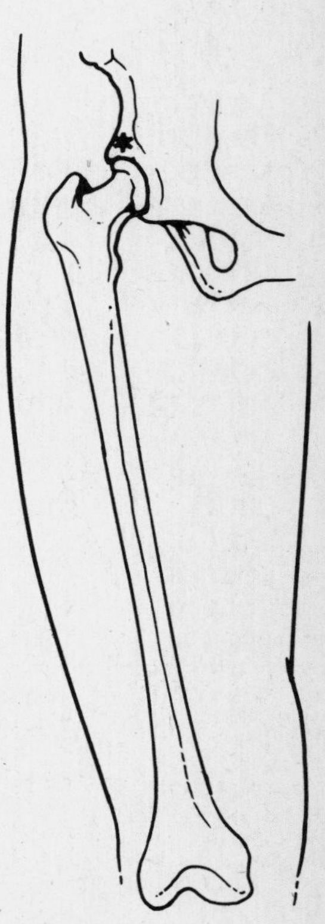

INVESTIGATION 11. DIAGRAM B

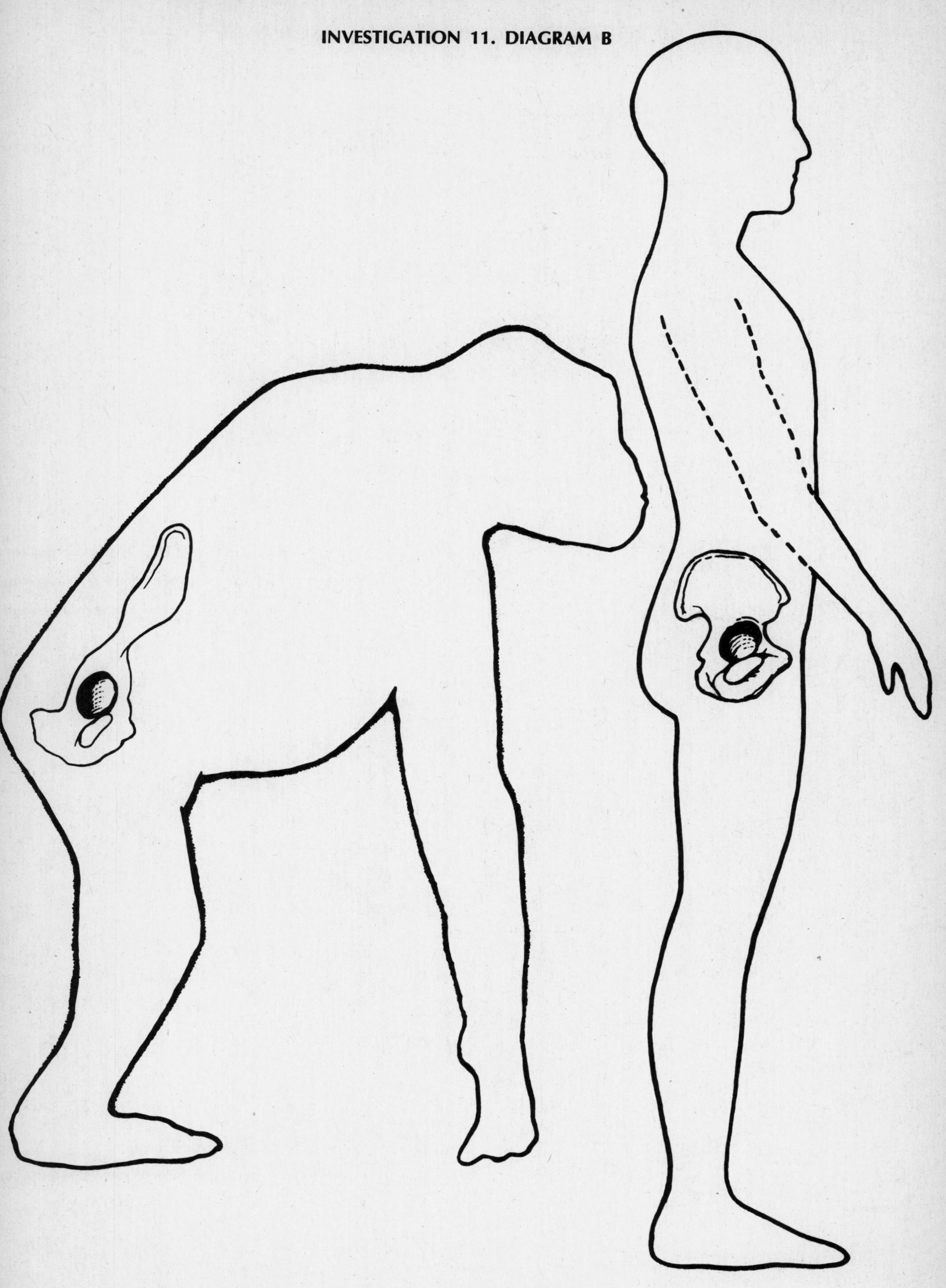

INVESTIGATION 16. POISONOUS SNAKE RANGES

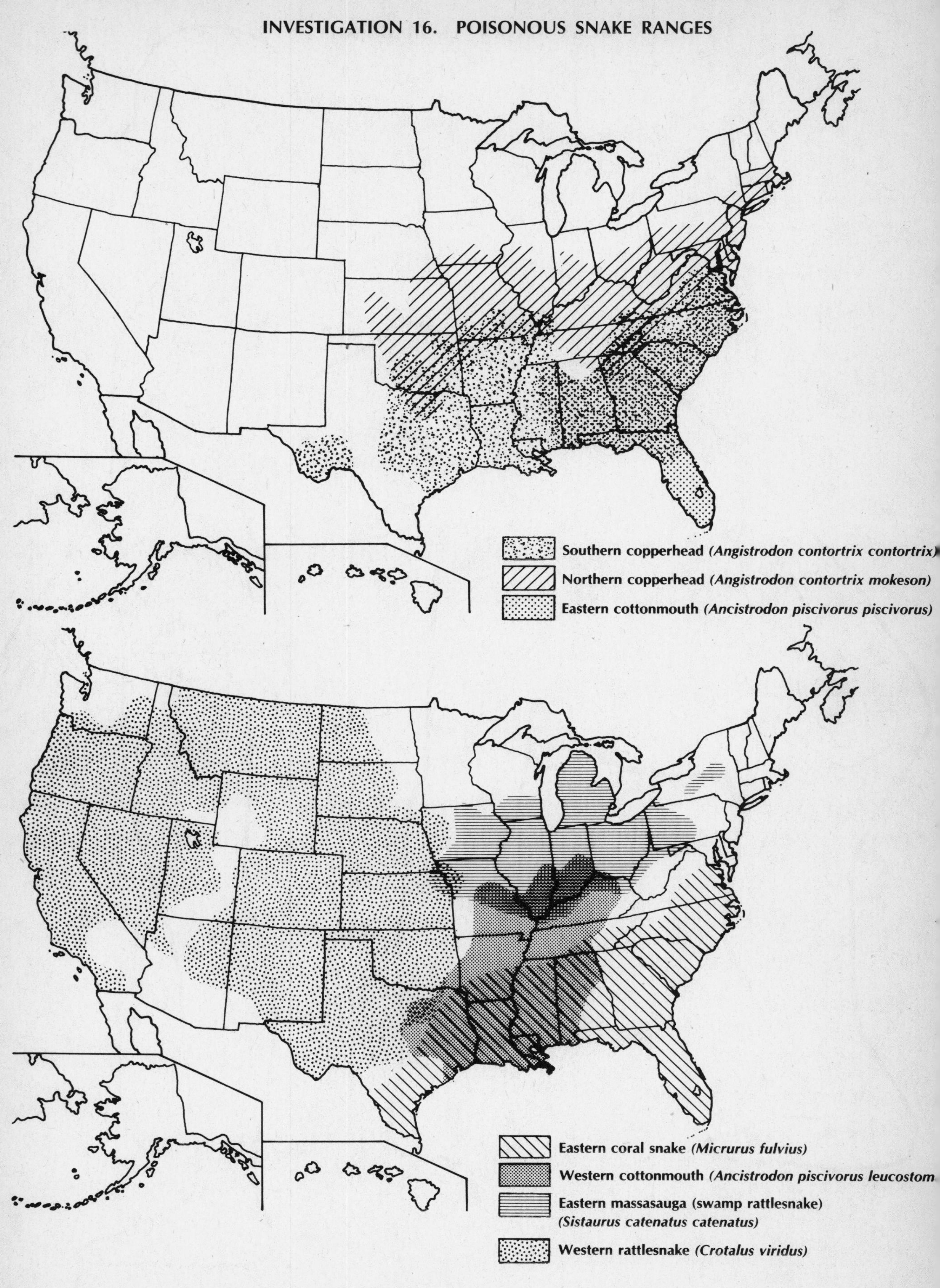

INVESTIGATION 23. REPRODUCTION IN *OBELIA*

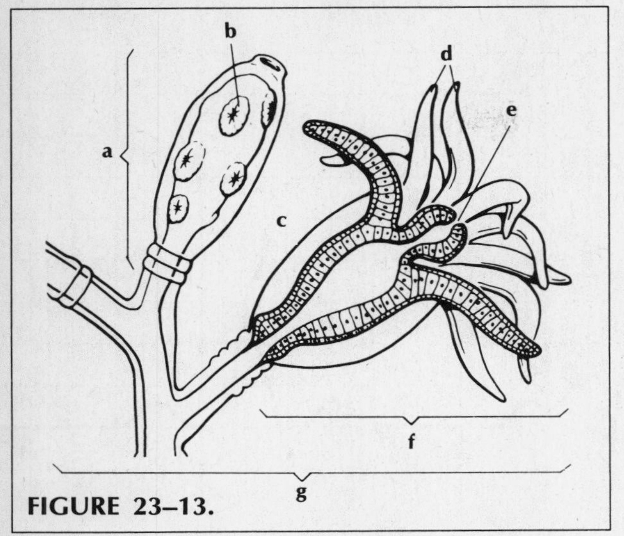

FIGURE 23–13.

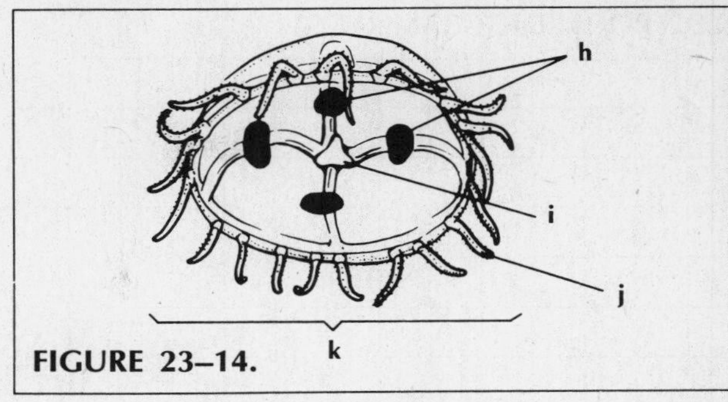

FIGURE 23–14.

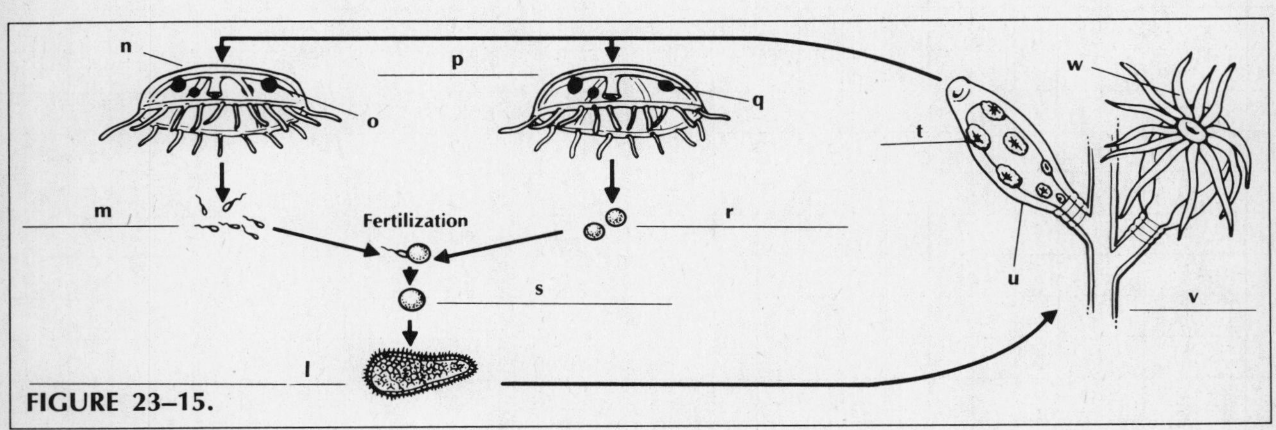

FIGURE 23–15.

INVESTIGATION 30. MUSCLE CONTRACTION

FIGURE 30–21.

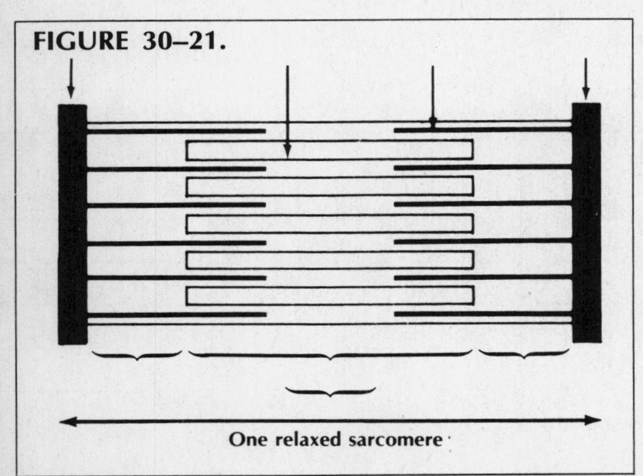

FIGURE 30–22.

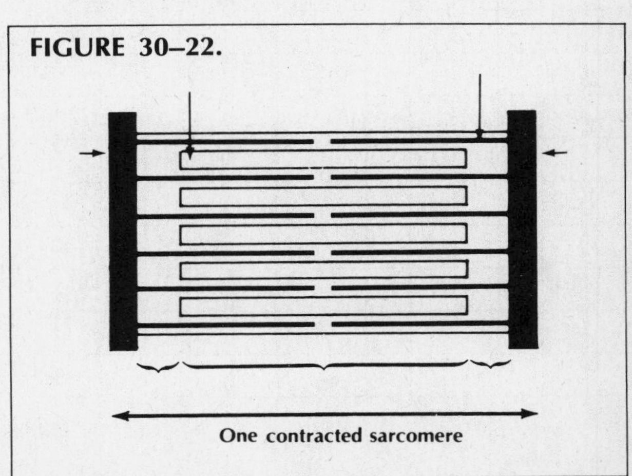

INVESTIGATION 26. ELECTROCARDIOGRAMS

FIGURE 26 A.
ELECTROCARDIOGRAM (ECG)

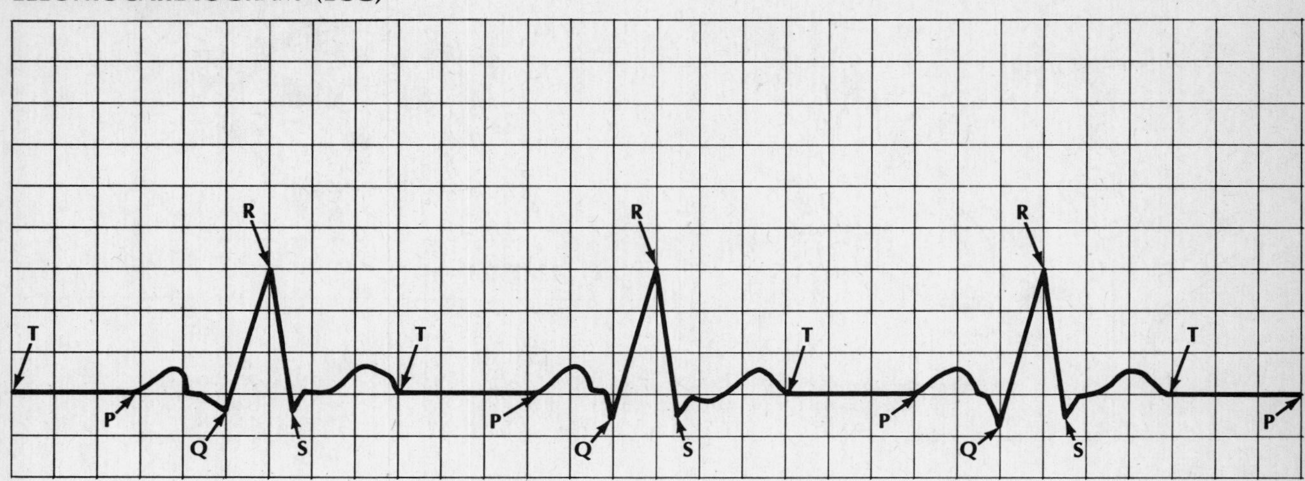

Each vertical line represents 0.1 seconds

FIGURE 26 B.
ECG OF HEART AT REST

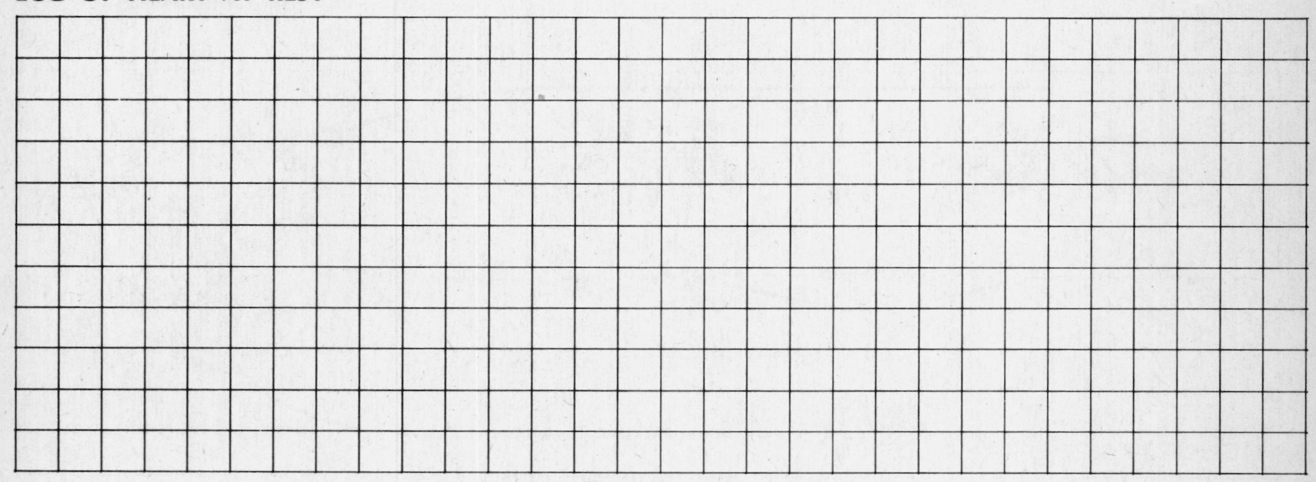

Each vertical line represents 0.1 seconds

FIGURE 26 C.
ECG OF HEART AT WORK

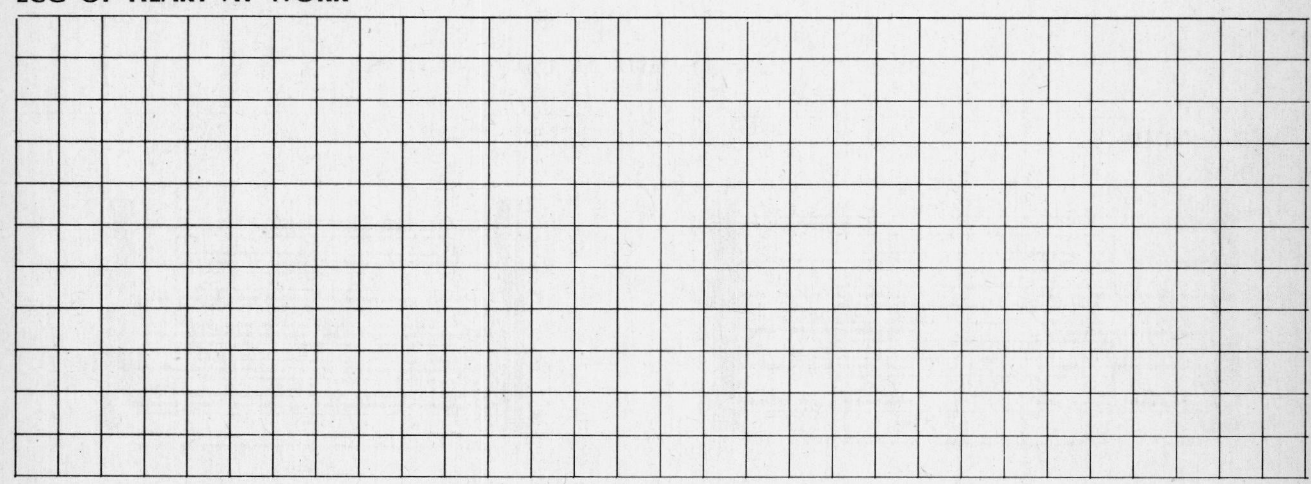

Each vertical line represents 0.1 seconds

INVESTIGATION 28. PICTOGRAPHS

Role of Calcitonin

a

Calcium is taken into the body through diet of foods such as

________________.

b

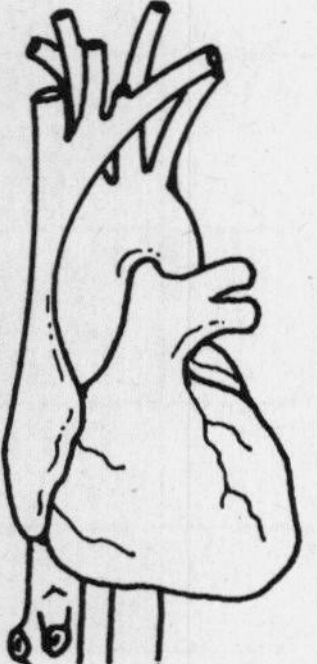

Concentration of calcium in

____

is ________________.

c

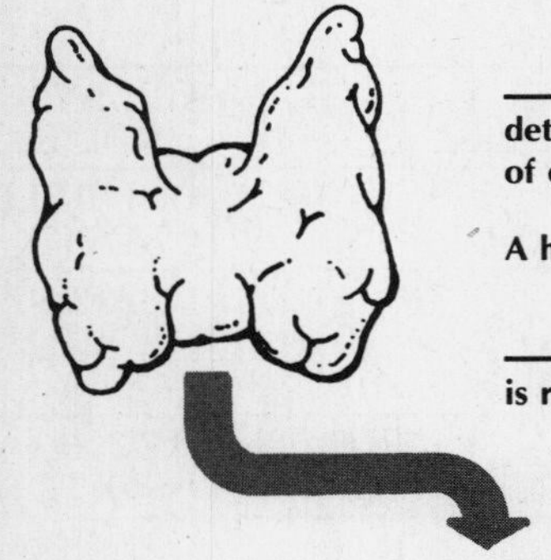

____

detects this amount of calcium.

A hormone called

____

is released.

d

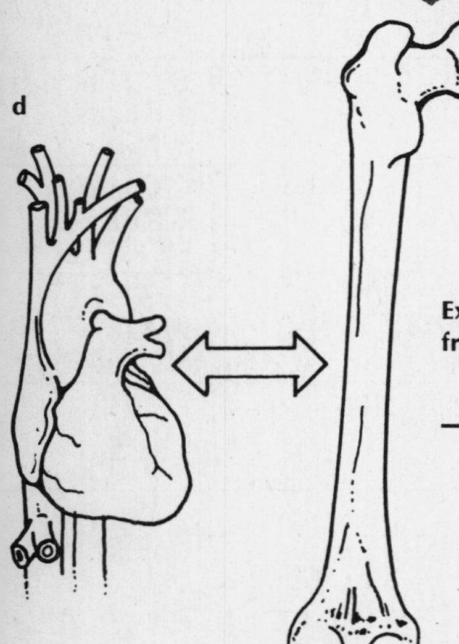

Excess calcium is removed from blood and stored in

________________.

Role of Parathormone

e

Calcium is not taken into the body through diet.

f

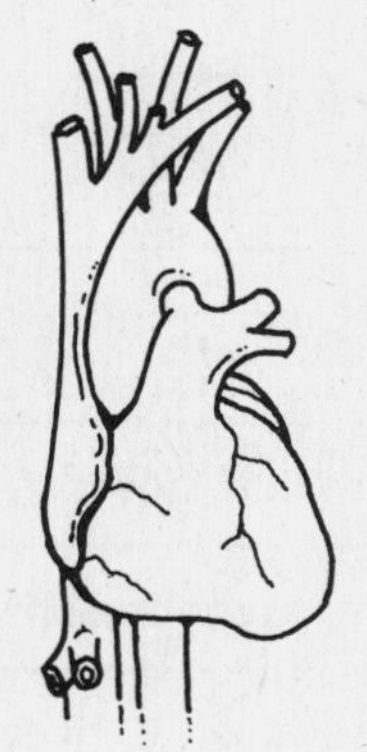

Concentration of calcium

in ________________

is ________________.

g

____

detect this amount of calcium.

A hormone called

____

is released.

h

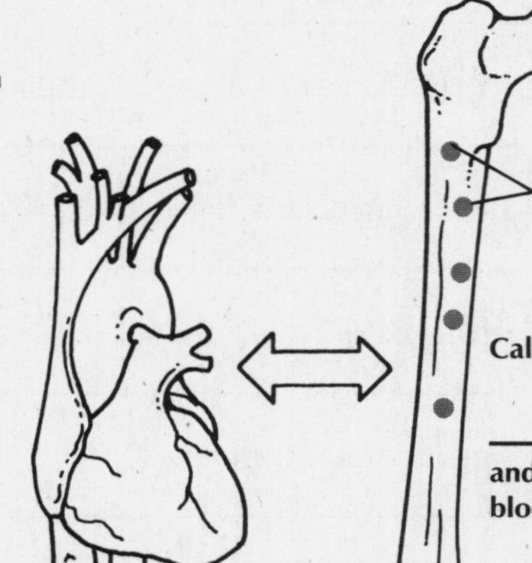

Calcium is removed from

____

and enters the bloodstream.

INVESTIGATION 29. BRAIN FUNCTIONS

FUNCTION	BRAIN SIDE	LOCATION	COLOR
a. Movement of right leg and right side of body	left	M–2 O–1,2 N–1,2	RED, SOLID
b. Movement of left leg and left side of body	right	M–2 O–1,2 N–1,2	RED, STRIPE
c. Movement of right arm and right hand	left	J–5 M–3,4 K–4,5 N–3 L–3,4,5	DARK BLUE, SOLID
d. Movement of left arm and left hand	right	J–5 M–3,4 K–4,5 N–3 L–3,4,5	DARK BLUE, STRIPE
e. Movement of right side of face	left	J–6,7,8,9,10 K–6,7,8,9	DARK GREEN, SOLID
f. Movement of left side of face	right	J–6,7,8,9,10 K–6,7,8,9	DARK GREEN, STRIPE
g. Detection of odors from left nostril	left	D–12 F–12 E–12	YELLOW, SOLID
h. Detection of odors from right nostril	right	D–12 F–12 E–12	YELLOW STRIPE
i. Comprehension (understanding) of spoken words	left	N–9 P–8,9,10 O–8,9,10 Q–8,9,10	GREY, SOLID
j. Objects seen on left side of both eyes	left	V–11,12,13,14 W–11,12,13,14 X–11,12	ORANGE, SOLID
k. Objects seen on right side of both eyes	right	V–11,12,13,14 W–11,12,13,14 X–11,12	ORANGE, STRIPE
l. Production of speech	left	G–7,8,9 I–7,8,9 H–7,8,9	BLACK, SOLID
m. Hearing from left and right ear	left and right	K–10,11 M–10,11 L–10,11	PURPLE, SOLID
n. Personality	left and right	A–7,8,9,10 B–5,6,7,8,9,10 C–5,6,7,8,9,10	BROWN, SOLID
o. Sensations felt in right leg and right side of body	left	P–1,2 R–2 Q–1,2	PINK, SOLID
p. Sensations felt in left leg and left side of body	right	P–1,2 R–2 Q–1,2	PINK, STRIPE
q. Sensations felt in right arm and right hand	left	M–5 O–3,4 N–4,5 P–3	LIGHT GREEN, SOLID
r. Sensations felt in left arm and left hand	right	M–5 O–3,4 N–4,5 P–3	LIGHT GREEN, STRIPE
s. Sensations felt on right side of face	left	L–6,7,8 N–6,7,8 M–6,7,8	LIGHT BLUE, SOLID
t. Sensations felt on left side of face	right	L–6,7,8 N–6,7,8 M–6,7,8	LIGHT BLUE, STRIPE

INVESTIGATION 29. CEREBRUM GRAPHS

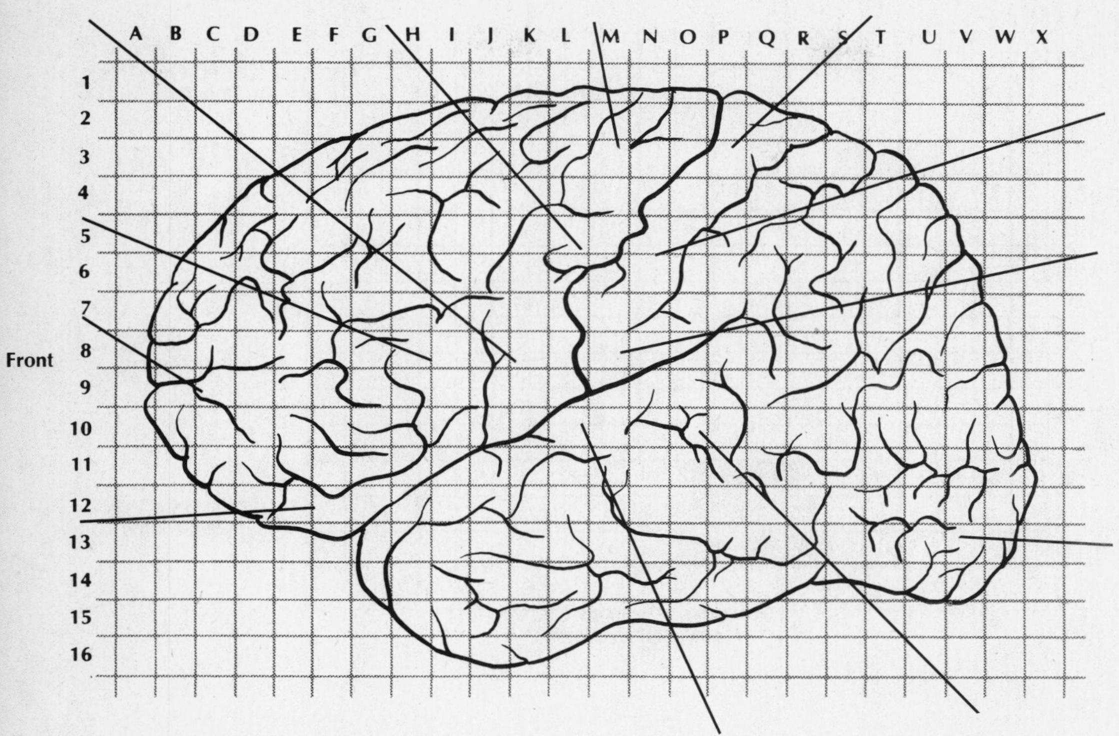

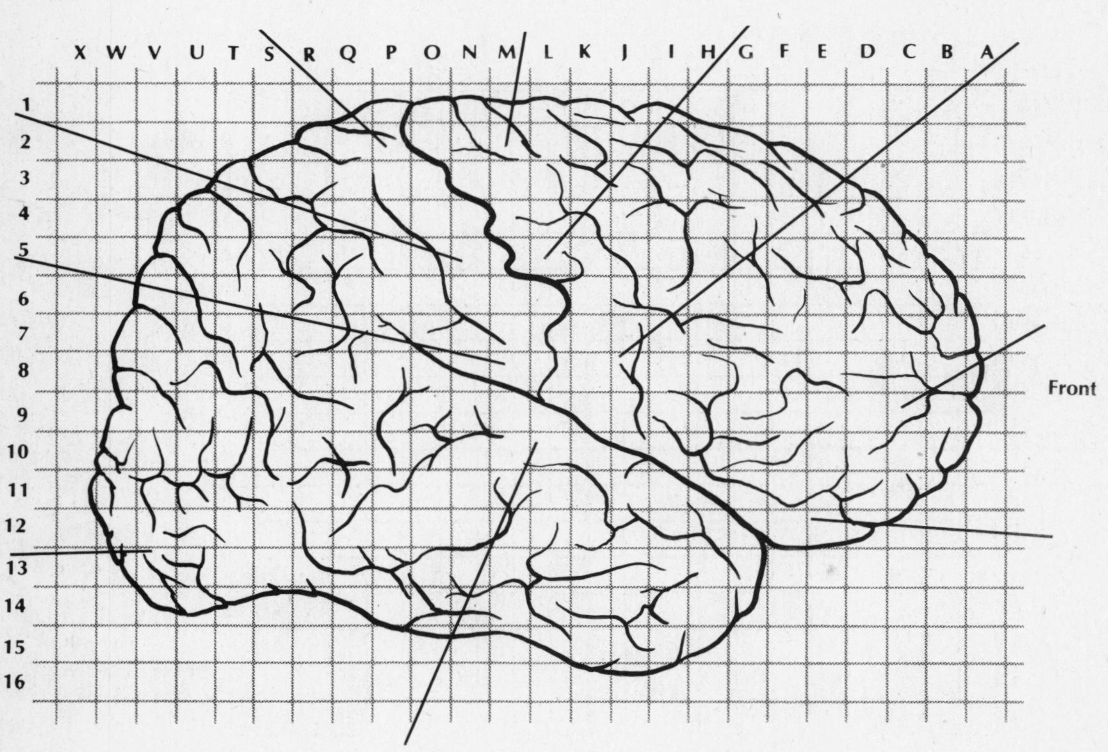

INVESTIGATION 32. POPULATION GRAPHS

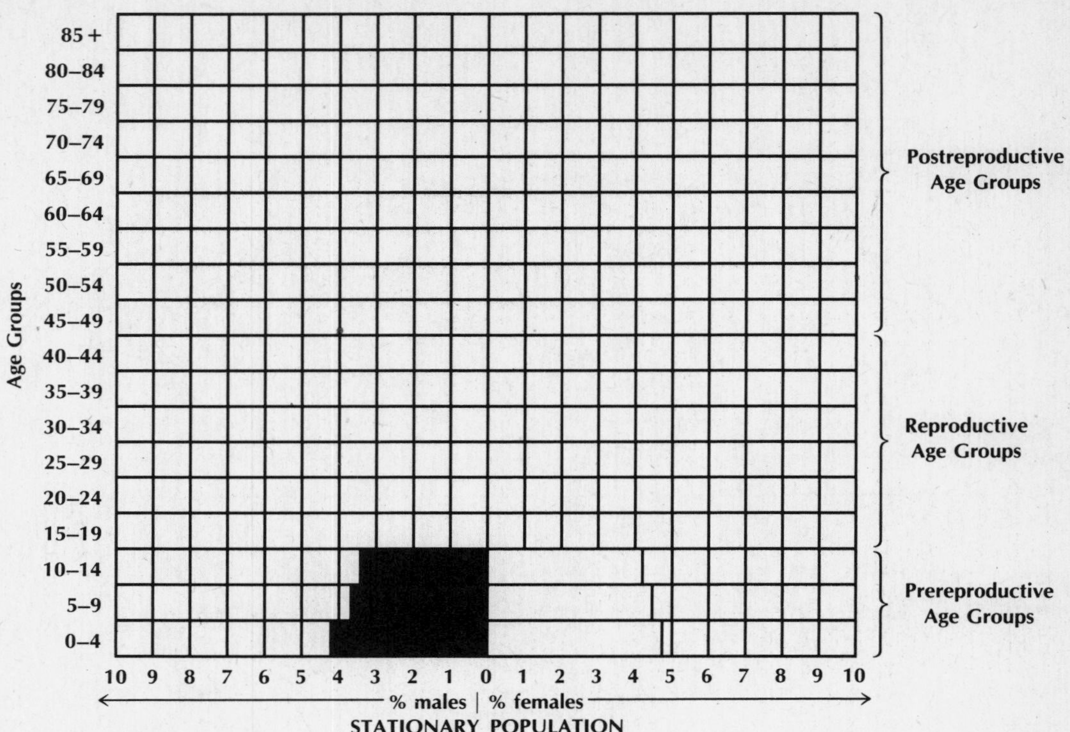

STATIONARY POPULATION

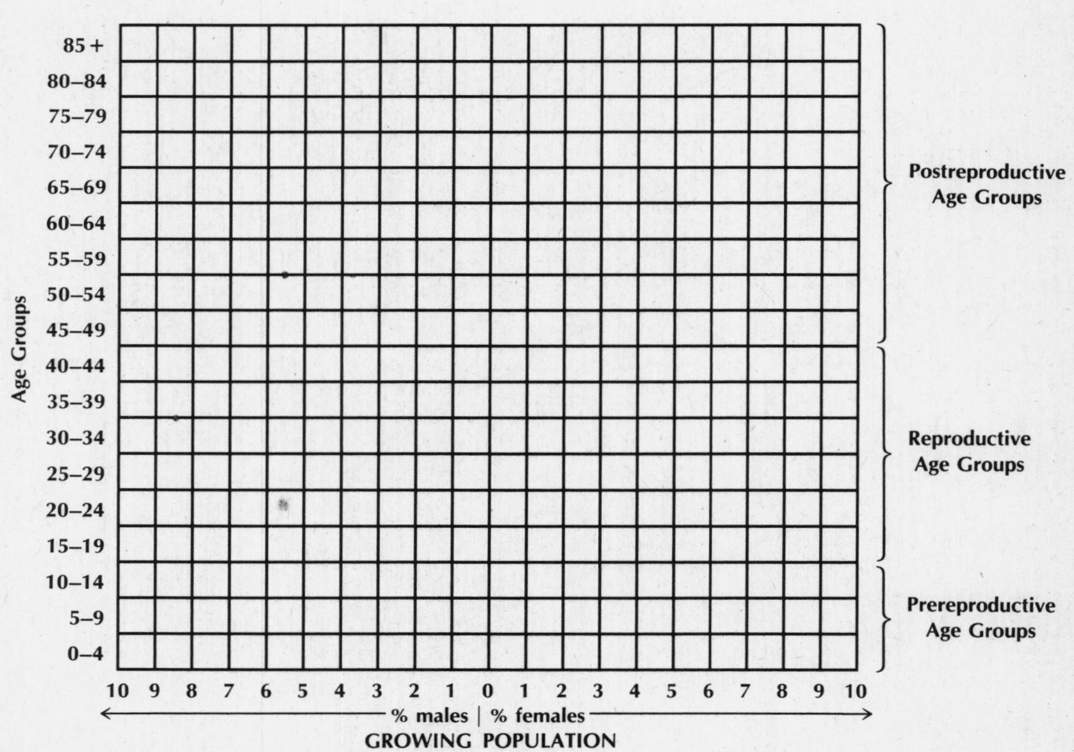

GROWING POPULATION

INVESTIGATION 32. AGE STRUCTURE DIAGRAMS

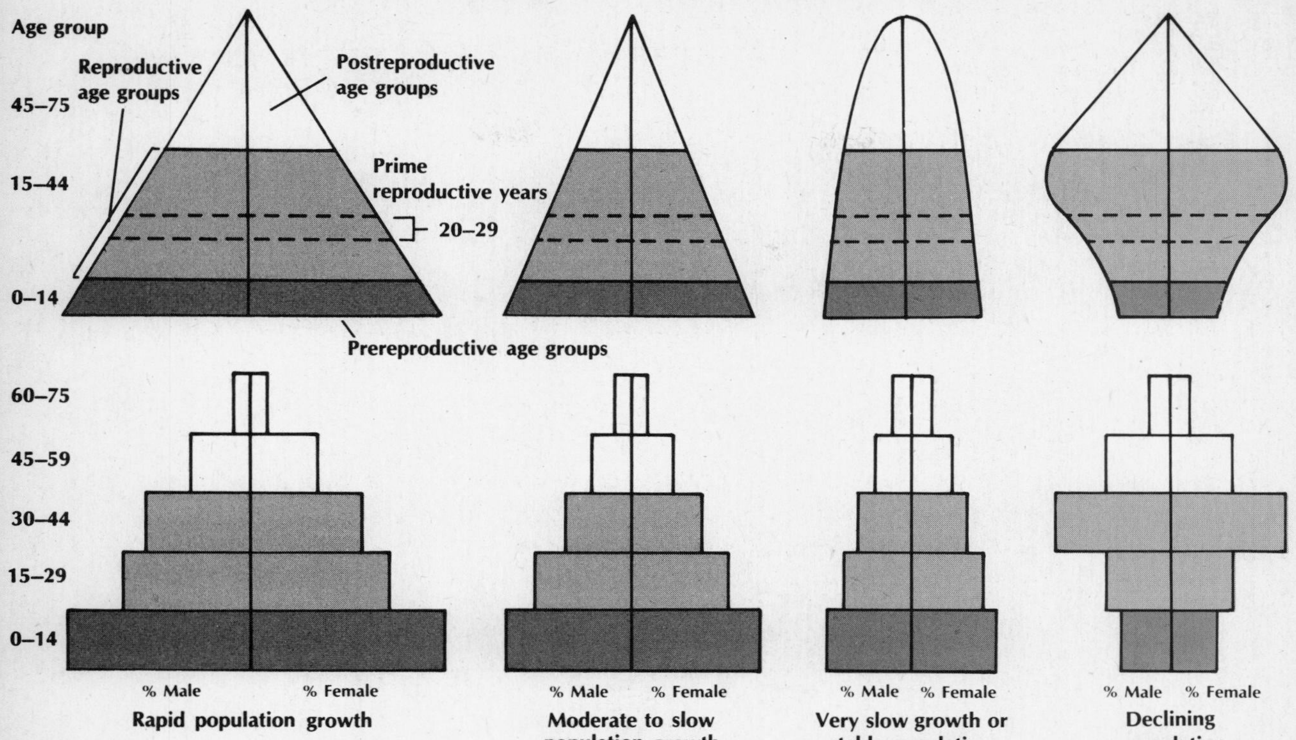

INVESTIGATION 34. CLIMATOGRAMS

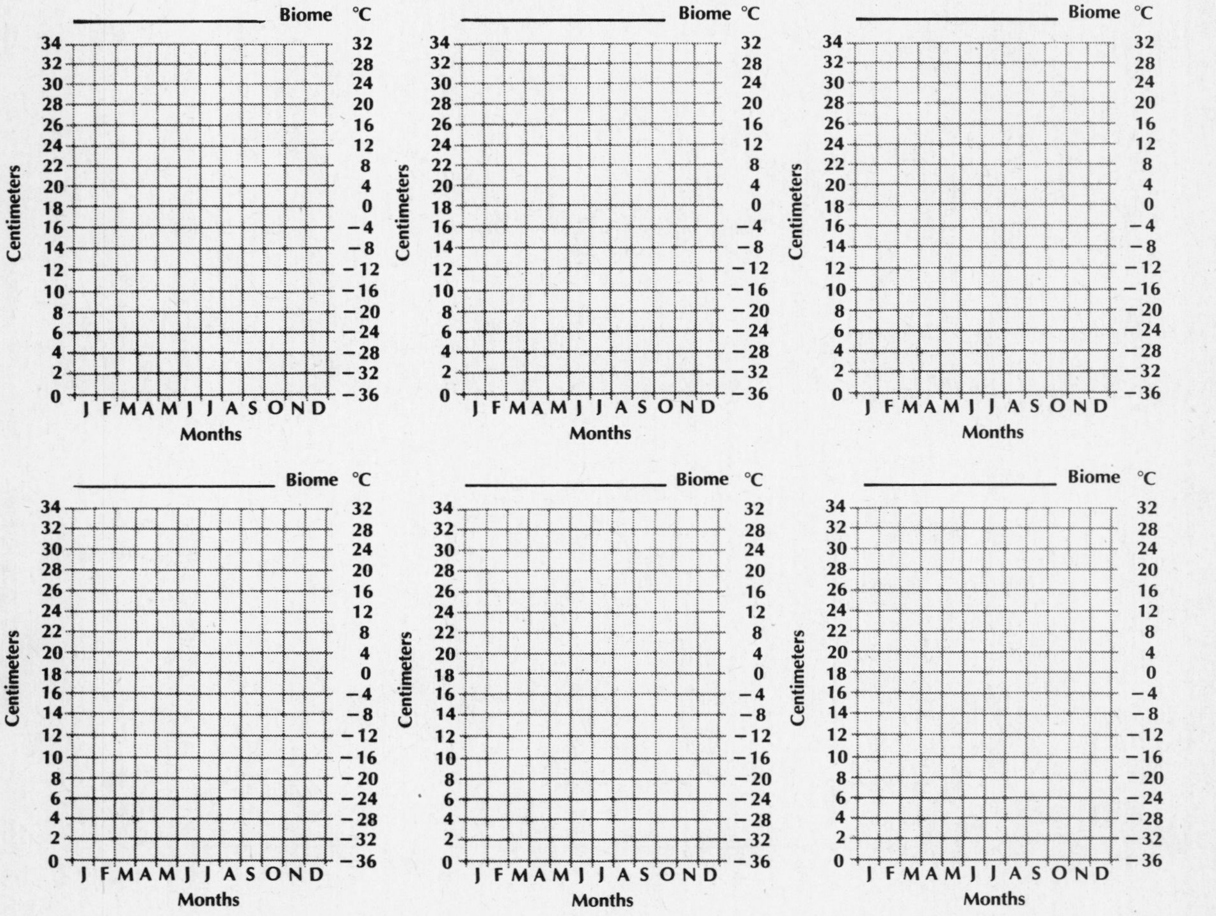

________ Biome °C

Centimeters: 34 32 30 28 26 24 22 20 18 16 14 12 10 8 6 4 2 0

°C: 32 28 24 20 16 12 8 4 0 −4 −8 −12 −16 −20 −24 −28 −32 −36

J F M A M J J A S O N D

Months

________ Biome °C

Centimeters: 34 32 30 28 26 24 22 20 18 16 14 12 10 8 6 4 2 0

°C: 32 28 24 20 16 12 8 4 0 −4 −8 −12 −16 −20 −24 −28 −32 −36

J F M A M J J A S O N D

Months

________ Biome °C

Centimeters: 34 32 30 28 26 24 22 20 18 16 14 12 10 8 6 4 2 0

°C: 32 28 24 20 16 12 8 4 0 −4 −8 −12 −16 −20 −24 −28 −32 −36

J F M A M J J A S O N D

Months

________ Biome °C

Centimeters: 34 32 30 28 26 24 22 20 18 16 14 12 10 8 6 4 2 0

°C: 32 28 24 20 16 12 8 4 0 −4 −8 −12 −16 −20 −24 −28 −32 −36

J F M A M J J A S O N D

Months

________ Biome °C

Centimeters: 34 32 30 28 26 24 22 20 18 16 14 12 10 8 6 4 2 0

°C: 32 28 24 20 16 12 8 4 0 −4 −8 −12 −16 −20 −24 −28 −32 −36

J F M A M J J A S O N D

Months

________ Biome °C

Centimeters: 34 32 30 28 26 24 22 20 18 16 14 12 10 8 6 4 2 0

°C: 32 28 24 20 16 12 8 4 0 −4 −8 −12 −16 −20 −24 −28 −32 −36

J F M A M J J A S O N D

Months

INVESTIGATION 35. TEMPERATURE AND CARBON DIOXIDE GRAPHS

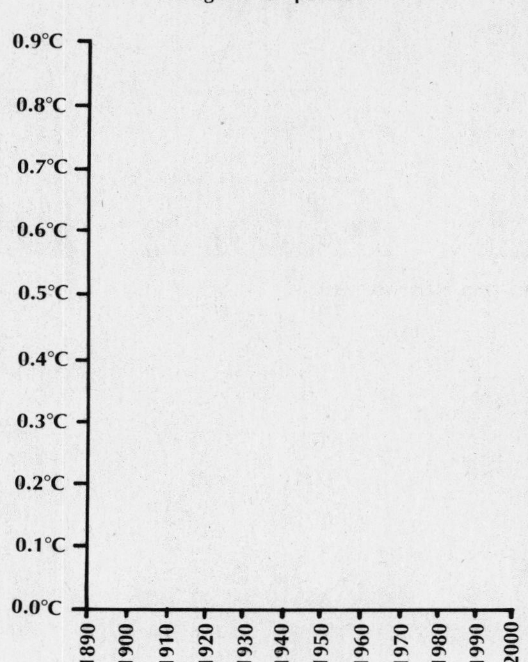

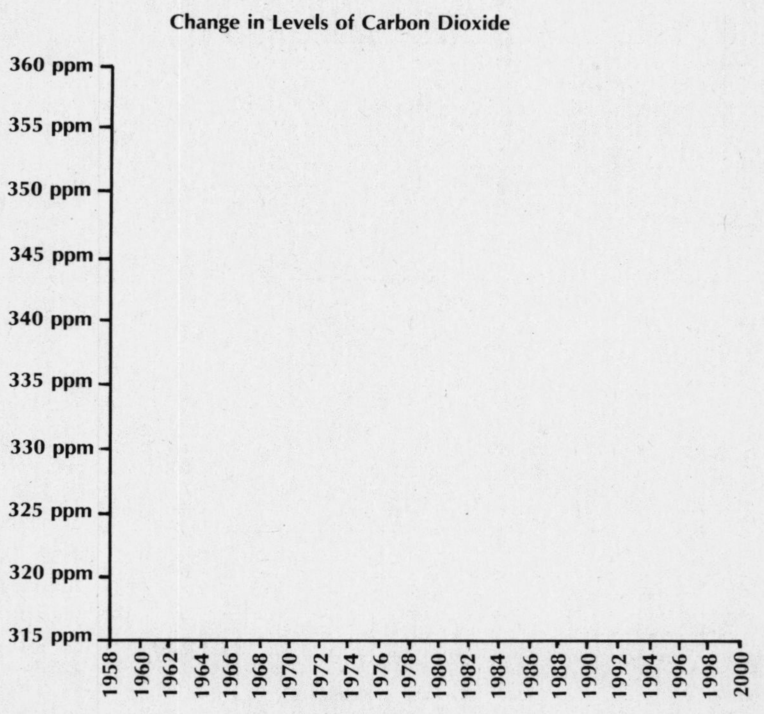

Coelenterate Anatomy: Hydra

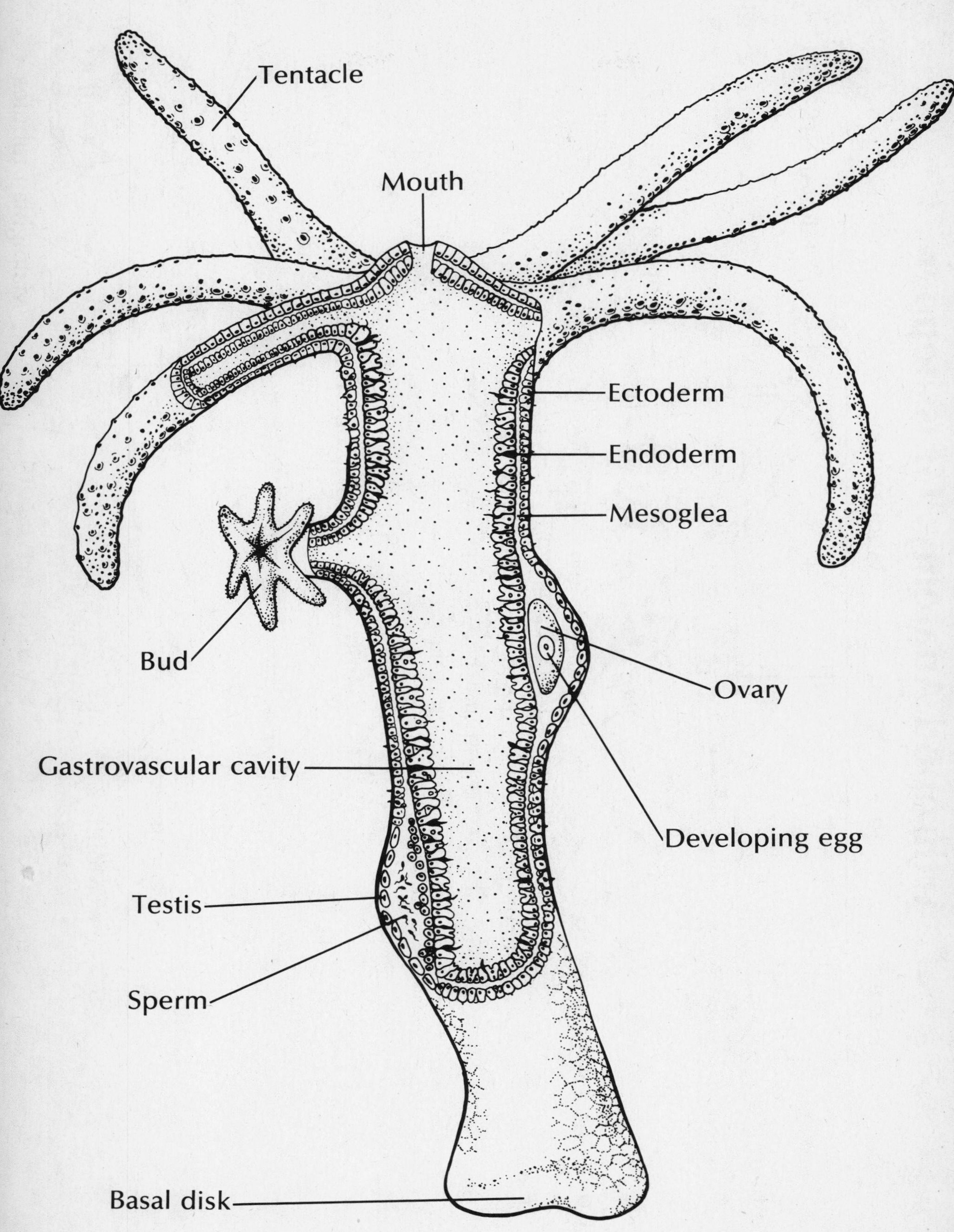

Arthropod Anatomy: Grasshopper

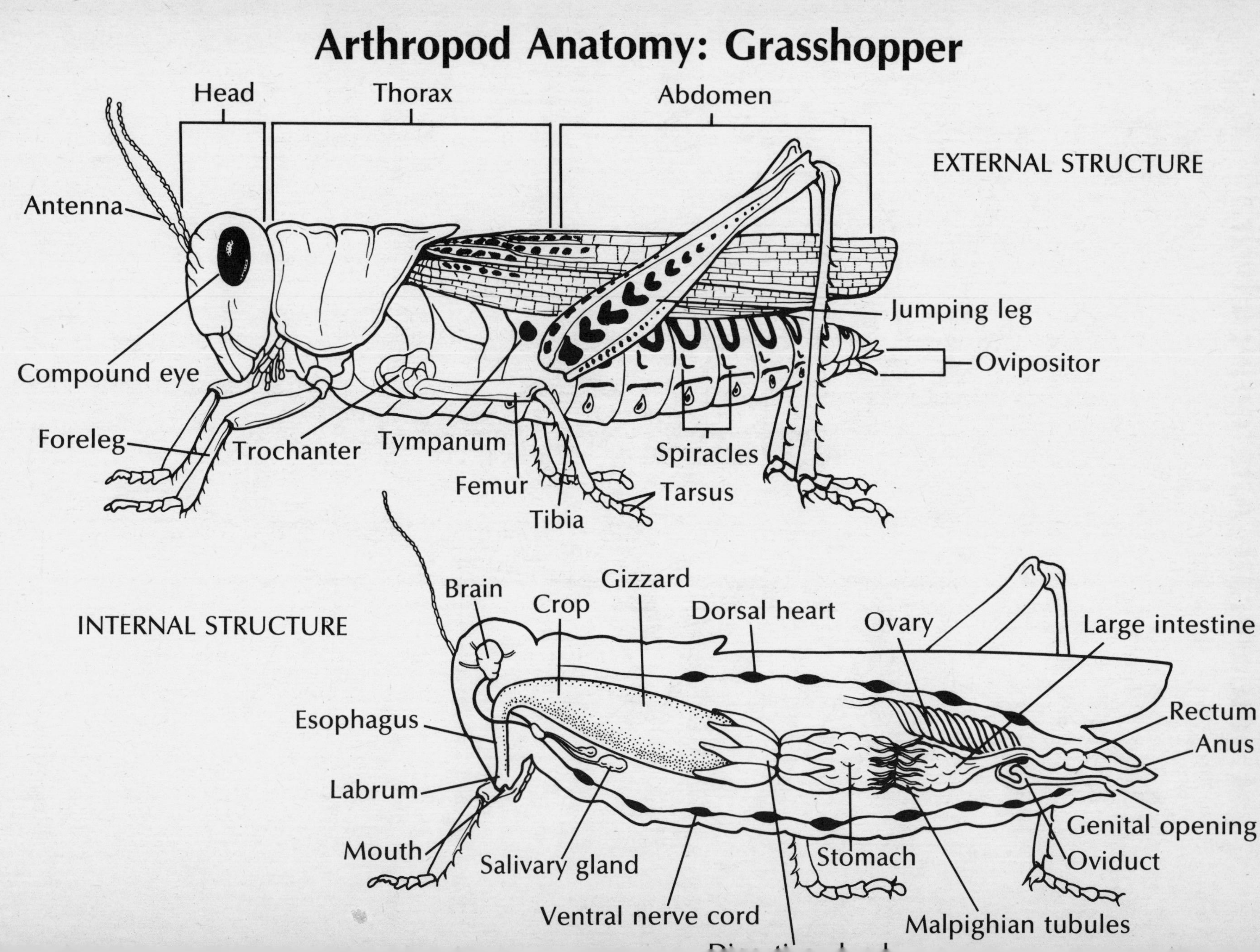

Echinoderm Anatomy: Starfish

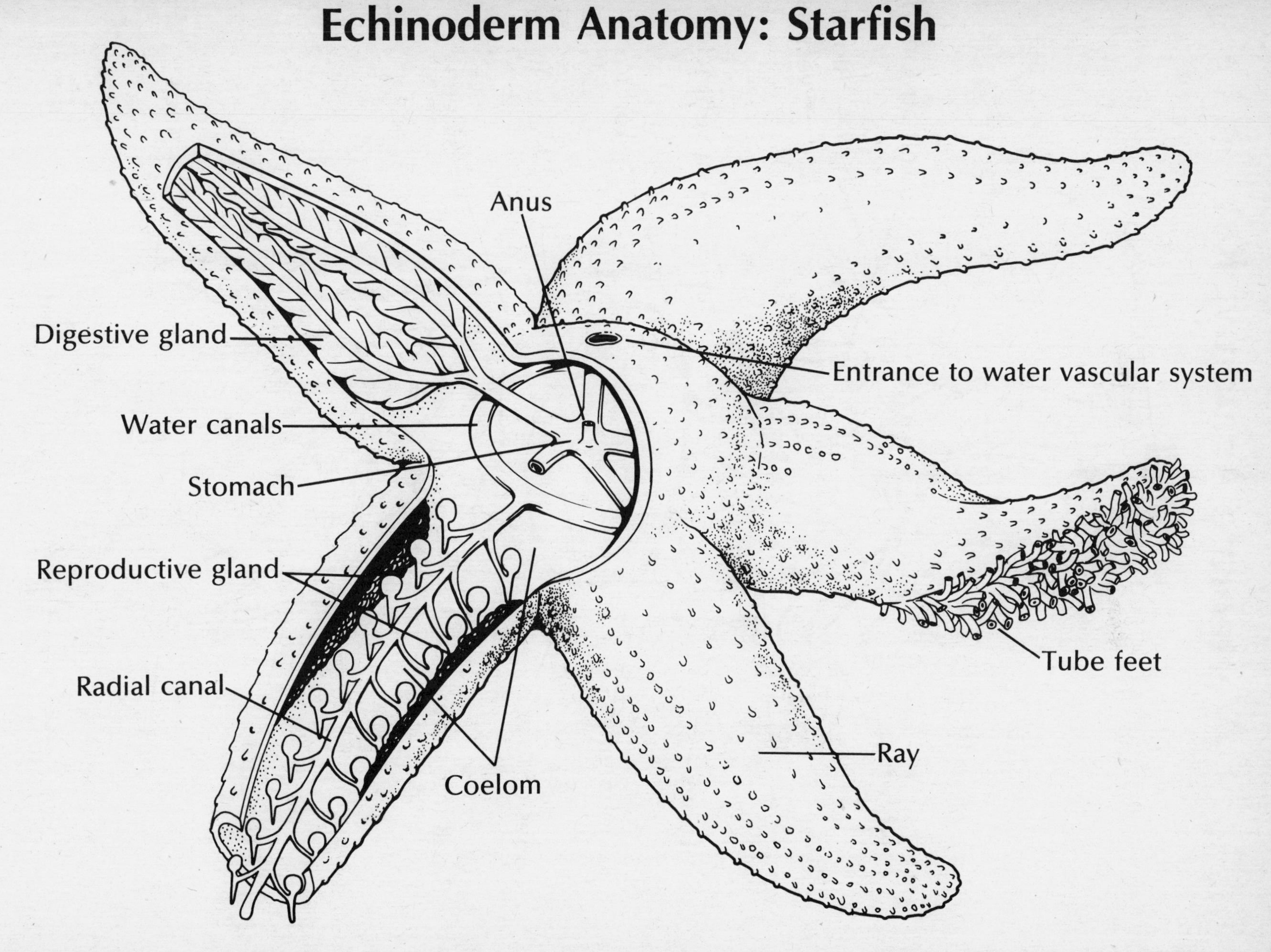

Vertebrate Anatomy: Rat

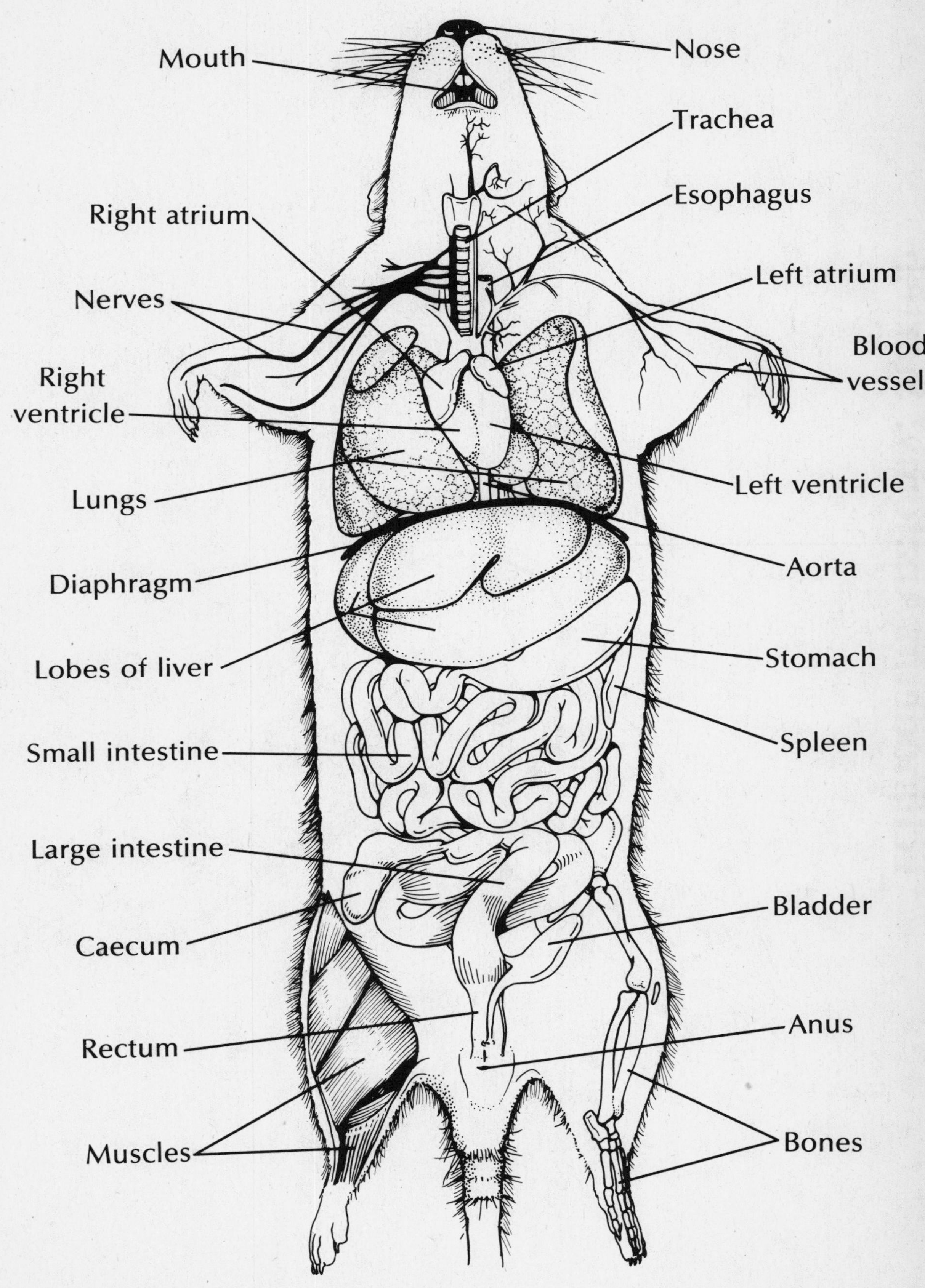

PLANNING GUIDE	
TEXT	**UNIT 1 Characteristics of Life** **Chapter 1 Life: Common Characteristics** **Investigation 1 Do living systems release carbon dioxide? p. 12**
TEACHER RESOURCE PACKAGE:	
READING AND STUDY GUIDE	Student Edition, p. 3 Teacher Edition, p. 3
RESOURCE MASTER BOOK	Student Master 1–1. A Study of Population Growth, p. 1–2 Student Master 1–2. Should the Rain Forests Be Preserved? p. 1–3 Teaching Master 1–1. Movement of Materials Through a Community, p. 1–4 Teaching Master 1–2. Movement of Energy Through a Community, p. 1–5 Investigation Worksheet, p. 1–6
EVALUATION PROGRAM	Test Masters, p. 1 Alternate Test Masters, p. 143
LABORATORY BIOLOGY: INVESTIGATING LIVING SYSTEMS	1 Biological Communities, p. 1 2 Use of the Light Microscope, p. 5 3 Techniques for Better Microscope Use, p. 9
PROBING LEVELS OF LIFE: A LABORATORY MANUAL	1 Life: Common Characteristics, p. 1 2 Life in a Square Meter Community, p. 3 3 The Compound Microscope—A Biological Tool, p. 6

Name ______________________ Date ______________

A Study of Population Growth

Population growth can be studied easily by using small organisms such as bacteria and yeast. The following graph represents the growth curve of bacteria that were put into a test tube of nutrient broth. The test tube was then exposed to conditions ideal for optimal growth. However, no additional food was added to the test tube. Because bacteria multiply rapidly, the population of the bacteria was determined every hour. Study the graph below. Then answer the questions that follow the graph.

FIGURE 1–1.

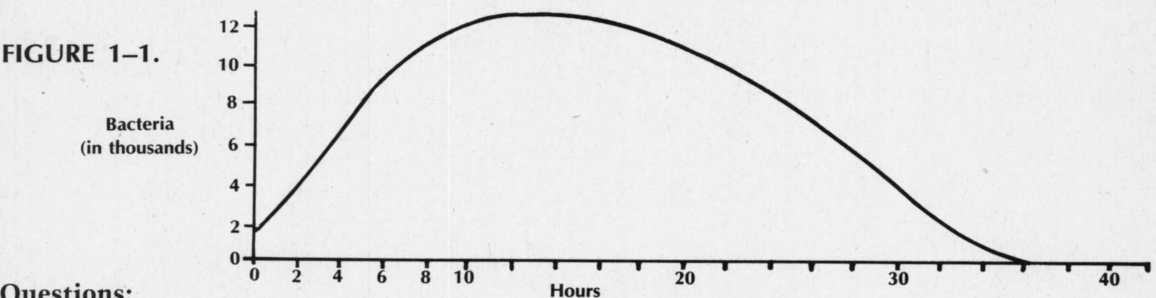

Questions:

1. Explain the results for the first 6 hours indicated by the curve on the graph. ______________

2. Explain the results that occurred from hour 10 to hour 16. ______________

3. Explain the results that occurred from hour 18 to hour 37. What caused this result? ______________

4. The human population of the world is continuously increasing. Will Earth be able to support an unlimited human population? Explain your answer. ______________

5. What do you suppose will happen if the world's population increases beyond its carrying capacity? ______________

Name ______________________ Date ______________

Should the Rain Forests Be Preserved?

Amazonia is the world's largest and oldest rain forest. It is slightly larger than Australia and more than half the size of Europe. Amazonia contains two-thirds of all the river water in the world, one-third of the world's forests, and produces one-half of all the oxygen generated by land plants in the world.

Amazonia's towering jungle trees are the homes of numerous species of plants and animals. Lianas, mosses, orchids, and other flowers of stunning brilliance offer extraordinary beauty. It is home to spiders so large that they are able to catch birds, and to butterflies with ten-centimeter wingspans. Amazonia is also home to a greater variety of mammals with grasping tails (mostly monkeys) than anywhere else in the world. It is one of the few places where new species of plants and animals are still being discovered.

Yet, Amazonia is facing perilous pressures from development. At least a million trees are cut down every 24 hours. Satellite photographs indicate that as many as 161 000 square kilometers of forest are being leveled every year. At this rate, Amazonia could disappear by the year 2000.

What has caused such large and rapid deforestation? The cleared land is used for farming, raising cattle, oil drilling, and coal mining. These activities produce the precious resources needed to meet increasing demands for food and energy. Timber mills operating in the middle of the rain forest provide forest products for a growing world population. Iron-ore mines produce the raw material needed to make steel.

Environmentalists are trying to halt the deforestation of Amazonia because destruction of the rain forest will result in the extinction of many organisms, the destruction of the Amazon Basin (including its river), and serious harm to the climate of the rest of the world.

Deforestation destroys entire communities of plants and animals. Many of the plants and animals in the rain forests are adapted to conditions found only within a few square kilometers. It destroys the areas in which wildlife breed, forage, hunt, and rest and even disturbs migration routes. Scientists believe that many of the plants in the rain forest could provide new, useful products such as medicines, spices, and food. Environmentalists estimate that if deforestation continues at the present rate, up to one million plant and animal species will be lost forever.

Destruction of the forest and its inhabitants is soon followed by the destruction of the forest's soil. Studies have shown that once the forests are cut down and the soil is exposed, rainfall washes away the soil within a few years. The soil erosion from farming and mining is causing small tributaries of the Amazon River to choke with silt. Food crops and pastures can be grown on the rain forest's infertile soil for only a few years before the farmlands and pastures have to be abandoned. The tropical sun quickly bakes the surface of the abandoned land into a hard-packed crust, creating a wasteland out of an area that once supported plant and animal communities of amazing diversity and extraordinary beauty.

Additional studies have shown that changes to the structure of the Amazonian rain forest can produce changes elsewhere in the environment. Drilling for oil not only results in contamination of the soil, it also creates oil slicks on the Amazon River, which in turn pollute the Atlantic Ocean. There is also concern that destruction of the rain forest will change the world's climate. The wide expanse of Amazonia influences both the balance of carbon dioxide in the atmosphere and the amount of heat reflected from Earth's surface. Many scientists believe that deforestation could cause a change in global wind patterns and rainfall and result in changes in the climates of different regions of the world.

Questions:

1. What benefits result from the cutting of the rain forests?
2. What negative effects might result from the cutting of the rain forests?
3. Many people feel that Amazonia and other rain forests should be saved from deforestation, whatever the cost. Do you agree with this opinion? Why?
4. Some people feel that deforestation of Amazonia and other rain forests should continue in order to meet the increasing need for food, energy, and other resources. Do you agree? Why?
5. How would you propose to deal with Amazonia? Can some parts of Amazonia be used for development and some parts preserved?

Movement of Materials Through a Community

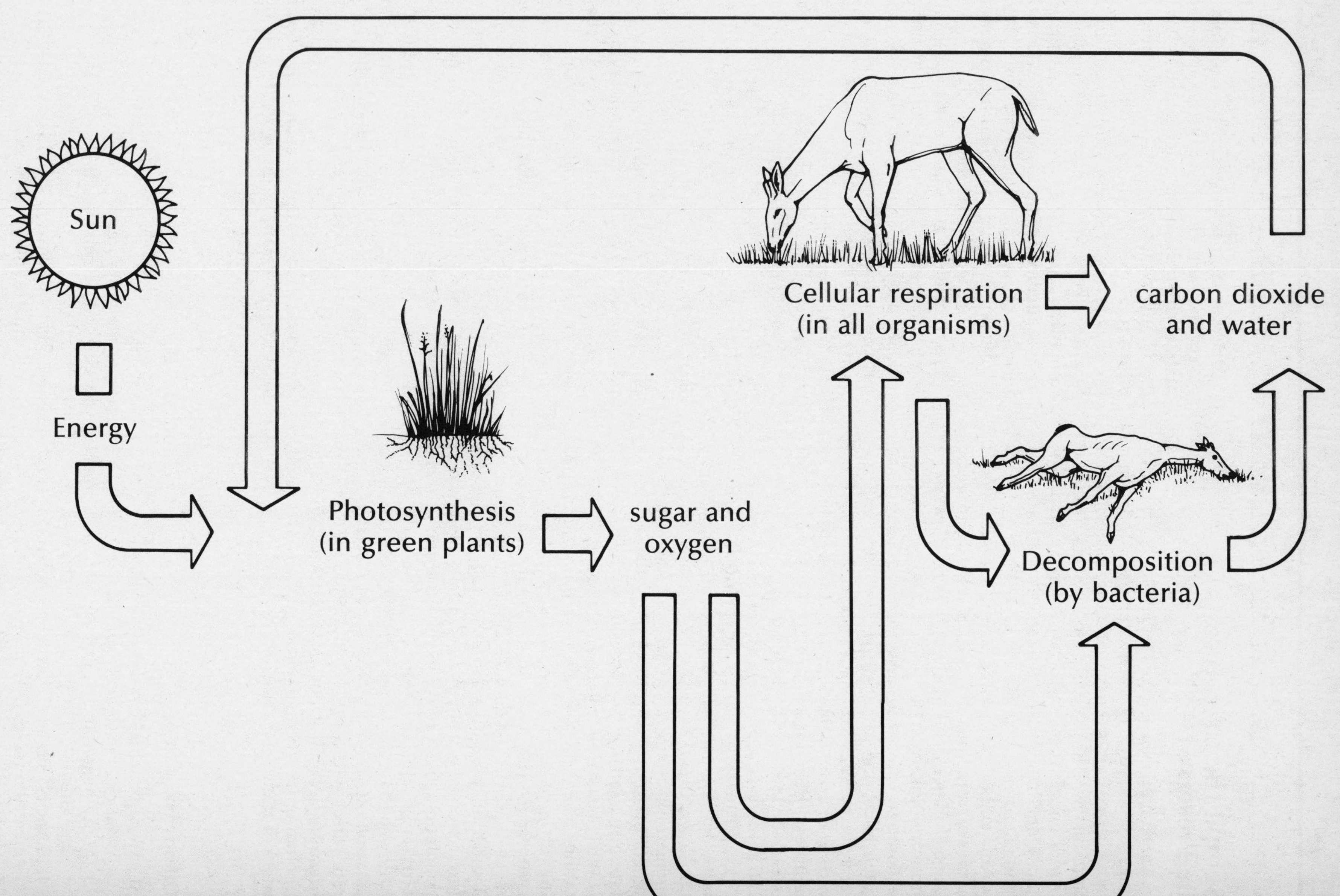

Movement of Energy Through a Community

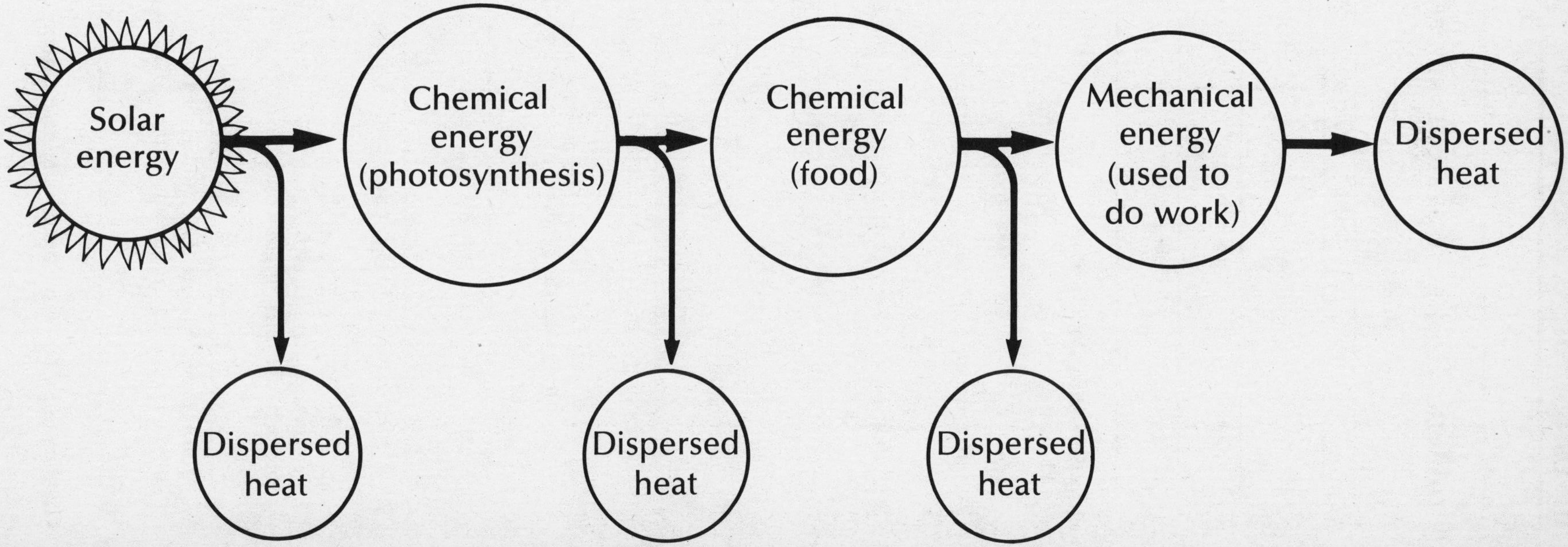

Solar energy → Chemical energy (photosynthesis) → Chemical energy (food) → Mechanical energy (used to do work) → Dispersed heat

Solar energy → Dispersed heat

Chemical energy (photosynthesis) → Dispersed heat

Chemical energy (food) → Dispersed heat

Name ______________________ Date ______________________

Problem: Do living systems release carbon dioxide? (text page 12)

Data and Observations:

TABLE 1-1. OBSERVATIONS OF BROMTHYMOL BLUE				
	Part A Detecting CO_2	Part B Do Producers Release CO_2?	Part C Do Consumers Release CO_2?	Part D Do Decomposers Release CO_2?
Color of:	Tube B "before"	Tube C	Flask E "before"	Tube F
Color of:	Tube B "after"	Tube D	Flask E "after"	Tube G

Questions and Conclusion:

1. Define each of the following terms: (a) producer (b) consumer (c) decomposer.

   ____

2. Put each organism in this activity into one of the following categories: (a) producer (b) consumer (c) decomposer. ______________________
3. Explain how to experimentally detect the presence of carbon dioxide gas.

   ____

4. Do producers release carbon dioxide into their surroundings? What is your evidence?

   ____

5. Do consumers release carbon dioxide into their surroundings? What is your evidence?

   ____

6. Do decomposers release carbon dioxide into their surroundings? What is your evidence?

   ____

7. What life process is responsible for the release of carbon dioxide by organisms into their surroundings? ______________________
8. In part B, why did you place a tube with no *Elodea* plant in the dark?

   ____

9. In part D, why did you place a tube that contained no yeast in the dark?

   ____

10. If you repeated parts B, C, and D of the experiment, but this time tested to see if water was given off, what results might you expect? Explain.

    ____

11. If you repeated part B, C, and D of the experiment but this time tested to see if oxygen was given off, what results might you expect? Explain.

    ____

Conclusion: Do living systems release carbon dioxide? ______________________

PLANNING GUIDE	
TEXT	**UNIT 1 Characteristics of Life** **Chapter 2 Biology as a Science** **Investigation 2 How does one test a hypothesis? p. 34**
TEACHER RESOURCE PACKAGE:	
READING AND STUDY GUIDE	Student Edition, p. 9 Teacher Edition, p. 5
RESOURCE MASTER BOOK	Student Master 2–1. Animal Rights? p. 2–2 Student Master 2–2. Solving the Mystery of Food Poisoning, p. 2–3 Teaching Master 2–1. Parts of the Microscope, p. 2–4 Teaching Master 2–2. Measuring Mass, p. 2–5 Investigation Worksheet, p. 2–6
EVALUATION PROGRAM	Test Masters, p. 5 Alternate Test Masters, p. 145
LABORATORY BIOLOGY: INVESTIGATING LIVING SYSTEMS	4 Solving a Problem with a Scientific Method, p. 13 5 Using SI Units, p. 17
PROBING LEVELS OF LIFE: A LABORATORY MANUAL	4 Microscopic Measurement, p. 11

Name ______________________ Date ______________

Animal Rights?

Animal rights and the prevention of cruelty to animals is a long and old issue. A law of the Massachusetts Bay Colony in 1641 states that, "No man shall exercise any Tirranny or Crueltie toward any Bruite Creatures which are kept for man's use." This early American law does not mention the types of "Tirranny or Crueltie" against certain "Bruite Creatures," but some of the colonists must have been treating animals in a way that others objected to.

Today, the debate continues. However, it does not focus on people who mistreat pets. There are effective laws that prevent this. The argument, today, focuses on the use and treatment of animals in laboratory experiments. And the main issue is whether or not many of these animals are unnecessarily exposed to pain and death.

One test that has been greatly criticized is the Draise test. In this test, researchers put shampoo, soap, eye liner, and various other cosmetic preparations in the eyes of albino rabbits. Depending on the strength of the chemical and the length of exposure, the effect on the rabbit's eyes can range from irritation to destruction of the eyeball. The tests are performed to determine product safety.

Other experiments that use animals involve those experiments that gain knowledge to prevent and/or cure various diseases. Animals are exposed to various substances to determine which of the substances may cause cancer in humans. Medicines developed to treat various diseases, such as cancer and AIDS, are tested first on animals in order to determine safety, correct dosage, and side effects. Furthermore, certain diseases in some animals are so similar to diseases of humans that these animals are considered perfect for studying ways of curing such diseases. Some of these diseases include hemophilia in dogs, muscular dystrophy in minks, and gallstones in squirrel monkeys. Some individuals believe that experiments using animals make for a safer, healthier life for people.

There seems to be no clear "Yes" or "No" side to the use of animals in experiments. There are dozens of opinions. At one extreme are people who would end all animal experimentation. At the other extreme are people who would set no restrictions. In the middle are those people who feel that useful research is essential and that some animals must be sacrificed. But these people also feel that the use and sacrifice of animals should take place only when necessary. Even this middle-of-the-road view raises debatable questions. Who should determine what research is useful and not? Who should determine when it is necessary to sacrifice an animal?

Questions:

1. Would you use a medicine knowing that it had not been tested on animals and therefore, that its effects are not fully known? Why?
2. Would you be willing to wait an additional five years for a breakthrough medicine that would save human lives in order to prevent testing on animals? Why?
3. Should animal testing be used to develop safe cosmetics? Defend your answer.
4. If you are in favor of animal testing, which animals should be used? Explain.

Name ______________________ Date ______________

Solving the Mystery of Food Poisoning

Food poisoning is caused by a toxic substance produced by several kinds of bacteria. When the bacteria contaminate food, they begin to grow and produce a toxin. One kind of bacteria, *Clostridium botulinum,* causes a specific form of food poisoning known as botulism. This type of food poisoning usually involves improperly smoked or uncooked meat or fish, canned vegetables, or low-acid foods. When the contaminated food is eaten, the toxin in the food is absorbed through the gastrointestinal tract into the blood stream and attacks the nerves. As a result, a person with botulism usually experiences weakness, double vision, uncoordinated eye movement, and difficulty in swallowing and speaking. Death is not uncommon and may be caused by respiratory failure or cardiac arrest. Fortunately, not all forms of food poisoning are deadly. The symptoms of food poisoning that are caused by toxins produced by other bacteria include nausea, vomiting, colicky pain, and diarrhea. These symptoms usually appear 8 to 12 hours after eating the contaminated food. Almost all people fully recover within one to several days.

You are the head of a research team assigned to investigate an outbreak of food poisoning in a city. You interview those people who have been diagnosed as having food poisoning. Through your interviews you made the following observations:

1. All of the victims experienced symptoms of food poisoning within 24 hours. The symptoms varied in severity, but included nausea, vomiting, colicky pain, and diarrhea. There were no reported deaths associated with the food poisoning.
2. All of the victims ate at the same restaurant for lunch or dinner within 24 hours of the onset of food poisoning symptoms.
3. All victims had ordered a lunch or dinner entree with the salad bar or they had ordered only the salad bar.

Questions:

1. How would you interpret your observations at this point? Give a reason for your answer.

____

____

____

2. What would your hypothesis be? ______________________________

____

3. How would you rewrite your hypothesis to make it very specific? ______________________________

____

____

____

4. How would you design an experiment to prove your hypothesis? ______________________________

____

____

____

____

Parts of the Microscope

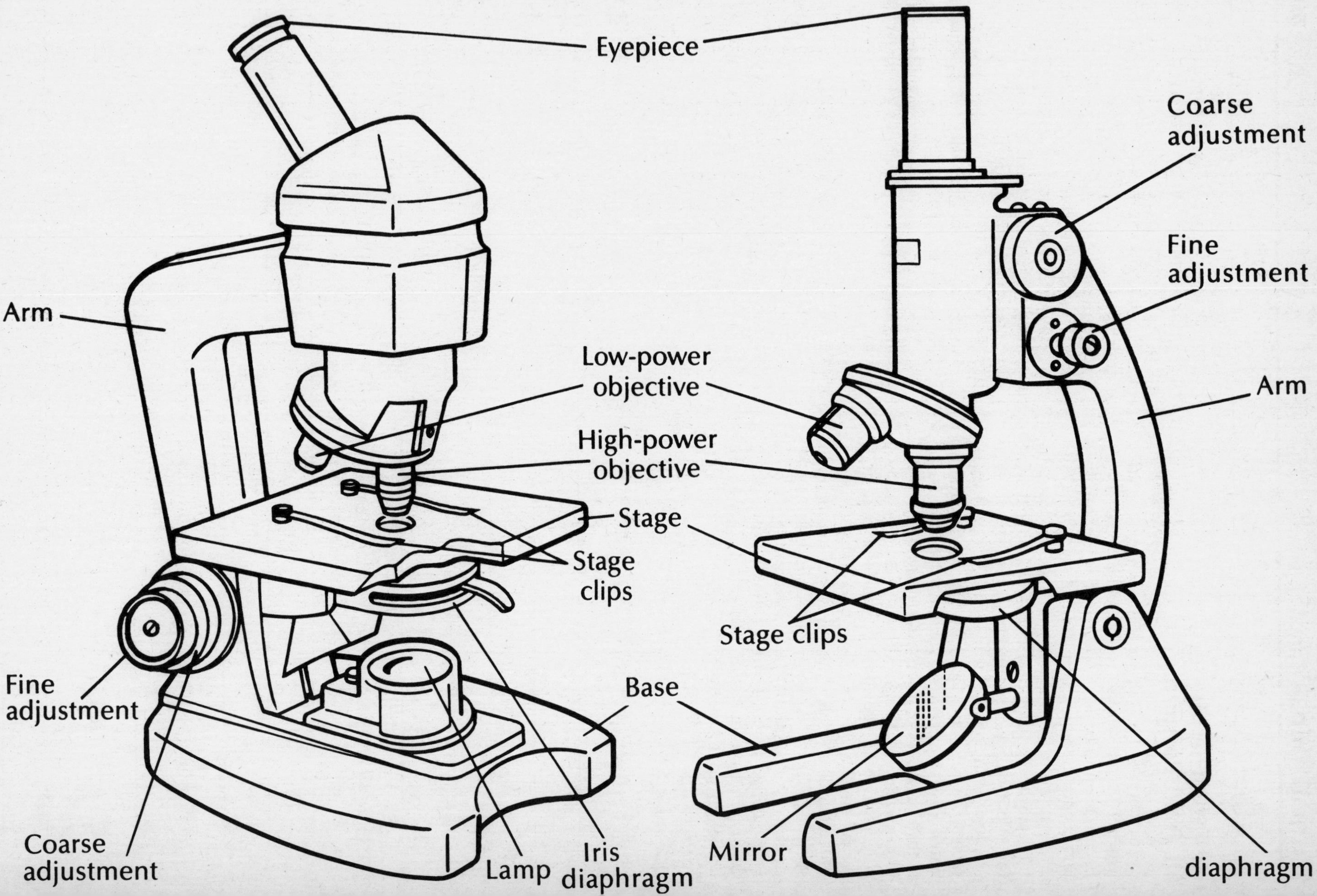

Eyepiece

Arm

Low-power objective

High-power objective

Stage

Stage clips

Fine adjustment

Coarse adjustment

Lamp

Iris diaphragm

Base

Mirror

Stage clips

diaphragm

Arm

Fine adjustment

Coarse adjustment

Measuring Mass

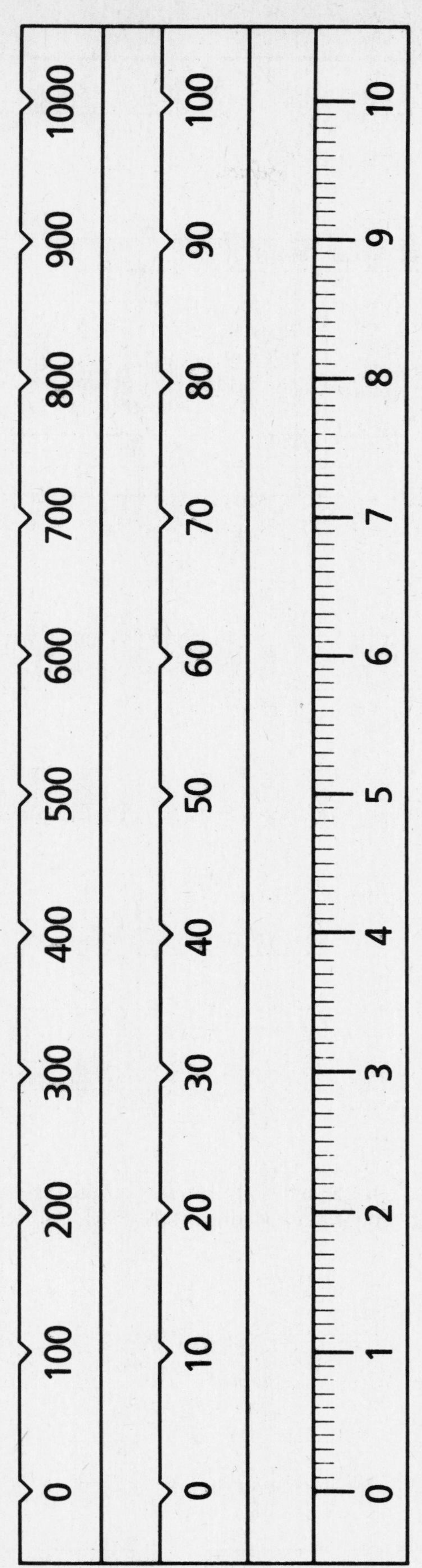

Name ______________________ Date ______________

Problem: How does one test a hypothesis?

(text page 34)

Data and Observations:

TABLE 2-1. RADISH SEED GROWTH						
	Individual Results			Class Results		
Treatment	Number of Seeds Used	Number of Seeds Growing	Number of Seeds Not Growing	Number of Seeds Used	Number of Seeds Growing	Number of Seeds Not Growing
Water	20					
Water and aspirin	20					

Questions and Conclusion:

1. Define: (a) hypothesis (b) control (c) variable. ______________________

2. Which part of this experiment represents the: (a) data (b) control (c) variable?

3. Based on your original hypothesis, does the class data appear to support it? Explain. ______

4. Restate a new hypothesis based on experimental findings for the class. Use the "if-then" format.

5. Explain why testing or experimentation is needed before one can accept a hypothesis.

6. Suggest a reason why it was best to use class totals rather than only your data when drawing conclusions about your hypothesis. ______________________

7. A hypothesis helps to predict new facts. Determine if the following could possibly be predicted based on your corrected hypothesis regarding aspirin and seed growth. Explain.

   (a) Aspirin added to pea seeds will reduce amount of growth. ______________________

   (b) Aspirin added to soil will help house plants to form greener leaves. ______________

   (c) Aspirin added to corn seeds will increase amount of growth. ______________________

Conclusion: How does one test a hypothesis? ______________________

PLANNING GUIDE	
TEXT	**UNIT 1 Characteristics of Life** **Chapter 3 Materials of Life** **Investigation 3 How does one determine if a solution is an acid or a base? p. 58**
TEACHER RESOURCE PACKAGE:	
READING AND STUDY GUIDE	Student Edition, p. 15 Teacher Edition, p. 6
RESOURCE MASTER BOOK	Student Master 3–1. Models of an Atom, p. 3–2 Student Master 3–2. Ionic Compounds and Electricity, p. 3–3 Teaching Master 3–1. Formulas of Organic Compounds, p. 3–4 Investigation Worksheet, p. 3–5
EVALUATION PROGRAM	Test Masters, p. 9 Alternate Test Masters, p. 147
LABORATORY BIOLOGY: INVESTIGATING LIVING SYSTEMS	6 Carbohydrates: Chemistry and Identification, p. 21 7 Proteins: Chemistry and Identification, p. 27 8 Fats: Chemistry and Identification, p. 31
PROBING LEVELS OF LIFE: A LABORATORY MANUAL	5 Detecting Compounds Made by Living Things, p. 15 6 Molecules of Biological Importance, p. 18 7 Amino Acid Chromatography, p. 20

Name ______________________ Date ______________

Models of an Atom

The model of the atom can be illustrated in two ways. One way is based upon the theory of an atom developed by Danish physicist Niels Bohr in 1913. In this model, an electron travels in a specific orbit around the nucleus. In Figure 3–1, a single hydrogen atom, indicate what represents the nucleus and what represents the electron's orbit.

Another way that the atom can be illustrated is using what is called a probability cloud. This model is based upon discoveries made a decade after Bohr developed his theory of the atom. These discoveries make up the quantum of the atom. Simply put, this theory states that the electrons move about within a probability cloud that forms a certain pattern in space. Figure 3–2 is of a probability cloud for a single hydrogen atom. Indicate where the nucleus is located and where there would be a high probability of finding the electron.

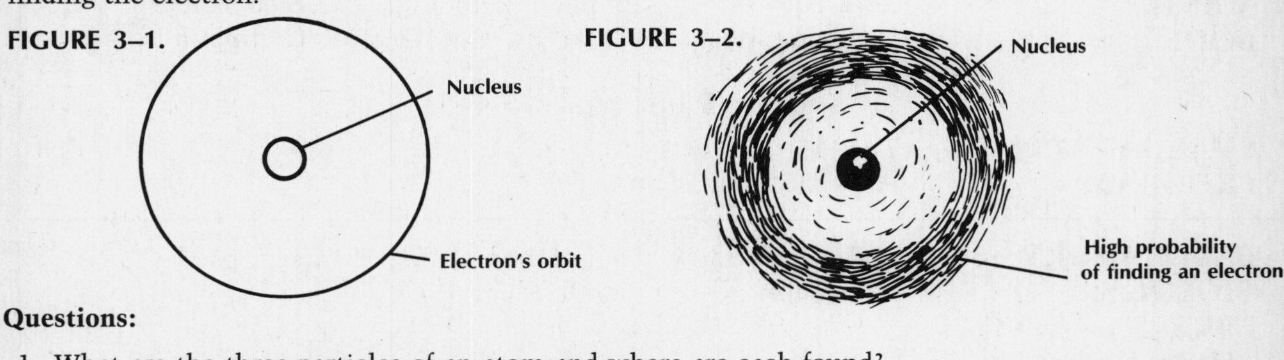

Questions:

1. What are the three particles of an atom and where are each found? ______________________

2. How are the two models of the atom described above similar? ______________________

3. How are the two models of the atom described above different? ______________________

4. Why is it important to understand the structure of an atom? ______________________

5. Which model would you say is more accurate, Bohr's model or the probability cloud model? Explain. ______________________

Name ______________________ *Date* ______________

Ionic Compounds and Electricity

Ionic compounds are made up of charged particles—ions—that are tightly bound together. If the attractive forces between the ions are weakened, the ions are free to move. Freely-moving, charged particles such as ions conduct electricity. To learn more about ionic compounds and electricity, work through the following activity.

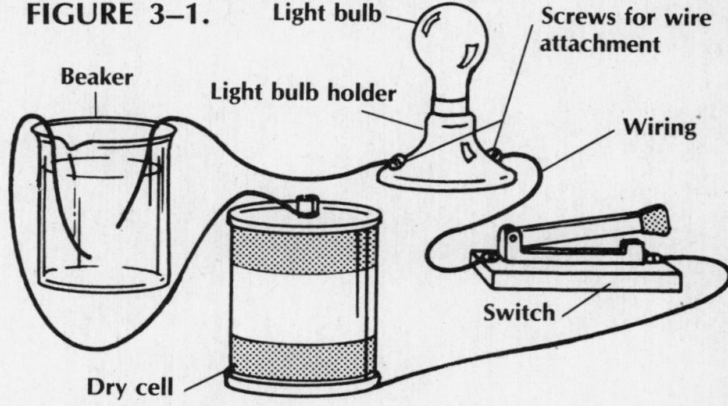

FIGURE 3–1.

Materials:

250-mL beaker	light bulb
dry cell	light bulb holder
electrical wires	distilled water
switch	salt
masking tape	glass stirring rod

Procedure:

1. Set up a series circuit like the one shown in Figure 3-1. Do not add anything to the beaker until your circuit is set up completely. Make sure the switch is open. You will need to remove a short length of insulation from the ends of the wires that come into contact with the switch, the dry cell, the light bulb holder, and the distilled water. To help keep the wires along the side of the beaker, you may wish to use masking tape to hold the wires in place. **CAUTION:** *Do not touch both ends of the wire in the beaker with your bare hands at the same time that the switch is closed, as you may receive a mild shock.*
2. Add distilled water to the beaker until the bare ends of the wire are covered with the water. Close the switch. Observe what happens to the light bulb. Open the switch.
3. Now, add about 5 to 10 grams of salt to the distilled water. Using the glass stirring rod, gently stir the water so that the salt dissolves. Close the switch. Observe what happens to the light bulb. Open the switch before you disassemble your series circuit.

Questions:

1. What happened to the light bulb when there was only distilled water in the beaker and you closed the switch? ______________________

2. What happened to the light bulb when you dissolved salt in the distilled water and then closed the switch? Give a reason for the result. ______________________

3. How does distilled water differ from a saltwater solution? ______________________

4. How would you classify distilled water and salt in terms of ionic compounds? ______________________

Formulas of Organic Compounds

Suffix identifies single, double, or triple bonds.

```
      H   H   H
      |   |   |
  H — C — C — C — H
      |   |   |
      H   H   H
```

prop*ane*

```
      H
      |
  H — C — C = C — H
      |   |   |
      H   H   H
```

prop*ene*

```
      H
      |
  H — C — C ≡ C — H
      |
      H
```

prop*yne*

Prefix identifies number of carbon atoms in a chain.

Name	Carbon atoms	Formula	Name	Carbon atoms	Formula
*meth*ane	1	CH_4	*pent*ane	5	C_5H_{12}
*eth*ane	2	C_2H_6	*hex*ane	6	C_6H_{14}
*prop*ane	3	C_3H_8	*hept*ane	7	C_7H_{16}
*but*ane	4	C_4H_{10}	*oct*ane	8	C_8H_{18}

Name ______________________ Date ______________

Problem: How does one determine if a solution is an acid or a base? (text page 58)

Part A Answers:

3(a) ______ (b) ______ (c) ______ (d) ______ (e) ______ (f) ______ (g) ______

Data and Observations:

TABLE 3-4. pH OF KNOWN SUBSTANCES	
Solution	pH
Known Acid	
Known Base	
Known Neutral	

TABLE 3-5. pH OF UNKNOWN SUBSTANCES					
	A	B	C	D	E
Sample Number	Sample Name	Your Guess Acid, Base, Neutral	pH	Actual Results Acid, Base, Neutral	Did your guess match results?
1					
2					
3					
4					
5					
6					
7					
8					
9					
10					
11					
12					

Name ______________________ Date ______________

Questions and Conclusion:

1. Define: (a) acid (b) base (c) neutral solution (d) pH scale (e) ion.

2. Using numbers of the pH scale, describe how you can indicate if a solution is (a) acid (b) base (c) or a neutral solution. ______________________

3. Identify these symbols: (a) OH^- ______________ (b) H^+ ______________
4. Of the solutions tested, name: (a) the weakest acid (b) the strongest acid (c) the weakest base (d) the strongest base (e) any that were neutral. ______________________

5. (a) What was the expected pH of the drinking water? ______________

   (b) What was the actual pH of the drinking water? ______________

   (c) List several factors that may affect the pH of the drinking water. ______________

Conclusion: How does one determine if a solution is an acid or a base?

PLANNING GUIDE	
TEXT	**UNIT 1 Characteristics of Life** **Chapter 4 Cell Structure and Function** **Investigation 4 How can cells be measured with the microscope? p. 84**
TEACHER RESOURCE PACKAGE:	
READING AND STUDY GUIDE	Student Edition, p. 21 Teacher Edition, p. 8
RESOURCE MASTER BOOK	Student Master 4–1. Prokaryotes and Eukaryotes, p. 4–2 Student Master 4–2. Osmosis, p. 4–3 Teaching Master 4–1. Plant Cell, p. 4–4 Teaching Master 4–2. Animal Cell, p. 4–5 Investigation Worksheet, p. 4–6
EVALUATION PROGRAM	Test Masters, p. 13 Alternate Test Masters, p. 149
LABORATORY BIOLOGY: INVESTIGATING LIVING SYSTEMS	9 The Basic Unit of Life, p. 35 10 Cell Membranes and Permeability, p. 43 11 Normal and Plasmolyzed Cells, p. 47
PROBING LEVELS OF LIFE: A LABORATORY MANUAL	8 Basic Cell Structure, p. 23 9 Qualitative and Quantitative Plasmolysis, p. 26

Name ______________________ *Date* ______________

Prokaryotes and Eukaryotes

Biologists have come to realize that the differences between plants and animals are not as significant as the differences between two basic cellular types—prokaryotic and eukaryotic. The eukaryotic cell is the structural unit of all modern, or higher, organisms, including humans. Bacteria and cyanobacteria are the only known prokaryotic cells. It is generally thought that eukaryotic cells represent a more advanced stage of evolution than the prokaryotic cells. As a result of genetic evolution, there are fewer similarities between prokaryotic cells and eukaryotic cells than there are between plants and animals.

The nature of cellular organization and reproduction in prokaryotic cells is quite different from that of eukaryotic cells. The nuclear material of a prokaryotic cell is found in an irregular mass in the cytoplasm called a nucleoid, while that of a eukaryotic cell is enclosed within a nuclear membrane. Prokaryotic cells also lack the mitochondria, endoplasmic reticulum, golgi bodies, and lysosomes found in eukaryotic cells. When chlorophyll is present in prokaryotic cells, it is not organized into chloroplasts as it is in eukaryotic cells that contain chlorophyll. In addition, the cell wall of prokaryotic cells, when present, is made up of a different chemical composition than the cell wall of eukaryotic plant cells. Prokaryotic cells reproduce simply by dividing in half while the reproductive process of eukaryotes is made up of several steps that involve the nucleus and often the combining of gametes, or sex cells.

Another striking difference between prokaryotes and eukaryotes is the fact that the cytoplasm of typical eukaryotes constantly moves and is said to "stream". This results in the motility of many protists, such as in the amoeba. The cytoplasm of prokaryotes, on the contrary, exhibits no apparent streaming.

At one time the prokaryotes were grouped together with all other microorganisms into the kingdom Protista. This kingdom was proposed in 1866 by Ernst Haeckel in order to include in a classification system the growing body of knowledge about microorganisms. The members of Protista were distinguished from members of the plant and animal kingdoms on the basis of a single characteristic: that they existed as unicellular (single-celled) organisms.

It is thought that prokaryotic cells exhibit a very primitive structure. Because of this primitive structure and their supposed ancient origin (bacteria are believed to be the first living things to have developed on Earth), these two groups were placed together by R. H. Whittaker, in 1969, into the Kingdom Monera.

Questions:

1. Why are prokaryotes considered to be primitive when compared to eukaryotes? ______________

____

____

2. At one time there were only two kingdoms, Plantae and Animalia. Then, a third kingdom was formed. What was this third kingdom? Why was it formed? ______________

____

____

3. In time, a fourth kingdom—Monera—was formed. Why? Is it necessary to have this kingdom?

____

____

____

____

____

Name ______________________ Date ______________

Osmosis

Osmosis is the passage of a solvent through a semipermeable membrane from a region of greater concentration to a region of lesser concentration. In an organism, the solvent is usually water and the semipermeable membrane is usually the cell membrane.

Because cell membranes are more permeable to water molecules than to other molecules or ions, cells will swell when placed in dilute solutions and shrink in solutions more concentrated than themselves, as a result of the osmotic movement of water. For example, a sea urchin egg is normally shed into seawater. The egg does not change size because the seawater has the same concentration of water and ions as the fluid within the cell. If the egg is placed in dilute seawater, the egg will swell as water enters the egg. The swollen egg will eventually burst. On the other hand, when placed in seawater to which excess salt has been added, the egg will shrink as water leaves the egg. Human red blood cells placed in solutions more dilute or more concentrated than blood do the same thing.

Solutions that have a concentration of water and ions different from that of a cell are given special names—hypo-osmotic and hyperosmotic. In a hypo-osmotic solution, or dilute solution, the cell swells and its contents become more dilute. In a hyperosmotic solution, or a concentrated solution, the cell shrinks and its contents become more concentrated. A solution that has the same concentration of water and ions as the cell is called an isosmotic solution. Because there is no difference in osmotic pressure, the cell stays the same size in an isosmotic solution.

Explain the following in terms of osmosis:

1. Slugs are perhaps the gardener's worst enemy. These creatures are fond of tender young leaves and shoots. Because slugs are slimy and considered repulsive by most gardeners, they prefer not to pick the slugs up with their hands to dispose of them. Instead, many gardeners kill the slugs by sprinkling salt on them. ______________________

2. You enjoy eating a delicious ham dinner. But you get very thirsty (indicating that your body cells are low on water) after eating the salty meal. ______________________

3. When growing living cells in test tubes, biologists are very careful to use a medium known as Ringer's solution. This solution has a salt concentration exactly equal to the salt concentration found in body and cellular fluids. ______________________

Plant Cell

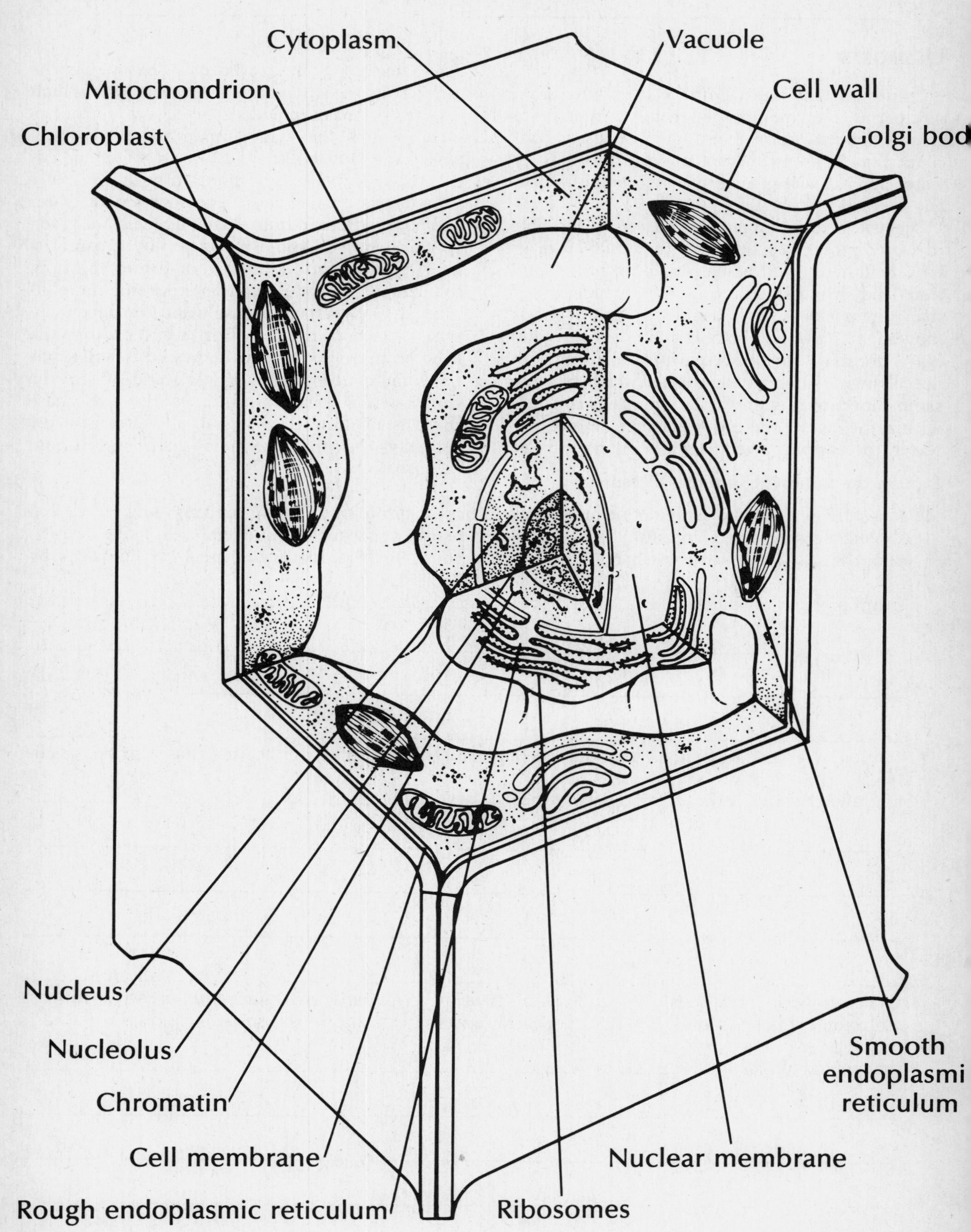
Cytoplasm
Vacuole
Mitochondrion
Cell wall
Chloroplast
Golgi bod
Nucleus
Nucleolus
Chromatin
Cell membrane
Rough endoplasmic reticulum
Ribosomes
Nuclear membrane
Smooth
endoplasmi
reticulum

Animal Cell

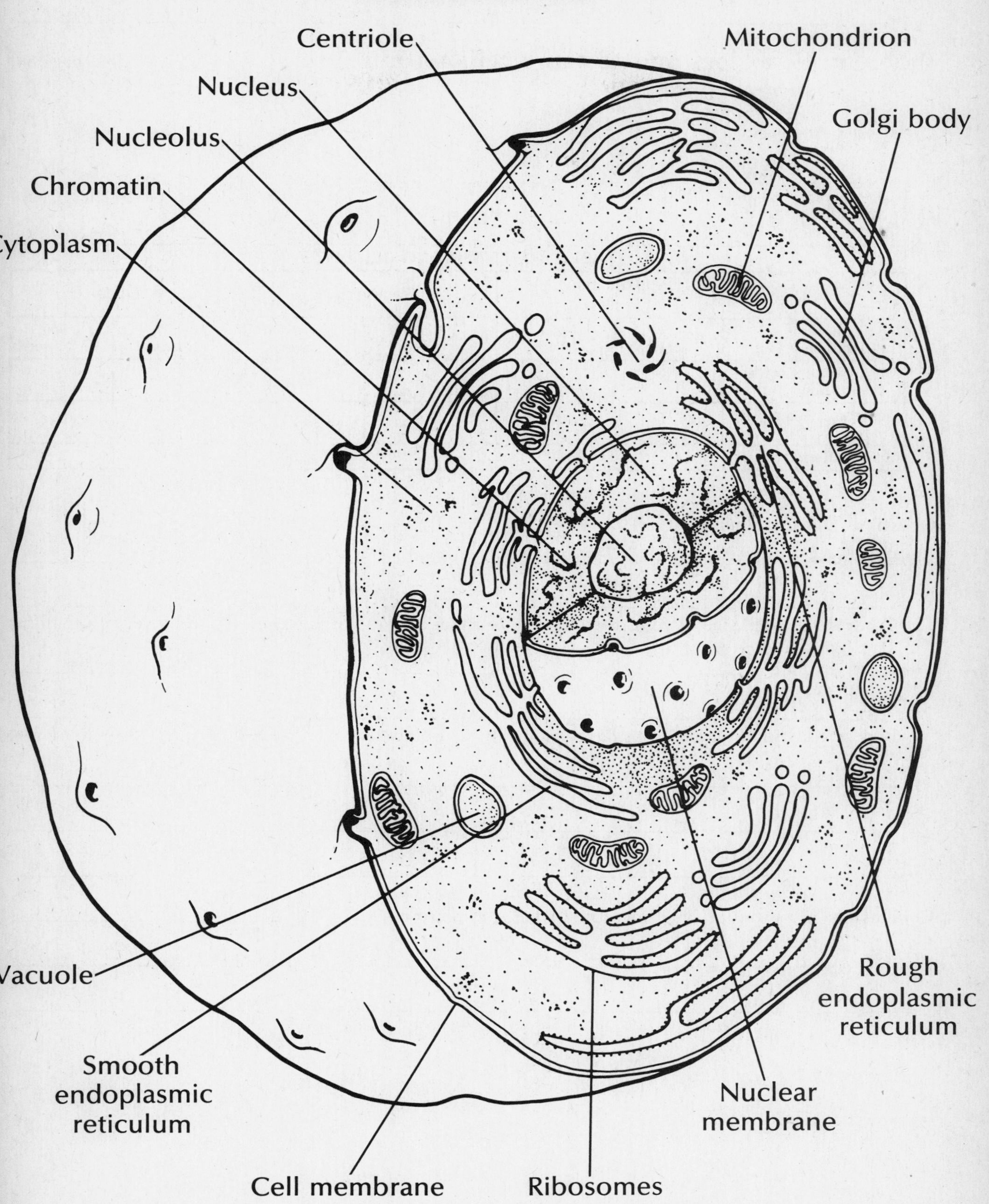
Centriole
Mitochondrion
Nucleus
Golgi body
Nucleolus
Chromatin
ytoplasm
acuole
Smooth endoplasmic reticulum
Rough endoplasmic reticulum
Nuclear membrane
Cell membrane
Ribosomes

Name ________________________ Date ____________

Problem: How does one measure cells within the microscope?

(text page 84)

Question 3 Answers:

(a) __________ (b) __________ (c) __________ (d) __________

Data and Observations:

TABLE 4-2. ESTIMATING CELL SIZE

	Frog red blood cells		*Paramecium*		*Elodea*	
Viewing under low or high power	Low power	High power	Low power	High power	Low power	High power
Number of cells that fit side-by-side						
Diameter of field of view						
Cell size in micrometers						

Questions and Conclusion:

1. Define: (a) millimeter (b) micrometer (c) field of view. ____________

2. Compare the cell size of your frog blood cells under low and high power. Are they very close or far apart? Explain. ____________

3. Repeat question 2, comparing *Paramecium* measurements. Then compare *Elodea* measurements. ____________

Conclusion: How can cells be measured with the microscope? ____________

PLANNING GUIDE	
TEXT	**UNIT 1 Characteristics of Life** **Chapter 5 Energy for Life** **Investigation 5 How does the amount of catalase enzyme compare in different tissues? p. 100**
TEACHER RESOURCE PACKAGE:	
READING AND STUDY GUIDE	Student Edition, p. 27 Teacher Edition, p. 9
RESOURCE MASTER BOOK	Student Master 5–1. Activation Energy and Catalysts, p. 5–2 Student Master 5–2. The Metabolism of Alcohol, p. 5–3 Teaching Master 5–1. Aerobic Respiration Cycle, p. 5–4 Investigation Worksheet, p. 5–5
EVALUATION PROGRAM	Test Masters, p. 17 Alternate Test Masters, p. 151
LABORATORY BIOLOGY: INVESTIGATING LIVING SYSTEMS	12 Proof of Enzyme Action, p. 49 13 Cell Energy, p. 53 14 Factors Influencing the Rate of Yeast Respiration, p. 57
PROBING LEVELS OF LIFE: A LABORATORY MANUAL	10 Extracellular Enzymes, p. 28 11 Measurement of Food Energy, p. 30 12 Yeast Fermentation, p. 32

Name ______________________ Date ______________

Activation Energy and Catalysts

If a chemical reaction is to occur, it is necessary for the reacting molecules to collide with one another as they move about in a random way. However, unless the temperature is high enough, most molecules simply rebound from collisions without reacting. An example is the reaction between hydrogen and oxygen that forms water. The reaction will take place explosively if the temperature is high enough. But in a mixture of hydrogen and oxygen at room temperature, the molecules collide repeatedly with one another and rebound without change. The situation is similar to that shown in Figure 5–1.

A ball that is resting in a depression on a hillside will give energy if it can roll down the hill. The ball will not roll down the hill unless its energy is first raised enough to get it out of the depression.

In the case of hydrogen and oxygen molecules in a container at room temperature, the molecules will not have enough energy to form the transition state. If a lighted match is placed in the container, the molecules near the flame gain enough energy to react when they collide with one another. The overall energy released is transferred to nearby molecules causing the reaction to spread quickly to all parts of the container. The added energy molecules must have to form the transition state is called the activation energy of the reaction.

In chemical reactions that have high activation energies, the reacting molecules can be lifted over the energy barrier by raising the temperature. Frequently, however, it is undesirable to carry out a given reaction at high temperatures. Another approach is to find a way to lower the energy barrier. The energy barrier can be lowered by a substance called a catalyst. A catalyst binds with certain molecules that form an intermediate compound. The intermediate compound has a transition state that has a lower energy. The reaction can then occur at lower temperatures and thus at a faster rate.

FIGURE 5–1.

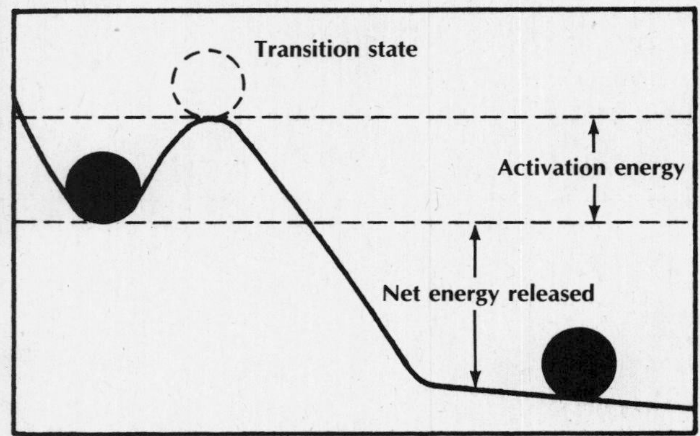

FIGURE 5–2.

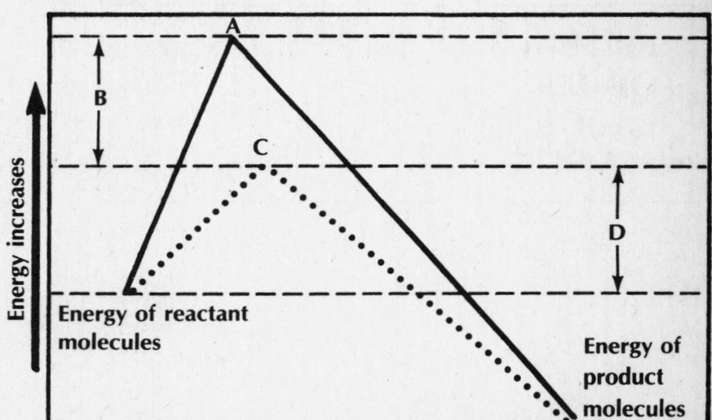

Questions:

Use Figure 5–2 to answer questions 1–4.

1. Which letter represents the transition state when a catalyst is absent? ______
2. Which letter represents the transition state when a catalyst is present? ______
3. The activation energy is represented by which letter when a catalyst is present? ______.
4. The activation energy is represented by which letter when a catalyst is absent? ______.
5. Chemical reactions within biological systems rarely take place without a catalyst. The catalysts are specific proteins called enzymes. Why are enzymes so beneficial (and necessary) to metabolic reactions? ______________________

Name ______________________ *Date* ______________

The Metabolism of Alcohol

Alcohol, when swallowed, is completely absorbed by the stomach and intestines, passing directly into the blood. From the blood, alcohol diffuses into all the body organs and has a marked effect on the central nervous system. Eventually, 95 percent of the alcohol taken into the body is broken down in the liver. The remaining 5 percent is excreted unchanged in the urine and the breath. This latter fact forms the basis for the use of the "Breathalyzer Test" in the detection of drunken drivers. Most alcoholic beverages contain little or no proteins or vitamins and therefore have little nutritional value.

The liver is the major organ that removes alcohol from the blood and converts the alcohol into other chemicals. The liver metabolizes alcohol in a two-step process. In the first step, two hydrogen atoms are removed from the alcohol molecule. In the second step, oxygen is added to the dehydrogenated molecule, producing the nontoxic acetate. Acetate leaves the liver, enters the blood and is eventually converted to carbon dioxide and water in other body tissues. These two steps are illustrated in Figure 5–1.

Each of the two steps are catalyzed by an enzyme. The enzymes are found in the cytoplasm of the liver cells. The hydrogen atoms that are removed from the alcohol molecules are carried by a substance known as NAD (nicotine adenine dinucleotide) to the mitochondria. There, the hydrogen atoms combine with oxygen atoms to form water.

The capacity of the liver to break down, or metabolize, alcohol is limited. Consuming large quantities of alcohol over a short period of time can be fatal. A high level of alcohol in the blood system can cause death, often from severe depression of the breathing centers at the base of the brain. Heavy drinkers can suffer from permanent physiological changes. These changes may negatively affect the intestines, circulatory system, lungs, kidneys, pancreas, and nervous system.

The organ most affected by heavy use of alcohol is the liver. Fat tends to accumulate in the liver's cells, producing a "fatty liver." Continued long term drinking causes cirrhosis, a condition in which parts of the liver degenerate and normal cells become replaced by scar tissue. Chronic cirrhosis can lead to death.

FIGURE 5–1.

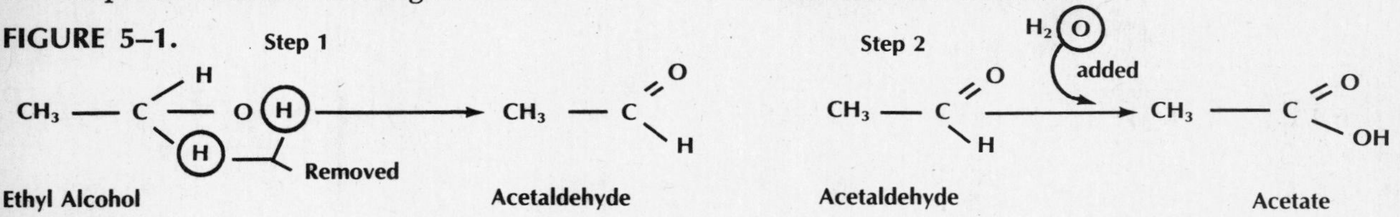

Step 1

CH_3 — C(H)(H) — O(H) → CH_3 — C(=O)H

(H) (H) Removed

Ethyl Alcohol → Acetaldehyde

Step 2

H_2(O) added

CH_3 — C(=O)H → CH_3 — C(=O)OH

Acetaldehyde → Acetate

Questions:

1. How does alcohol enter the circulatory system? ______________________

____

2. What metabolic fact has permitted the development and use of the "Breathalyzer Test"?

____

____

3. How does the liver metabolize alcohol? ______________________

____

____

4. Why can drinking a lot of alcohol over a short period of time be harmful?

____

____

____

Aerobic Respiration Cycle

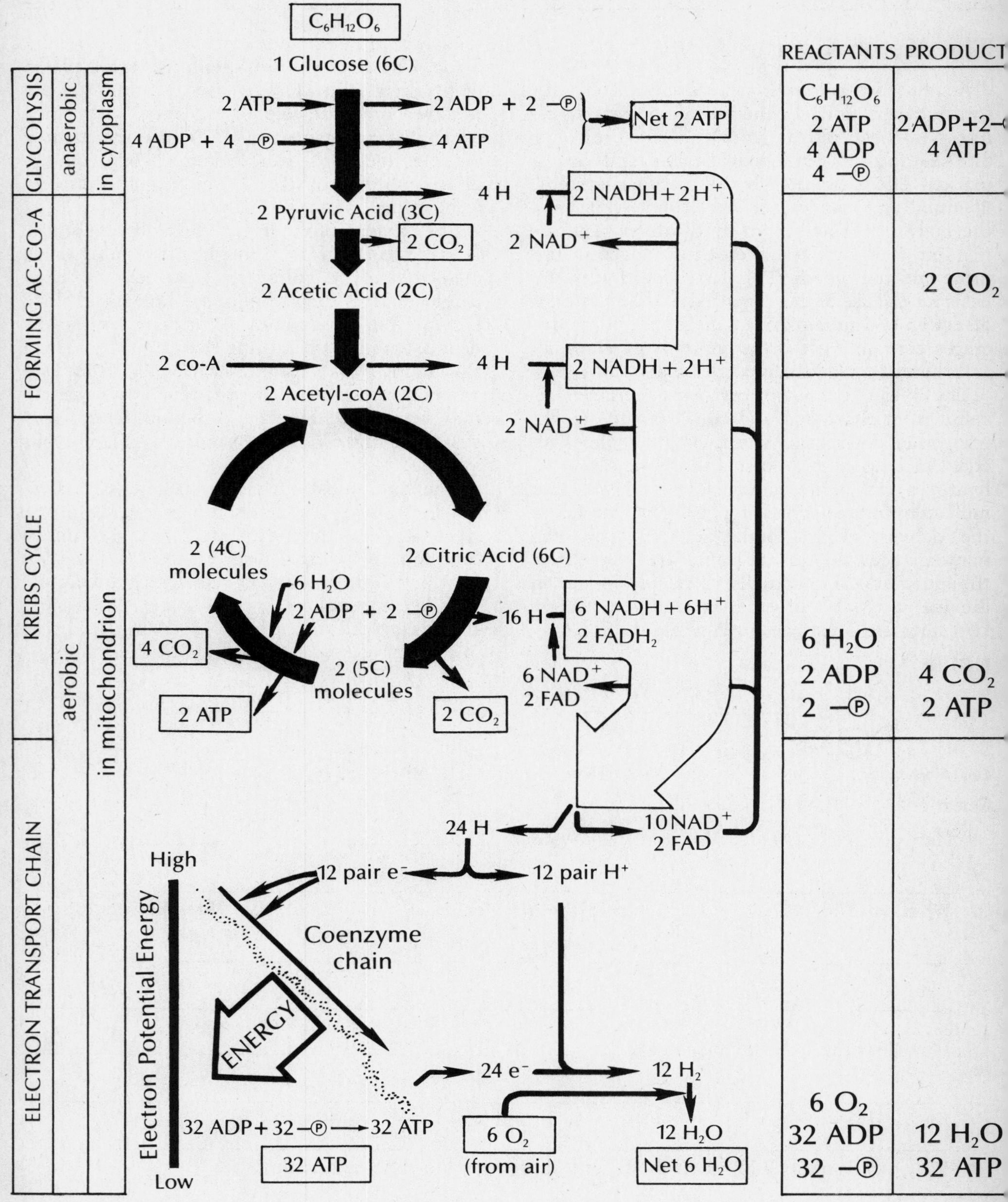

REACTANTS	PRODUCT
$C_6H_{12}O_6$ 2 ATP 4 ADP 4 –Ⓟ	2ADP+2– 4 ATP
	2 CO_2
6 H_2O 2 ADP 2 –Ⓟ	4 CO_2 2 ATP
6 O_2 32 ADP 32 –Ⓟ	12 H_2O 32 ATP

Net: 36 ADP + 36 –Ⓟ + $C_6H_{12}O_6$ + $6O_2$ ⟶ $6CO_2$ + $6H_2O$ + 36 ATP

Name ______________________ *Date* ______________

Problem: How does the amount of catalase enzyme compare in different tissues? (text page 100)

Part A Answers:

6. (a) ________ (b) ______________________ (c) ____________

(d) ______________ (e) ______________________________

____

Data and Observations:

TABLE 5-1. COMPARISON OF THE AMOUNTS OF CATALASE IN DIFFERENT TISSUES				
Cell Type	Unboiled		Boiled	
	Chunk	Chopped	Chunk	Chopped
Carrot				
Potato				
Liver				
Muscle				

Name ______________________ *Date* ______________

Questions and Conclusion:

1. List four properties of all enzymes. ______________________

2. How were you able to judge if the enzyme was or was not working in this activity? ______________________

3. In general, do plant or animal cells contain more catalase? Give evidence from your data.

4. (a) In general, do chunk, unboiled cells release more, less, or about the same amount of catalase, as chopped, unboiled cells? Give evidence from your data. (b) Offer a possible hypothesis to explain your data. ______________________

5. In general, do chunk, unboiled cells release more, less, or about the same amount of catalase as chunk boiled cells? Give evidence from your data. ______________________

6. In general, do chunk, boiled cells release more, less, or about the same amount of catalase as chopped boiled cells? Give evidence from your data. ______________________

7. Offer possible hypotheses to explain the data you obtained in questions 5 and 6. ______________________

Conclusion: How does the amount of catalase enzyme compare in different tissues? ______________________

PLANNING GUIDE	
TEXT	**UNIT 2 Heredity** **Chapter 6 The Cellular Basis of Heredity** **Investigation 6 How do you observe chromosomes in cells? p. 124**
TEACHER RESOURCE PACKAGE:	
READING AND STUDY GUIDE	Student Edition, p. 33 Teacher Edition, p. 11
RESOURCE MASTER BOOK	Student Master 6–1. Radiation and Mutations, p. 6–2 Student Master 6–2. The Genetic Peril of the Cheetah, p. 6–3 Teaching Master 6–1. Stages of Mitosis, p. 6–4 Teaching Master 6–2. Stages of Meiosis, p. 6–5 Investigation Worksheet, p. 6–6
EVALUATION PROGRAM	Test Masters, p. 21 Alternate Test Masters, p. 153
LABORATORY BIOLOGY: INVESTIGATING LIVING SYSTEMS	15 Mitosis, p. 61 16 Time for Mitosis, p. 65 17 Comparing Mitosis and Meiosis, p. 69
PROBING LEVELS OF LIFE: A LABORATORY MANUAL	13 Spontaneous Generation, p. 34 14 Significance of Time and Mitosis, p. 36

Name ______________________ Date ______________

Radiation and Mutations

For more than 50 years it has been known that X rays and the energy emitted by the decay of radioactive elements can be dangerous to humans and plants. At extremely high dosages of such radiation, there is massive destruction to the animal nervous system and death occurs almost instantly. But most of the effects of radiation appear gradually and usually are due to the genetic damage, or mutations, of individual cells. A single, low exposure to radiation may not cause immediate symptoms, but permanent damage to body cells can occur. These harmful types of radiation are said to be mutagenic.

When mutations occur in the germ cells of the gonads, the parts of the body that produce either sperm or eggs, the mutations can be passed on to future generations. If mutations occur in other body cells, they can interfere with the normal genetic controls, causing cells to undergo rapid and uncontrolled divisions. These uncontrolled growths of cells are called cancers.

There are two types of radiation. One type is electromagnetic radiation. This type of radiation includes sunlight, radio waves, X rays, and microwaves. High-energy radiation, such as X rays, are capable of penetrating deep into living tissue. Sunlight, however, only affects the surface of the skin. The other type of radiation is called particulate radiation. This type of radiation is released as radioactive elements disintegrate. Uranium and radium are two well-known examples of elements in Earth's crust that are radioactive.

The amount of damage to the cells of a tissue by harmful radiation depends upon the amount of radiation that is absorbed by the tissue. Bone, for example, is a dense tissue and will absorb more of a certain radiation than will muscle, kidney, or brain tissue. Health physicists, scientists concerned with the biological effects of radiation, have established a unit that takes into account the biological effectiveness of radiation in humans. This unit is known as a rem. It indicates a standard amount of biological damage resulting from various sources. For example, people receive about 100 to 110 mrems (a mrem represents a millirem, one-thousandth of a rem) per year from natural background radiation such as sunlight and radioactive elements in Earth's crust.

The amount of radiation a person may receive safely depends on many factors. One of these factors is the rate at which radiation is received. About 60 percent of the people who are exposed to a single dose of high-energy radiation equivalent to 100 rems will develop moderate radiation sickness. The same dose, spread out over an entire lifetime, will not produce illness, but will probably shorten one's life by about 1 percent, or 8 months.

1. How many total rems of radiation must be absorbed in order for about 60 percent of the population to experience radiation sickness? ______________
2. A 100 rem dose of radiation spread over a lifetime may shorten a person's life by how much? ______________
3. The effects of radiation are cumulative. If a person were to receive 110 mrems of natural radiation per year, how many mrems would that add up to in 70 years? ______________ How many rems would that be? ______________
4. With knowledge of the relationship between radiation and mutations, how might you explain the relationship between exposure to the sun and skin cancer? ______________

Name ______________________ Date ______________

The Genetic Peril of the Cheetah

The cheetah is truly one of nature's marvels. A virtual running machine, its skull is small and lightweight, its limbs are long and slender, and its spinal column is unusually flexible. The cheetah's heart, lungs, and adrenal glands are all enlarged, enhancing the animal's ability to accelerate during a high-speed chase—a chase often clocked at up to 112 kilometers per hour. Unlike other cats, the cheetah's claws are always extended like cleats, enabling it to grip the ground. These adaptations have made the cheetah an effective hunter on the flat, open savannahs of central and southern Africa.

In spite of the cheetah's skill as a runner and hunter, the species seems to be headed for extinction. While the cheetah's body structure is superbly adapted to a running existence, the cheetah has traits that are considered maladaptive. It is extremely vulnerable to disease, and there is a high infant mortality rate. Although the cheetah is the world's fastest mammal, it can run rapidly for only a few hundred yards before it tires. After a typical chase, the cheetah collapses for half an hour in order to regain its strength. During this time, it is vulnerable to attack by other predators and can lose either its life or its catch. Cheetahs are rather timid creatures, with some 50 percent of their kills snatched away by more aggressive lions, leopards, and hyenas. The cheetah is now limited to a few, small areas in Africa. There are about 20 000 cheetahs left on Earth today.

Research over the last six years suggests that the cheetah has somehow lost most of its genetic variation. Scientific studies have revealed that, genetically, each cheetah is nearly identical to every other cheetah. In other words, the species exhibits genetic uniformity. Genetic uniformity hampers the ability of a species to adapt to environmental changes, such as temperature shifts, drought, glaciation, and even the emergence of new viruses or bacteria. Such uniformity is usually the result of intensive inbreeding.

Scientists have recently puzzled over the causes for the probable inbreeding and resultant genetic uniformity in the cheetah. The most plausible hypothesis to date is that at some point in the past the cheetah went through a severe population reduction. The population reduction was followed by inbreeding, which diminished genetic variability. How severe would the population reduction have to be in order to lead to genetic uniformity? Studies have shown that a population reduced to only seven individuals will retain about 95 percent of its original genetic variation. The population can retain that variation only if the survivors reproduce rapidly enough to expand the size of the population. Slow reproduction in a small population decreases the likelihood that different genetic types will survive. Scientists suspect that at least once in the past the cheetah's population dropped to only a few individuals. What caused the cheetah population to dwindle is not known. The possibilities include catastrophic climatic changes, viral or bacterial plagues, and even hunting by humans.

Several other animals have gone through severe population reductions and seem to be recovering. One example is the northern elephant seal. This population was reduced to about 20 animals. Yet after the passage of protective legislation, the seal population grew. Today the number of elephant seals reaches into the tens of thousands. Can the cheetah have the same good fortune?

Questions:

1. Provide a definition of genetic uniformity. ______________________

2. How does genetic uniformity occur? ______________________

3. How does genetic uniformity hamper the survival of the cheetah? ______________________

Stages of Mitosis

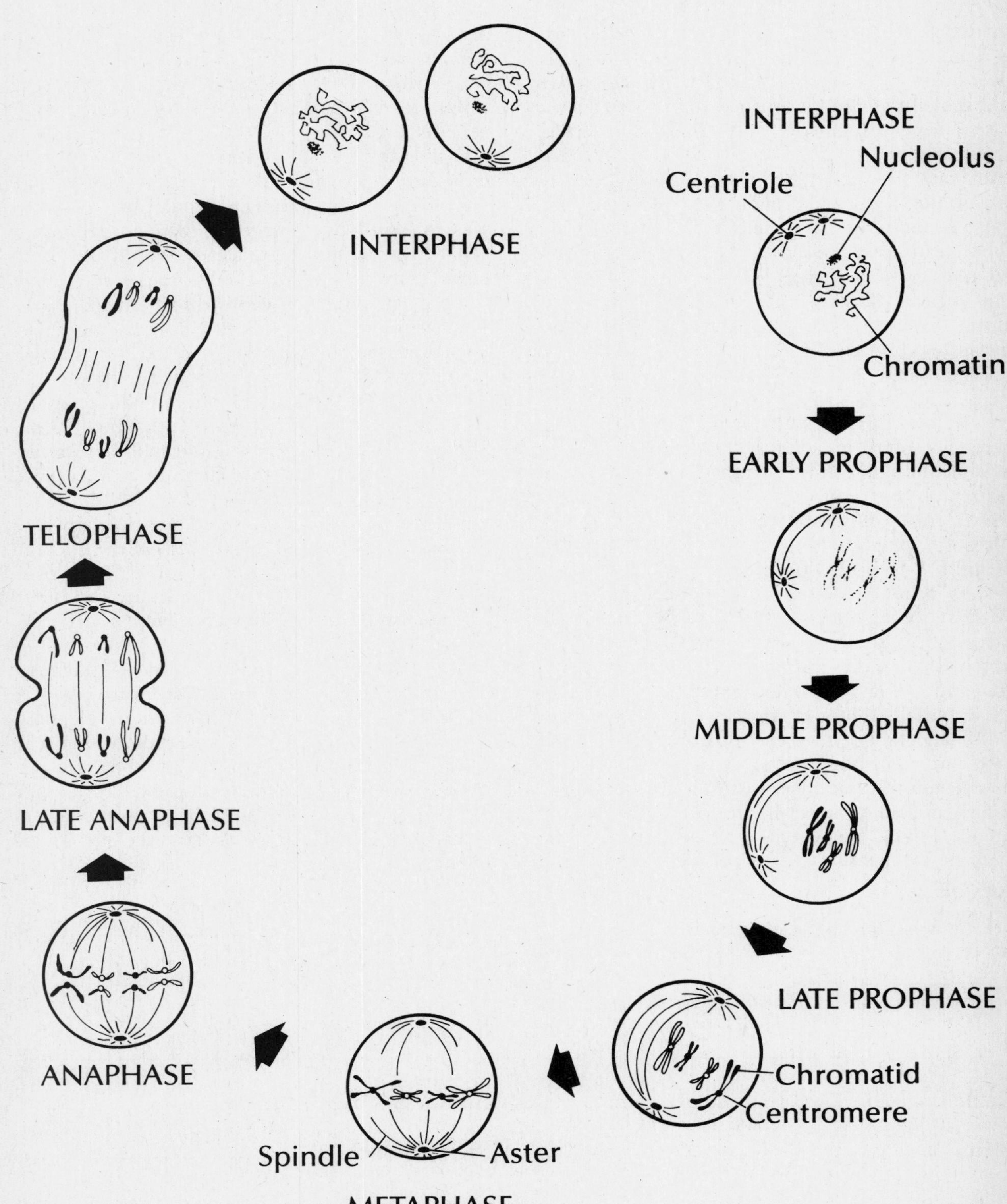

Stages of Meiosis

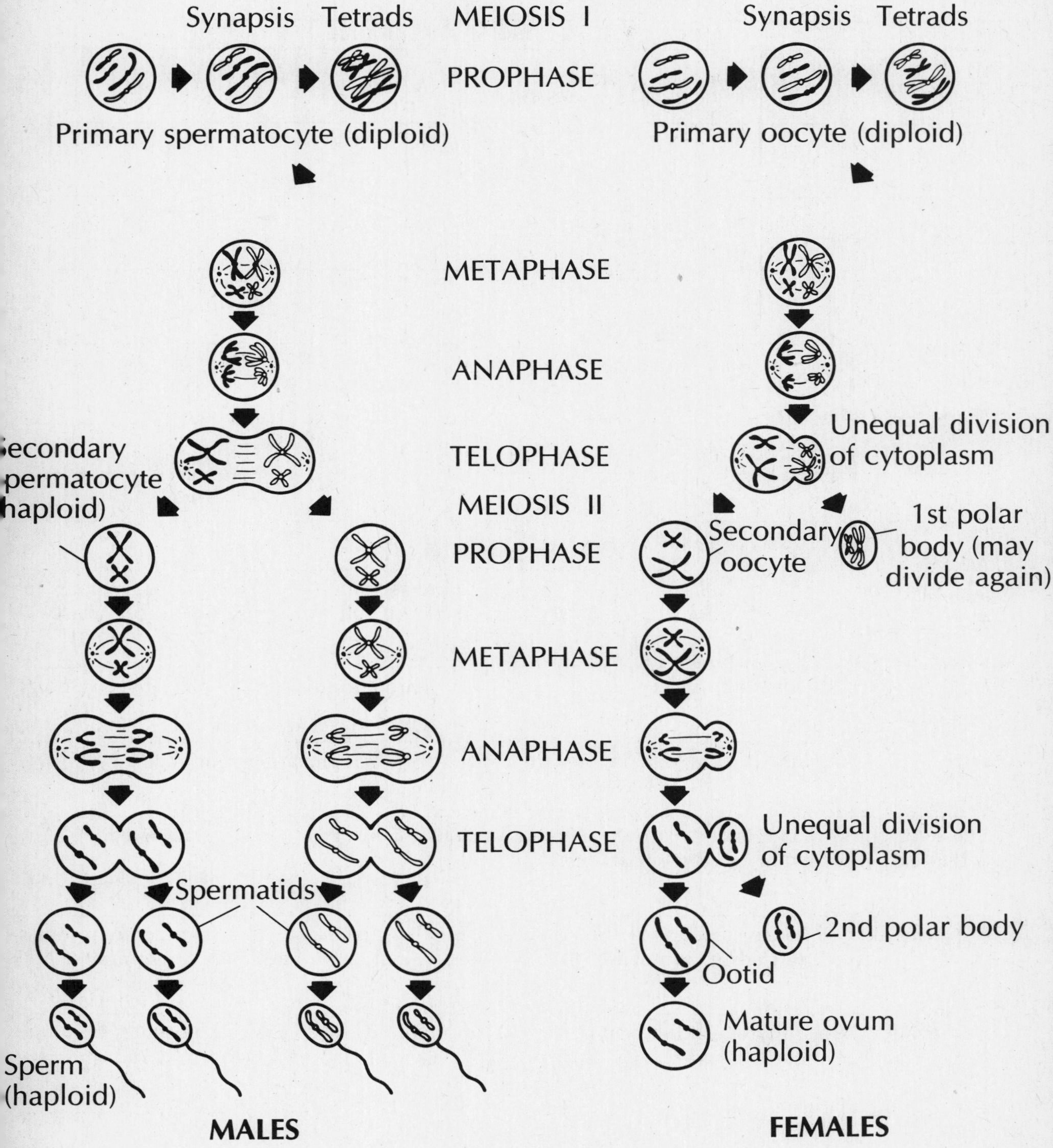

Name ______________________ Date ______________

Problem: How can one observe chromosomes in cells? (text page 124)

Data and Observations:

TABLE 6-2. CHROMOSOME APPEARANCE		
Organism	Diagram of Chromosomes	Phases of Mitosis Seen
Bean root tip		
Bean root tip		
Drosophila salivary gland		X

Questions and Conclusion:

1. Define the following terms: (a) chromosome (b) mitosis (c) interphase (d) cell cycle. ______________
2. (a) Using your data from Table 6-2, list the phases of mitosis you observed in the bean root tip. (b) Were there more cells undergoing a particular phase of the cell cycle than any other phase? If so, which phase did you observe most often? ______________
3. How did the following help in the observations of the chromosomes: (a) staining (b) squashing?
4. Why did you use the tip of the root and not the entire root when preparing your slide?
5. The term chromosome is derived from chromo- (meaning color) and -some (meaning body). How is the term chromosome an appropriate one?
6. If human skin tissue instead of root tips had been used in part A: (a) how many chromosomes would you expect to find in each cell? (b) would the skin cells have been undergoing mitosis? (c) explain your answer to (b). ______________
7. (a) Consider the tissue from the salivary glands of *Drosophila.* How do the chromosomes from one cell compare to those from any other cell? (b) How does the situation described in 7(a) illustrate genetic continuity? ______________

Conclusion: How can you observe chromosomes in cells?

PLANNING GUIDE	
TEXT	**UNIT 2 Heredity** **Chapter 7 Principles of Heredity** **Investigation 7 How similar are traits of offspring to those of the parents? p. 142**
TEACHER RESOURCE PACKAGE:	
READING AND STUDY GUIDE	Student Edition, p. 39 Teacher Edition, p. 12
RESOURCE MASTER BOOK	Student Master 7–1. Punnett Square, p. 7–2 Student Master 7–2. Pedigrees, p. 7–3 Teaching Master 7–1. Punnett Squares I, p. 7–4 Teaching Master 7–2. Punnett Squares II, p. 7–5 Investigation Worksheet, p. 7–6
EVALUATION PROGRAM	Test Masters, p. 25 Alternate Test Masters, p. 155
LABORATORY BIOLOGY: INVESTIGATING LIVING SYSTEMS	18 Finding Phenotypes and Genotypes for One Trait, p. 73 19 Finding Phenotypes and Genotypes for Two Traits, p. 77 20 Pedigree Studies, p. 81
PROBING LEVELS OF LIFE: A LABORATORY MANUAL	15 Probability and Mendelian Genetics, p. 38 16 *Drosophila* Genetics, p. 43

Name ______________________ Date ______________

Punnett Square

One way to quickly calculate the possible genotypes and phenotypes of offspring is to use the so-called checkerboard or Punnett Square method. Use of the Punnett square is quite easy when dealing with one pair of genes for each parent. When dealing with several pairs of genes, the probability method for calculating genotypes and phenotypes becomes easier.

To use the Punnett square, the genotype of one parent is written above the checkerboard and the genotype of the other parent is written along the left side of the checkerboard. The new gene pairs of the offspring are obtained by combining the parent's genes that are above each row of the checkerboard with those along the side of the checkerboard.

A Punnett square for leaf shape in *Coleus,* a plant of the mint family is provided below. In *Coleus* deep-lobed leaves are dominant over shallow-lobed leaves. One parent is homozygous dominant (and deeply-lobed) and its genotype is *DD.* This genotype is written above the checkerboard. The other parent is homozygous recessive (and is shallowly lobed). It's genotype is *dd* and is written along the left side of the checkerboard. The possible genotypes of the possible offspring are determined by multiplying the parent's gene (located along the top of each row of boxes) by the parent's gene located along the side of each row of boxes. In square 1 the genotype would be *Dd.* By using the same method, the genotype of square 2 would also be *Dd.* Complete the Punnett square in Figure 7–1 by filing squares 3 and 4.

The Punnett square you have completed represents the possible genotypes and phenotypes of the first filial (or F_1) generation. Based on your understanding of this Punnett square, answer questions 1 and 2.

Complete the Punnett square (still dealing with *Coleus* leaf shape) in Figure 7–2 using the two offspring from the F_1 generation above as parents. Remember that the dominant gene is always written first. This new Punnett square represents the second filial (or F_2) generation. Use the information gained from the F_2 generation to answer questions 3–6.

FIGURE 7–1.

	D	*D*
d	*Dd*	*Dd*
d		

FIGURE 7–2.

	D	*d*
D		
d		

Questions:

1. What is (are) the genotype(s) of the F_1 generation? ______________
2. What is (are) the phenotype(s) of the F_1 generation? ______________
3. What is (are) the genotype(s) of the F_2 generation? ______________
4. What is (are) the phenotype(s) of the F_2 generation? ______________
5. What ratio expresses the possible relative numbers of the genotype(s) of the F_2 generation? ______________
6. What ratio expresses the possible relative numbers of the phenotype(s) of the F_2 generation? ______________

Name ______________________ Date ______________

Pedigrees

Human geneticists and animal breeders apply Mendelian principles and laws when analyzing pedigrees, the family diagrams that represent the phenotypes of offspring. Pedigrees are useful because traits with simple patterns of inheritance can often be traced accurately. For many traits prediction can be made about the likelihood of expression of a trait in future generations.

A stumbling block to the use of human pedigrees is that most human traits are too complex to be identified as dominant or recessive, and many that are do not have simple patterns of inheritance. For some traits, phenotypes (for example, deafness) may behave as dominant in some families while as recessive in other families. This can occur if several genes are responsible for a particular phenotype. Recessive genes in families are sometimes difficult to keep track of in a pedigree because they remain hidden by their dominant alleles generation after generation. It may not be known if an individual actually carries a recessive allele.

A few human traits, however, have been associated with specific genes and their patterns of inheritance are well known. For these traits, pedigrees can be helpful in determining the genetic patterns within a family. The usefulness of a pedigree to determine the genotypes and phenotypes of a known trait for a particular family is illustrated in the following example. In this pedigree, attached earlobes result from a double-recessive genotype *(aa)*. Study the pedigree and, with your knowledge of genetics, answer the questions that follow.

FIGURE 7–1.

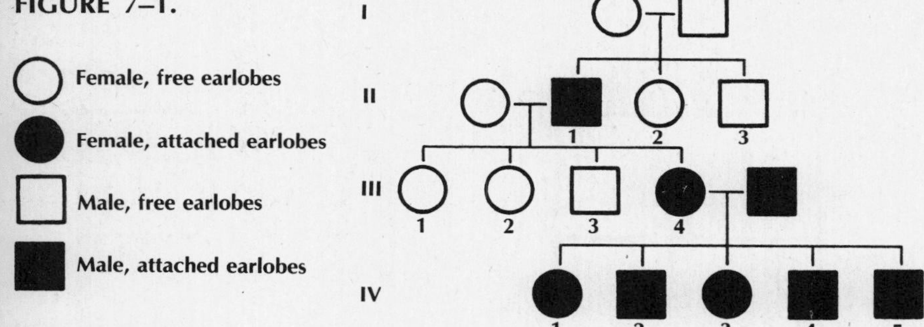

Questions:

1. In generation II, one male offspring has attached ear-lobes. (A = free ear-lobes, a = attached ear-lobes). What are the genotypes of his parents? ______________________
2. In generation II, what are the possible genotypes of children 2 and 3? Explain.

____

____

3. What must the genotype of the wife of child 1 in generation II be in order to have a child in generation III that has attached ear-lobes? Explain. ______________________

____

4. What is (are) the genotype(s) of children 1, 2, and 3, in generation III? Explain.

____

____

5. What would be the possible genotype(s) and phenotype(s) of the offspring in generation V if one of the children in generation IV were to marry a person who was homozygous for free ear-lobes? Explain. ______________________

____

Punnett Squares I

Punnett Squares II

Name ______________________ Date ______________

Problem: How similar are traits of offspring to those of the parents? (text page 142)

Data and Observations:

TABLE 7-3. PHENOTYPES OF PARENTS AND CHILDREN					
Trait	Father	Mother	1st Child	2nd Child	3rd Child
Fingers					
Hair color					
Teeth					
Earlobes					
Rh blood type					
Tongue rolling					
Mid-digit hair					
Height					
Huntington's disease					

Questions and Conclusion:

1. (a) In this simulation, how many chromosomes did each child receive from each of the parents? (b) If this were an actual situation, how many chromosomes would each child receive from each parent? ______________________
2. Explain how the element of chance enters into inheritance of traits. ______________________
3. Using the data you generated for the first child, determine: (a) the number of traits it inherited that were exactly like those of the father (b) the number of traits it inherited that were exactly like those of the mother. ______________________
4. (a) Using your data from the second child, answer questions 3(a) and 3(b). (b) How many traits does the second child have in common with the first child? ______________________
5. (a) Using your data from the third child, answer questions 3(a) and 3(b). (b) How many traits does the third child have in common with the second child? ______________________

Conclusion: How similar are traits of offspring to those of the parents? ______________________

PLANNING GUIDE	
TEXT	**UNIT 2 Heredity** **Chapter 8 Genes and Chromosomes** **Investigation 8 How does a genetic disease affect red blood cells? p. 162**
TEACHER RESOURCE PACKAGE:	
READING AND STUDY GUIDE	Student Edition, p. 45 Teacher Edition, p. 14
RESOURCE MASTER BOOK	Student Master 8–1. Sex-Related Traits in Humans, p. 8–2 Student Master 8–2. Purebred Dogs, p. 8–3 Teaching Master 8–1. Sex-linked Traits, p. 8–4 Investigation Worksheet, p. 8–5
EVALUATION PROGRAM	Test Masters, p. 29 Alternate Test Masters, p. 157
LABORATORY BIOLOGY: INVESTIGATING LIVING SYSTEMS	21 A Chromosome Study, p. 85 22 Heredity or Environment, p. 87 23 Sex-linked or not Sex-linked, p. 89
PROBING LEVELS OF LIFE: A LABORATORY MANUAL	17 Detecting Chromosome Problems by Karyotyping, p. 47 18 Human Pedigree Genetics, p. 49

Name ______________________ Date ______________

Sex-Related Traits in Humans

The fact that human males have an X and a Y chromosome, and females have two X chromosomes and no Y chromosome, raises some interesting genetic possibilities. This is especially so when it is realized that the sex chromosomes carry genes other than those that determine sex. One should expect to discover that inheritance patterns are related to the sex of an individual. Genes located exclusively on the X chromosome are said to be sex-linked. Genes located exclusively on the Y chromosome are said to be holandric. Because holandric genes appear only on the Y chromosome, these genes produce their effect only in the males. Other mechanisms produce traits that are limited to one sex or another. The genes responsible for these traits are said to be sex-limited. The dominance of a given allele may depend upon the sex of the bearer. The trait that is expressed is said to be sex-influenced.

There are more than 60 sex-linked traits that have been identified in humans. Most of these appear to be due to recessive genes. Red-green color blindness was the first sex-linked trait to be described, and it is the most commonly encountered sex-linked trait. Hemophilia, a well known disorder in which blood clotting is deficient, is also controlled by a sex-linked gene. Other sex-linked traits in humans include two forms of diabetes, nonfunctional sweat glands, absence of central incisors, certain forms of deafness, night blindness, juvenile glaucoma, juvenile muscular dystrophy, and white forelock (a patch of light hair on the front of the head).

There are not many clearly established, holandric genes. One common to the population of India, however, is one that causes excessive hair development on the ears.

Sex-limited genes are different from sex-linked genes. Sex-linked genes may be expressed in either sex, although they may be expressed more in one sex than the other. Sex-limited genes express their effects only in one sex or the other, and their action is clearly related to the production of sex hormones. Sex-limited traits are mostly responsible for secondary sex characteristics. Beard development is such a sex-limited trait. Men normally have beards while women usually do not.

Sex-influenced genes are those whose dominance is influenced by the sex of the bearer. Pattern baldness exhibits such a genetic relationship. In pattern baldness, hair gradually thins on the top of the head. This characteristic is more common in males but may occur in females due to the fact that the gene for pattern baldness is dominant in males but recessive in females.

Questions:

1. Defective tooth enamel is due to a dominant sex-linked gene (E). A female homozygous for defective tooth enamel and a male with normal tooth enamel have three children, 2 girls and 1 boy.

   What are the possible genotypes and phenotypes of these children? ______________________

   ____

   ____

   ____

2. A female is heterozygous for hemophilia (Hh). Her husband does not have hemophilia. Could they produce a hemophiliac son? Could they have a hemophiliac daughter? Explain.

   ____

   ____

   ____

3. A male and a female are both heterozygous for pattern baldness. Will both be bald? Explain.

   ____

   ____

Name ______________________ Date ______________

Purebred Dogs

You have probably heard that mutts, dogs that are not purebred, are healthier than purebred dogs. Whether that statement always holds true is a matter for debate. One has to wonder, however, how much a breeder can guarantee the health of a purebred dog when one sees the many genetic disorders that affect such animals.

Perhaps the most common genetic disorder of purebred dogs is hip dysplasia. This disorder occurs mostly in larger dogs, such as German shepherds, Labrador retrievers, and Great Danes. Hip dysplasia occurs when the muscles do not develop and reach maturity at the same rate as the skeleton. This allows the hip, which depends upon muscle power for stability, to pull apart. A series of events is triggered that ultimately causes the hip socket and the head of the femur, or hip bone, to begin pulling apart from one another. Hip dysplasia often cripples a dog.

Hip dysplasia was recognized as a disease in the 1950s. At that time, most dog breeders believed it was caused by a dominant gene and it was assumed that hip dysplasia could be eliminated by destroying or by not breeding affected dogs. This soon proved to be a futile exercise as breeders found that they could mate two normal dogs, yet still end up with offspring that suffered from hip dysplasia. Additional research has revealed that the disease is caused by the cumulative effects of a number of genes. Hip dysplasia is said to be a polygenic disorder.

To date, the best way to eliminate hip dysplasia is to breed dogs who have pedigree depth for normal hips. Pedigree depth for normal hips means that the bloodline has been free of hip dysplasia for at least three generations. While this method does not guarantee that all offspring will be free of the disease, it does substantially reduce the number of offspring that will suffer from it.

Hip dysplasia is not the only genetic disorder that affects purebred dogs. Disorders of the eyes, ears, and nose can cause more than discomfort for the dog and can needlessly handicap the animal. Deafness is inherited by dalmatians, bulldogs, bullterriers, and many white-coated breeds. Breathing difficulties often plague pugs, bulldogs, boxers, and other breeds with very short noses. They often suffer fits of sneezing and snorting.

Disorders of the eyes include cataracts, entropion, and glaucoma. Cataracts are opaque areas that develop within the lens of the eye. Cataracts interfere with vision and can lead to blindness. Accidents, injuries, and old age can cause cataracts, and they can also be inherited. Irish setters, Afghan hounds, German shepherds, poodles, schnauzers, cocker spaniels, and several types of retrievers are breeds that suffer from inherited cataracts. A dog with entropion has an upper or lower eyelid that is turned, a condition that causes the cornea of the eye to become irritated. Permanent corneal damage can result. Nearly all cases of entropion are inherited and particularly afflict chow chows, Irish setters, Kerry blue terriers, Saint Bernards, and several breeds of retrievers. Glaucoma occurs when drainage of the fluid in the eyes is impaired. The fluid builds up in the eyes and can result in blindness if not corrected. Glaucoma can be caused by an injury or infection, and it is inherited as well. The following breeds of dogs are known to carry genes for glaucoma: cocker spaniels, beagle, poodle, Alaskan malamute, basset hound, and many kinds of terriers.

Questions:

1. You plan to buy a German shepherd puppy. You soon discover that the mother is a two year old with a mild case of hip dysplasia. The hip condition of the father is unknown but he is five years old and has some eye problems. Would you buy a puppy from this litter? Why? Why not?
2. You have purchased a Saint Bernard puppy from a well-known breeder. The breeder assures you that the puppy's parents have pedigree depth for normal hips. You hope to breed this dog when it is three years old. However, at the age of two your dog begins to show signs of hip dysplasia. Will you still breed your dog? Why? Why not?
3. You plan to buy a white, toy poodle. What questions might you ask the breeder before you purchase a puppy? What would you do if the breeder did not have enough information about the puppy's pedigree to answer your questions?
4. Should a dog breeder assume any responsibilities when selling his or her animals? What responsibilities?

Sex-linked Traits

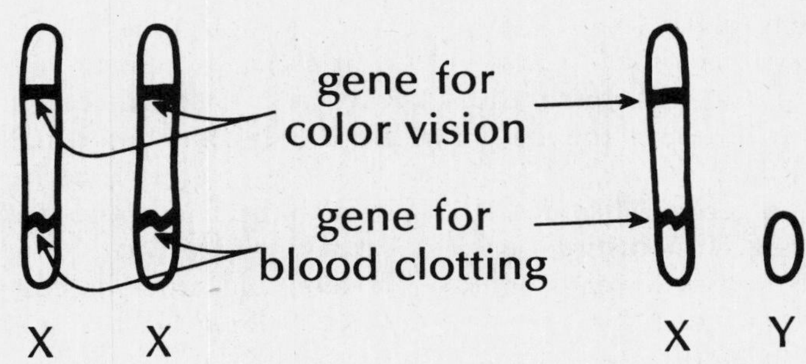

Let ▬ show a gene for normal color vision (dominant).

Let ▭ show a gene for color blindness (recessive).

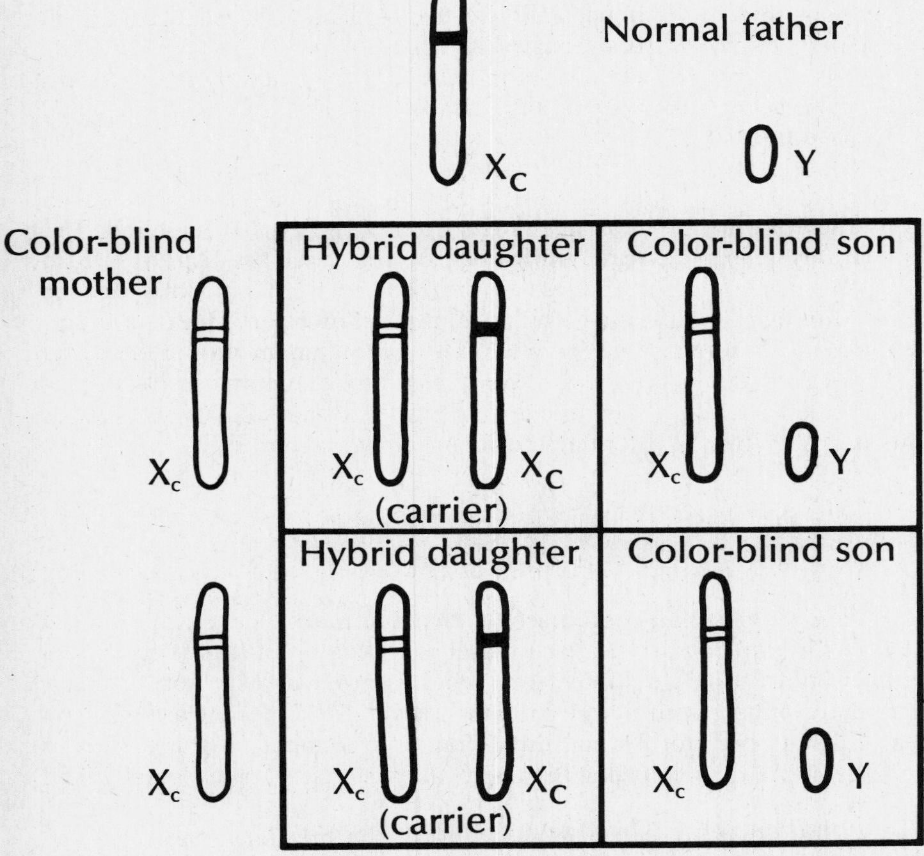

Corresponding Punnett square

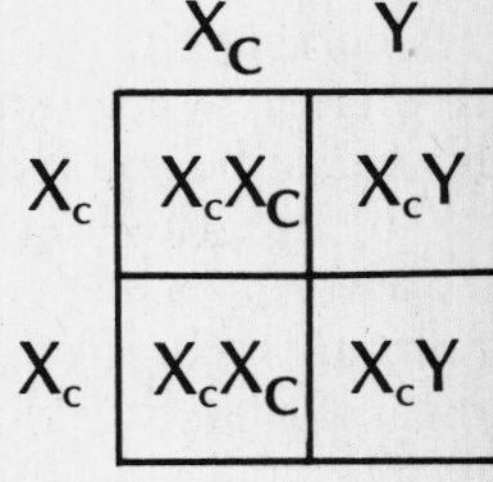

	X_C	Y
X_c	X_cX_C	X_cY
X_c	X_cX_C	X_cY

Name ______________________ Date ______________

Problem: How does a genetic disease affect red blood cells? (text page 162)

Part A Answers:

3(a) ______ (b) ______________ (c) ______ (d) ______ (e) ____________

Data and Observations:

TABLE 8-2. OBSERVATIONS OF RED BLOOD CELLS		
	Appearance	Description
Normal red blood cells		
Sickled red blood cells		

Questions and Conclusion:

1. Explain why sickle-cell trait and sickle-cell anemia illustrate the inheritance pattern known as incomplete dominance.

2. (a) Where is hemoglobin found? (b) What is the job of hemoglobin? (c) Explain why abnormal, sickled hemoglobin is a problem. ______________

3. Explain why sickle-cell trait is less severe than sickle-cell anemia.

4. How might it be possible to check one's phenotype for normal red cells, sickle-cell trait, or sickle-cell anemia? ______________

5. Once the phenotype is determined for one's hemoglobin type, is the genotype also determined? Explain. ______________

6. Assume that you are a genetic counselor as you complete the following problems. Show the parents how you have arrived at your answers by using Punnett squares. (a) A mother has normal red blood cells and the father has all sickled red blood cells. What are the chances of their children being born with sickle-cell trait? Sickle-cell anemia? (b) A mother has sickle-cell trait and the father has sickle-cell anemia. What are the chances of their children being born with sickle-cell trait? Sickle-cell anemia?

Conclusion: How does a genetic disease affect red blood cells? ______________

PLANNING GUIDE	
TEXT	**UNIT 2 Heredity** **Chapter 9 The Genetic Code** **Investigation 9 What is a method for extracting DNA from cells? p. 184**
TEACHER RESOURCE PACKAGE:	
READING AND STUDY GUIDE	Student Edition, p. 51 Teacher Edition, p. 15
RESOURCE MASTER BOOKLET	Student Master 9–1. The Genetic Code, p. 9–2 Teaching Master 9–1. Replication of DNA, p. 9–4 Investigation Worksheet, p. 9–5
EVALUATION PROGRAM	Test Masters, p. 33 Alternate Test Masters, p. 159
LABORATORY BIOLOGY: INVESTIGATING LIVING SYSTEMS	24 DNA and RNA, p. 93 25 tRNA and Protein Building, p. 97
PROBING LEVELS OF LIFE: A LABORATORY MANUAL	19 DNA Models, p. 52 20 Protein Synthesis, p. 54

Name ______________________ Date ______________________

The Genetic Code

One major group of molecules in living cells is the nucleic acids. The nucleic acids include deoxyribonucleic acid (DNA) and ribonucleic acid (RNA). DNA makes up the chromosomes and contains information that is passed from generation to generation. RNA is the messenger molecule that takes the information coded for in the DNA and uses it to make proteins. It is through these proteins that the contents of the chromosomes, the genes, are expressed and metabolism is controlled.

The exact organization and structures of the nucleic acids were first described in 1953 when Rosalind Franklin, James Watson, and Francis Crick, among others, discovered DNA to be a double helix that consists of two strands (made of a five-carbon sugar called deoxyribose, nitrogen bases, and phosphate groups) spiraled about one another and weakly joined by specific pairing of the nitrogen bases. Messenger RNA (mRNA) was shown to be a single-stranded molecule with a structure comparable to half of the structure of the DNA molecule, but containing a different sugar (ribose) and a different nitrogen base (uracil).

The expression of genes occurs through a process called protein synthesis. This is a complex process that involves two steps, *transcription* and *translation.* Transcription begins with the temporary splitting of the DNA molecule. The nitrogen bases of one-half of this DNA molecule then serve as a template for the creation of an mRNA molecule. In translation, the nitrogen bases of mRNA pair with transfer RNA (tRNA) molecules and produce protein molecules. These pairings are precisely governed by the relative ability of the nitrogen bases to form bonds with one another. The rules for base-pairing are summarized in Table 9-1.

TABLE 9-1. PAIRING OF NITROGEN BASES

DNA with DNA	DNA with mRNA	mRNA with tRNA
A–T	T–A	A–U
T–A	A–U	U–A
G–C	C–G	G–C
C–G	G–C	C–G

Use the information in Table 9-1 to fill in the missing nitrogen bases (the blanks) in Figures 9–1, 9–2, and 9–3.

The information in the DNA is transcribed and translated in groups of three bases, called triplets. A triplet of mRNA is called a codon, while a triplet of tRNA is called an anticodon. DNA triplets pair with codons of mRNA, mRNA codons then pair with tRNA anticodons, and the amino acids carried by the tRNA molecules are joined to form long chains. These long chains are proteins. Each tRNA molecule carries a specific kind of amino acid, and different proteins are the result of different amounts and different arrangements of amino acids. Selected triplets and the amino acids they code for are presented in Table 9-2.

TABLE 9-2. DNA TRIPLETS AND AMINO ACIDS FOR WHICH THEY CODE

DNA	mRNA Codon	tRNA Anticodon	Amino Acid
AAA	UUU	AAA	phenylalanine
TTT	AAA	UUU	lysine
AAC	UUG	AAC	leucine
GGC	CCG	GGC	proline
TGG	ACC	UGG	threonine

FIGURE 9–1.

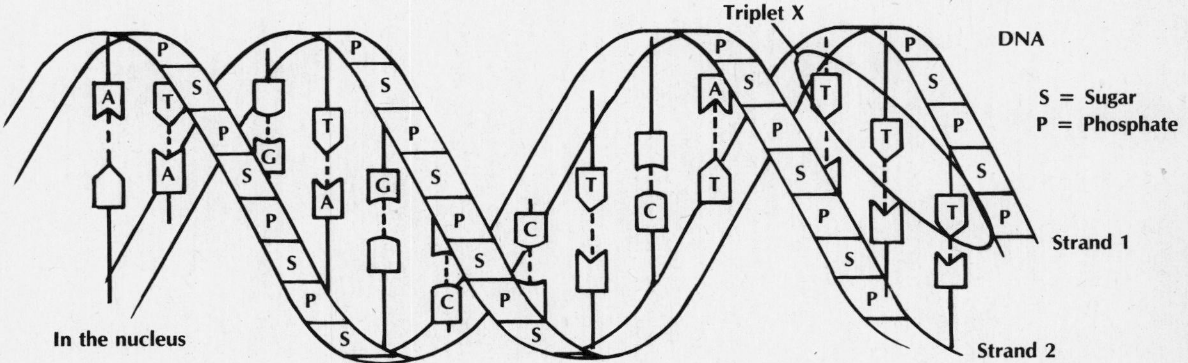

FIGURE 9–2.

FIGURE 9–3.

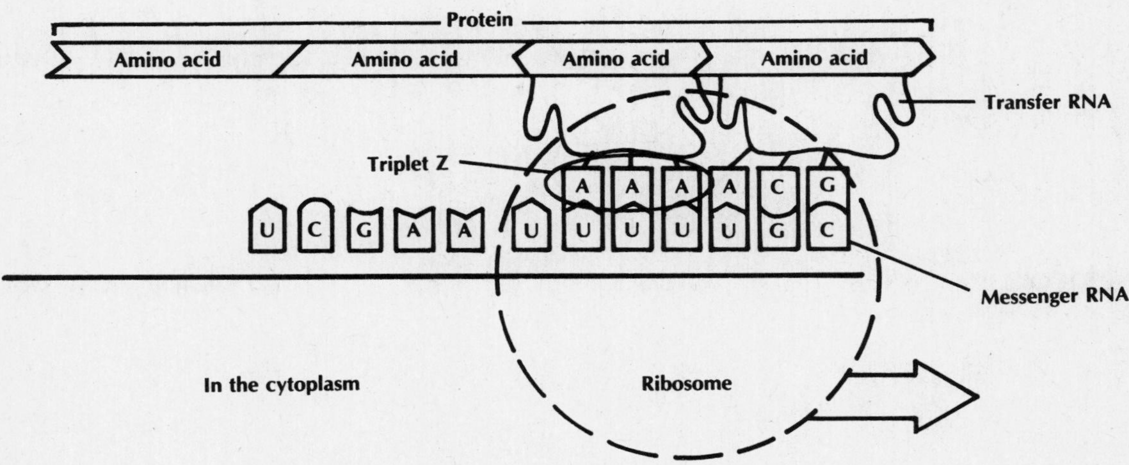

Questions:

1. The DNA triplet labeled X in Figure 9–1 codes for what amino acid? ____________________
2. In Figure 9–2, what amino acid is coded for by the mRNA codon labeled Y? ____________
3. In Figure 9–3, what amino acid is carried by the tRNA molecule whose anticodon is labeled triplet Z? ____________________
4. The DNA triplet TCC codes for the amino acid arginine. By using the base-pairing rules expressed in Table 9-1, with what codon does this triplet pair? For what anticodon does this DNA triplet code? ____________________

Replication of DNA

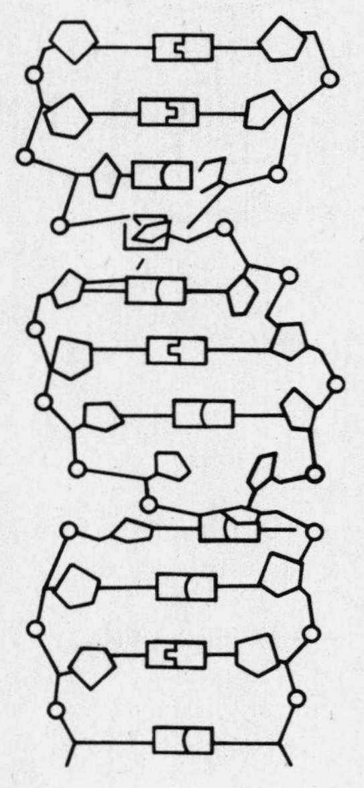

Uncoiling

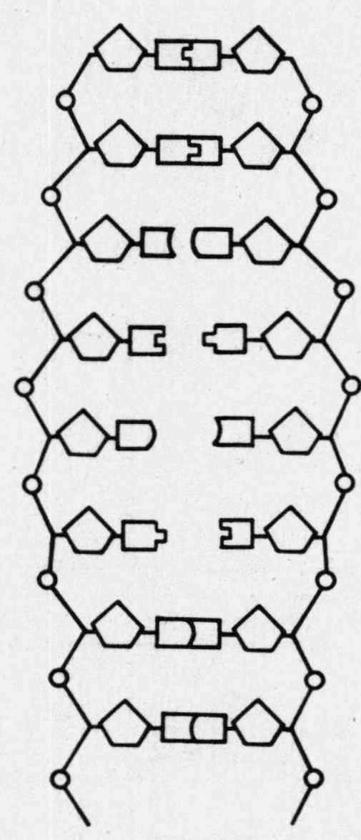

Unzipping

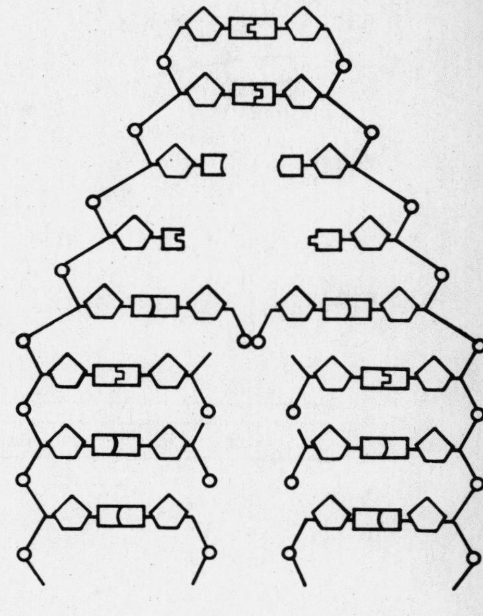

Adding new parts

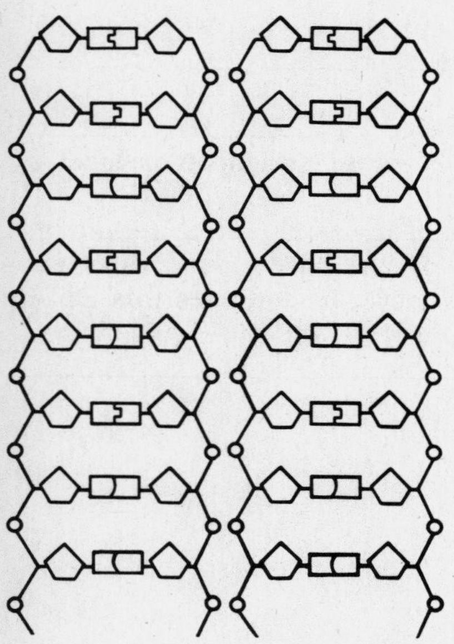

Two DNA molecules

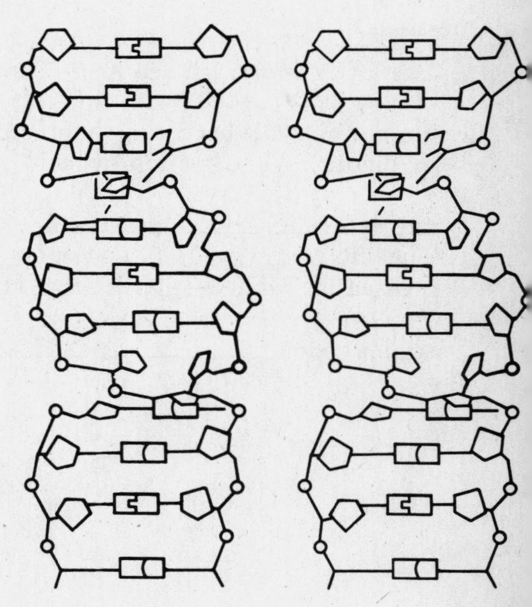

Recoiling

Name ______________________ Date ______________

Problem: What is a method for extracting DNA from cells?

(text page 184)

Data and Observations:

FIGURE 9–17.

Questions and Conclusion:

1. What is the role of DNA in living cells? ______________________
2. Describe the structural and chemical makeup of DNA. ______________________
3. What was the source of DNA in this lab? ______________________
4. What might have been the role of lysozyme (an enzyme) in this lab? ______________________
5. Would your results have been different if carrot, chicken, or mushroom cells had been used instead of bacterial cells? Explain. ______________________
6. How might the interface have appeared if you had used only frog cell cytoplasm? ______________________
7. How might the concentration of DNA have compared between two test tubes if human sperm were placed in one tube and equal numbers of human body cells were placed in another? Explain.

Name ______________________________ Date ______________

8. How might the concentration of DNA have compared between two test tubes if human sperm were placed in one tube and equal numbers of human eggs were placed in another? Explain.

____

____

9. Study the chart below.

Organism	Percentage of Each Nitrogen Base Contained in DNA			
	A	T	G	C
human	30.2	29.8	19.9	19.8
wheat	27.3	27.1	22.7	22.8
bacteria	36.9	36.3	14.0	14.0

(a) Why is the percent adenine (A) always nearly equal to the percent thymine (T) in an organism? (b) Why is the percent cytosine (C) always nearly equal to the percent guanine (G) in an organism? ______________________________

Conclusion: What is a method for extracting DNA from cells? ______________________________

____

PLANNING GUIDE	
TEXT	**UNIT 3 Changes** **Chapter 10 Change with Time** **Investigation 10 How does comparative biochemistry support the theory of evolution? p. 216**
TEACHER RESOURCE PACKAGE:	
READING AND STUDY GUIDE	Student Edition, p. 57 Teacher Edition, p. 17
RESOURCE MASTER BOOKLET	Student Master 10–1. The Evolution of the Horse, p. 10–2 Student Master 10–2. Death of the Dinosaurs—How Did It Happen? p. 10–3 Teaching Master 10–1. Geologic Time Scale, p. 10–4 Investigation Worksheet, p. 10–5, p. 7
EVALUATION PROGRAM	Test Masters, p. 37 Alternate Test Masters, p. 161
LABORATORY BIOLOGY: INVESTIGATING LIVING SYSTEMS	26 Biochemical Evidence for Evolution, p. 101 27 A Human Variation with Possible Adaptive Value, p. 105
PROBING LEVELS OF LIFE: A LABORATORY MANUAL	21 Natural Selection in Populations, p. 58 22 Coacervates—The Road to Life, p. 62

Name ______________________ Date ______________________

The Evolution of the Horse

The fossil records of a number of organisms, although incomplete, demonstrate a progression of changes from an initial form (ancestor) to that of the modern descendants. An especially well-documented case history of such evolution has been described for the horse. As the horse evolved, numerous evolutionary side branches developed and became extinct. There is also a major evolutionary line in which changes led from a terrier-sized, four-toed, forest-dwelling *Eohippus* to the larger, one-toed, plains-grazing species of *Equus.* The changes that have taken place during the evolution of today's horse represent adaptations to new habitats and living conditions. These adaptations arose as a consequence of random mutations that have become fixed by natural selection.

Questions:

1. What is the earliest ancestor of the modern horse, and when did it first appear? ______________________

2. How does the foot structure of *Merychippus* differ from the foot structure of *Equus?* ______________________

3. How does the skull of *Miohippus* differ from the skull of *Equus?* ______________________

4. What obvious evolutionary changes have taken place between *Eohippus* and *Equus?* ______________________

FIGURE 10–1.

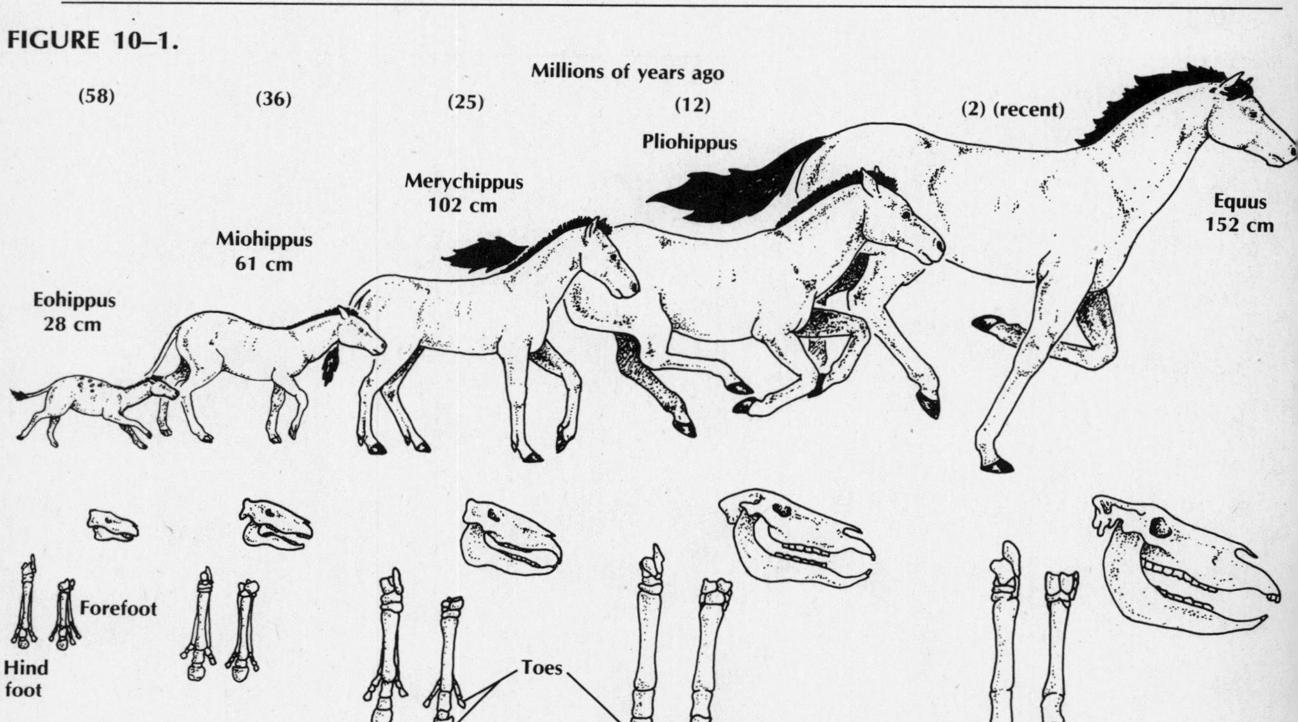

Name ______________________ Date ______________

Death of the Dinosaurs–How Did It Happen?

Approximately 65 million years ago an event of such magnitude took place that it ended the 160 million year reign of the dinosaurs. In 1980 a team of scientists composed of physicist Louis Alvarez and his son, Walter, a geologist, and two associates proposed a theory that attempts to explain the sequence of events that led to the extinction of the dinosaurs.

The Alvarez team had discovered a rare substance, iridium, in a thin layer of sedimentary clay deposited over a layer of rock that belonged to the same period of time as the rock layers bearing dinosaur fossils. Iridium, although nearly nonexistent in Earth's crust, is about 10 000 times more abundant in extraterrestrial rocks and is common in meteorites and asteroids. The iridium layer was found in two parts of the world in clay deposits of exactly the same age, thus prompting the Alvarez team to propose that the iridium had come from an asteroid that hit Earth with enough force to vaporize and scatter iridium atoms into Earth's atmosphere.

A controversial aspect of the team's theory was the idea that the impact of the asteroid blasted so much dust into the atmosphere that it prevented much of the sunlight from reaching Earth. In the darkness, photosynthesis would have been severely impaired, if not impossible, and many of the plants would have died. The deaths of large numbers of plants would have been followed by the extinction of plant-eating dinosaurs and then flesh-eating dinosaurs. Other scientists have suggested that the blocked sunlight would have also precipitated a global freeze, making the world fiercely hostile for the giant beasts that were well-adapted to a tropical world.

No one knows how long the dark, winterlike conditions might have lasted if they did indeed occur. They may have lasted only a few weeks, but significant environmental disruptions could have occurred that may have persisted for thousands of years. In any case, the result was the mass extinction of many plants and animals in many parts of the world.

Most evolutionary theorists have declared themselves supporters of this impact theory. Some scientists have modified or expanded the theory. They believe that perhaps a comet, instead of an asteroid, struck Earth. A comet could have been routed toward Earth by the gravitational pull of a hypothetical companion star to our sun, called Nemesis. Others speculate that a tenth planet, Planet X, might have upset the normal orbit of comets and sent one or more of them toward Earth. A few scientists do not accept the impact theory at all. They assert that no single, catastrophic event was responsible for the extinction of the dinosaurs because the dinosaurs (and other organisms) did not disappear from Earth as rapidly as is presently believed. These scientists maintain that only our faulty interpretation of the dinosaur fossil record supports the idea of rapid, mass extinctions, and that the extinctions occurred gradually over a longer period of time.

Whether the mysteries surrounding the death of the dinosaurs are ever solved, the fact remains that the dinosaurs no longer walk Earth. The event or series of events that closed the dinosaur era also permitted the rapid evolution of a class of animals that have replaced the dinosaurs on Earth. These animals were the mammals, a prolific group that has produced many highly complex animals, including humans and other primates.

Questions:

1. Dinosaurs were the dominant life form on Earth for how many years? ______________
2. Who were the scientists behind the current, and most popular, theory on how the dinosaurs became extinct? ______________________________
3. Summarize the impact theory. ______________________________

____

____

____

Geologic Time Scale

Era	Period	Epoch	Age (years ago)	Representative Life Forms
Cenozoic	Quaternary	Recent	100 000	Humans; modern forms of plants and animals
		Pleistocene	1 000 000	Extinction of many mammals; primitive humans; grasslands
	Tertiary	Pliocene	10 000 000	Early humans; other mammals; herbs
		Miocene	30 000 000	Mammals; grasses
		Oligocene	40 000 000	Primates and other mammals; forests common
		Eocene	60 000 000	Primitive horse; other mammals; flowering plants
		Paleocene	75 000 000	Mammals predominant; more modern flowering plants
Mesozoic	Cretaceous		135 000 000	Extinction of giant reptiles; birds and insects; flowering plants
	Jurassic		165 000 000	Dinosaurs dominant; primitive birds and mammals; earliest flowering plants
	Triassic		205 000 000	Dinosaurs and other reptiles; early mammals; primitive seed plants
Paleozoic	Permian		230 000 000	Rise of insects; early reptiles
	Carboniferous		280 000 000	Insects and amphibians; mosses and ferns
	Devonian		325 000 000	Age of fishes; early amphibians; early bryophytes; ferns
	Silurian		360 000 000	Club mosses; insects and other invertebrates
	Ordovician		425 000 000	Primitive mollusks and fish; algae
	Cambrian		500 000 000	Protists; sponges; jellyfish; spore-producing plants
Precambrian			4 500 000 000	Monerans; simple protists; fungi; simple invertebrates

Name ______________________ Date ______________________

Problem: How does comparative biochemistry support the theory of evolution? (text page 216)

Data and Observations:

TABLE 10-2. COMPARISON OF RNA NITROGEN BASE SEQUENCES															
	Number of RNA Sequences in Common With Each Organism														
Organism	1	2	3	4	5	6	7	8	9	10	11	12	13	14	15
1															
5															
10															
15															

Questions and Conclusion:

1. Define: (a) mRNA (b) tRNA (c) DNA (d) nitrogen base (e) comparative biochemistry (f) homologous. ______________________

2. What do the following letters represent in an RNA nitrogen base sequence: (a) A (b) U (c) C (d) G? ______________________
3. In closely related organisms, the sequences of nitrogen bases in the RNA of each organism are very similar. Thus, they are thought to have evolved from a common ancestor. (a) Which two organisms show the most similar RNA sequences? (b) Which two organisms show the most similar biochemistry? (c) Which two organisms may have evolved from a common ancestor? (d) Which two organisms may have the most similar genetic material? (e) Which two organisms may have the most similar DNA? ______________________
4. Reading down column 2, (a) which two organisms are the most related biochemically? Explain. (b) Which two organisms may show the most homologous chemical similarities? (c) Which two organisms may have evolved from the same ancestor? (d) Which two organisms are the least related biochemically? Explain. ______________________

Name ______________________ *Date* ______________

5. Reading down column 9, (a) which two organisms are the most related biochemically? Explain. (b) Which two organisms may show the most homologous chemical similarities? (c) Which two organisms may have evolved from the same ancestor? (d) Which two organisms are the least related biochemically? Explain. ______________________

6. Closely related organisms often show many physical similarities. Which groupings would show the most physical similarities: (a) organisms 2 and 15 or 2 and 1 (b) organisms 3 and 15 or 3 and 5 (c) organisms 7 and 5 or 7 and 15? ______________________

7. How might organisms 5 and 6 be expected to appear when compared to one another? Explain. ______________________

8. How might organisms 1 and 12 be expected to appear when compared to one another? Explain. ______________________

9. An organism has the following mRNA nitrogen base sequence: ACCUCG. (a) Convert the mRNA base sequence into the proper corresponding DNA sequence of nitrogen bases. (b) Convert the mRNA base sequence into the proper corresponding tRNA sequence of nitrogen bases.

10. An organism has the following nitrogen base sequence: AUCCUG. (a) Convert the mRNA base sequence into the proper corresponding DNA sequence of nitrogen bases. (b) Convert the mRNA base sequence into the proper corresponding tRNA sequence of nitrogen bases. ______________________

11. When comparing a gorilla and a human, or a frog and a human: (a) which two animals show greater physical resemblance to each other? A lesser physical resemblance? (b) which two animals would have RNA sequences that are similar to each other? Not similar? ______________________

Conclusion: How does comparative biochemistry support the theory of evolution? ______________________

PLANNING GUIDE	
TEXT	**UNIT 3 Changes** **Chapter 11 Adaptation and Speciation** **Investigation 11 What evidence can be used to determine if an animal is or was a biped or quadruped? p. 240**
TEACHER RESOURCE PACKAGE:	
READING AND STUDY GUIDE	Student Edition, p. 63 Teacher Edition, p. 18
RESOURCE MASTER BOOK	Student Master 11–1. Human Evolution—New Views, p. 11–2 Teaching Master 11–1. Human Origins, p. 11–4 Investigation Worksheet, p. 11–5, pp. 8, 9
EVALUATION PROGRAM	Test Masters, p. 41 Alternate Test Masters, p. 163
LABORATORY BIOLOGY: INVESTIGATING LIVING SYSTEMS	28 Animal Adaptations, p. 109 29 Seed Adaptations, p. 111 30 Evolutionary Changes in Primates, p. 115
PROBING LEVELS OF LIFE: A LABORATORY MANUAL	23 Adaptation, p. 64 24 Variation within a Species and between Species, p. 67 25 Evolutionary Changes in Primates, p. 69

Name ______________________ Date ______________

Human Evolution—New Views

Paleoanthropology involves the study of hominids, the bipedal, primate mammals that include recent humans, their immediate ancestors, and related forms. Paleoanthropology, perhaps more than any other field of science, is characterized by feuds and scientific debates. One reason for such controversy is that many of the hypotheses presented by paleoanthropologists are based upon fragments of fossilized skull bones and incomplete skeletons. The reconstruction of an entire hominid and its possible behavior from so few fragments is based largely upon speculation.

Humans evolved from an initial, ancestral form that provided direct lineage to modern humans, *Homo sapiens,* along with various branches of hominids that have become extinct. Such a multibranched "family tree" is characteristic of that of most species. Paleoanthropologists attempt to reconstruct the sequence of the steps in human evolution based upon the age and structure of the skeletal remains of hominids that have been discovered. Discovery of a new species may require paleoanthropologists to find a place for the new species in the sequence of their fossil records. While sometimes an easy task, often it is not and controversies are frequent.

In 1974, a skeleton was discovered in Hadar, Ethiopia by a team of scientists led by Don Johanson, Maurice Taieb, and Yves Coppens. The skeleton was given the nickname "Lucy." There was little question that Lucy was a hominid. Controversy erupted when attempts were made to identify the type of hominid that Lucy represented. At the time, Lucy could have been identified as one of four types of known hominids: early *Homo, Australopithecus africanus, A. robustus,* or *A. boisei.* Johanson, Coppens, and an associate, Tim White, chose to recognize Lucy as an entirely new species and gave her a new scientific name, *Australopithecus afarensis.* Not only did the creation of a new species spark controversy, but so did the placement of this species in the sequence of the fossil record. Richard Leakey and his colleagues believed Lucy to be separate from the late australopithecines and *Homo.* They also asserted that Lucy, the late australopithecines, and *Homo* evolved from forms yet to be discovered. To Johanson, White, and several other scientists, Lucy represented the common ancestor from which *Homo* and the late australopithecines split less than three million years ago (Figure 11–1).

As the controversy over where Lucy fits into the fossil record continues, another has begun. In 1985, a skull of yet another hominid was discovered in Kenya by a team of scientists, which included Alan Walker and Richard Leakey. This new skull, numbered KNM-WT-17000, is clearly in the *A. boisei* lineage. The features of the skull show that *A. robustus* can be neither its ancestor nor its descendant because the skull is both older and more advanced than *A. robustus.* This discovery raises the possibility that *A. robustus* and *A. boisei* developed independently and were not as closely related to one another as was once thought (Figure 11–2). The skull also indicates that *A. robustus* may have developed from *A. africanus,* while *A. boisei* did not. *A. afarensis* (Lucy) could have been the common ancestor to all three. In yet another interpretation, *A. afarensis* is also the common ancestor to all of the hominid lines (Figure 11–3). In this view, *A. africanus, A. robustus, Homo,* and KNM-WT-17000 rapidly split from one another about three million years ago. It isn't known what might have caused the rapid split of all four hominid lines from *A. afarensis,* but there is no shortage of speculation. Was it a change in climate? Did some animal in competition with hominids become extinct? Did the hominids achieve some extraordinary evolutionary advantage?

Both Lucy and KNM-WT-17000 have brought into question the organization of the fossil record that attempts to explain human evolution. New information in many scientific fields often creates new controversies and raises new, exciting questions. This is the stuff of anthropology. This is science.

Questions:

1. How might an animal that competed with hominids and that suddenly became extinct cause a rapid split or development of hominids?
2. Does the new skull give any further evidence that *A. afarensis* could have been the common ancestor to *Homo* and other side branches of hominids? Explain.
3. How might the discovery of still another species of hominid affect the fossil record? Explain.

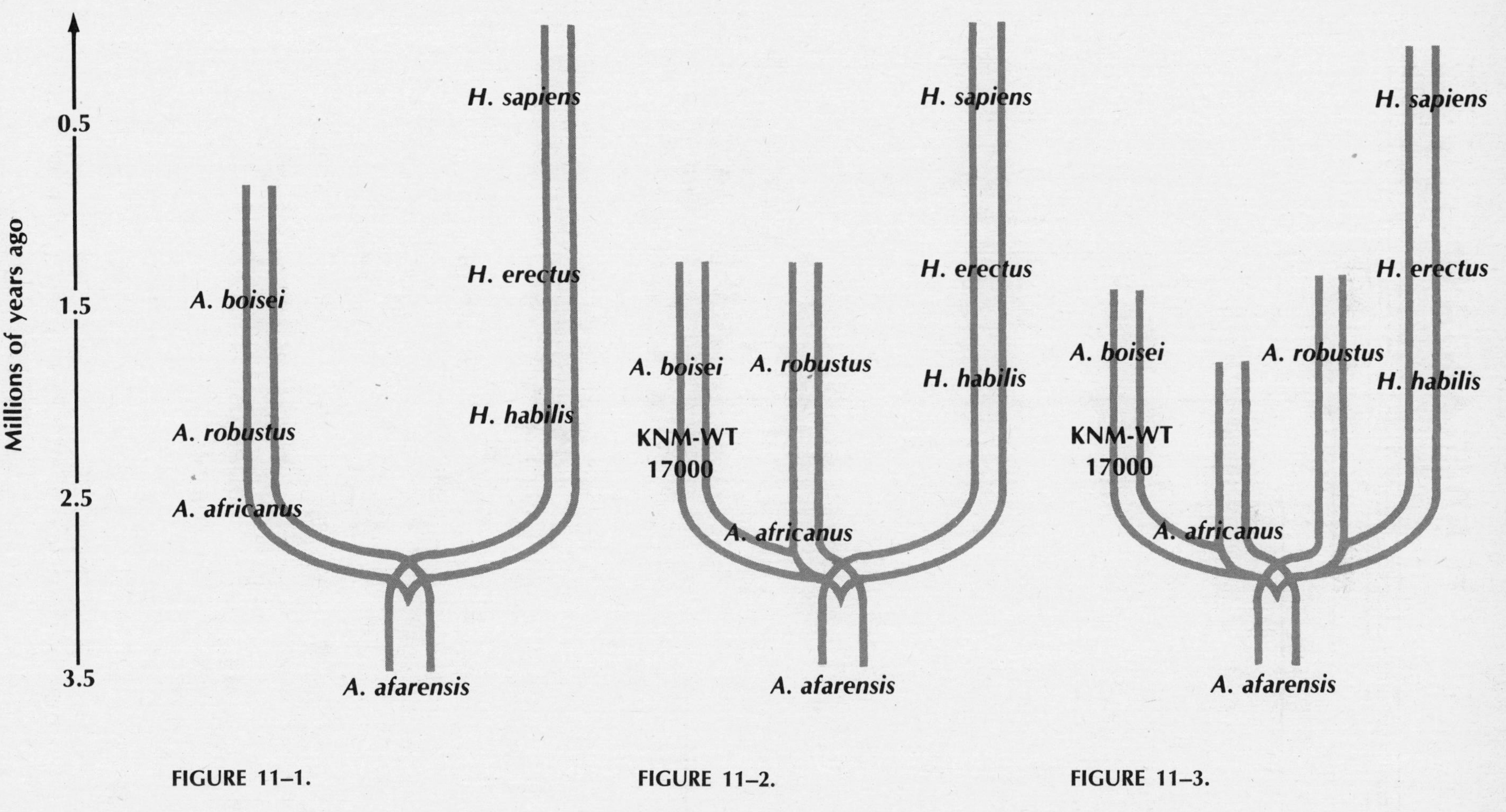

FIGURE 11–1.

FIGURE 11–2.

FIGURE 11–3.

Human Origins

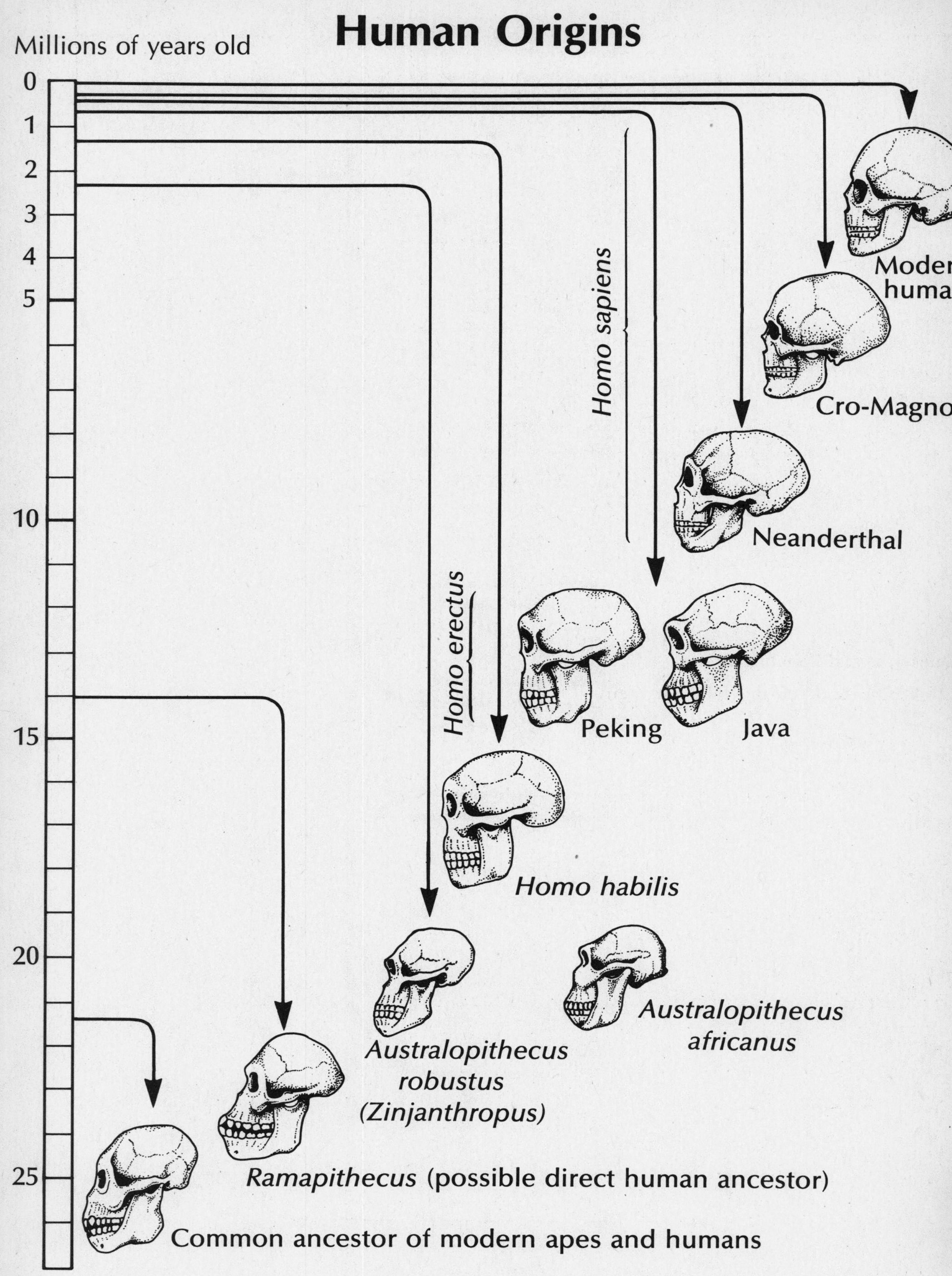

Name ______________________ Date ______________

Problem: What evidence can be used to determine if an animal is or was a biped or a quadruped?

(text page 243)

Data and Observations:

TABLE 11-1. COMPARISON OF QUADRUPED AND BIPED CHARACTERISTICS			
	Ape	Human	*Australopithecus*
Arm length			–
Leg length			–
Position of hind leg			–
Shape of lumbar region			–
Position of center of gravity			–
Location of weight-bearing axis			

Questions and Conclusion:

1. Define each of the following terms: (a) *Australopithecus* (b) natural selection (c) bipedalism (d) quadrupedalism. ______________________
2. Compare arm and leg lengths in a biped. ______________________
3. Compare arm and leg lengths in a quadruped. ______________________
4. Explain how the position of the hind legs in bipeds differs from the position of the hind legs in quadrupeds. ______________________
5. If the center of gravity is located above and in front of the pelvis of an animal, the animal has a tendency to fall over when standing on only two legs. Which animal that you studied in this investigation might have this problem? ______________________

Name ______________________ Date ______________________

6. An animal having more body weight in the upper trunk shows a center of gravity above the pelvis. (a) Describe how body weight is distributed in humans. (b) Explain how body weight distribution influences the ability of an animal to stand upright. ______________________

7. Explain how the shape of the lumbar region of a biped differs from the shape of the lumbar region of a quadruped. ______________________

8. Does the evidence indicate that *Australopithecus* was a biped or quadruped? Explain. ______________________

9. Explain if each of the following animals was bipedal or quadrupedal: (a) arm length = 452 mm; leg length = 520 mm (b) outside edge of knee joint worn more than inside edge (c) inside edge of knee joint worn more than outside edge. ______________________

Conclusion: What evidence can be used to determine if an animal is or was a biped or a quadruped?

____

PLANNING GUIDE	
TEXT	**UNIT 3 Changes** **Chapter 12 Classification** **Investigation 12 What information can be gained from classifying living organisms? p. 254**
TEACHER RESOURCE PACKAGE:	
READING AND STUDY GUIDE	Student Edition, p. 69 Teacher Edition, p. 20
RESOURCE MASTER BOOK	Student Master 12–1. Identifying Unusual Mammals, p. 12–2 Student Master 12–2. Hydrothermal-Vent Tube Worms, p. 12–3 Teaching Master 12–1. Classification of Organisms, p. 12–4 Investigation Worksheet, p. 12–5
EVALUATION PROGRAM	Test Masters, p. 45 Alternate Test Masters, p. 165
LABORATORY BIOLOGY: INVESTIGATING LIVING SYSTEMS	31 Classification, p. 121 32 Using and Making a Biological Key, p. 125
PROBING LEVELS OF LIFE: A LABORATORY MANUAL	26 Construction and Use of a Dichotomous Key, p. 74 27 Binomial Nomenclature—Scientific Names of Trees, p. 76

Name ______________________ Date ______________

Identifying Unusual Mammals

Use the identification key that follows in order to determine the names of the unusual mammals illustrated to the right. For each mammal identified by a letter, record its name in the accompanying chart.

Identification Key

1a. Animal possesses hooves 2
1b. Animal lacks hooves 6

2a. Animal possesses long horns 3
2b. Animal possesses short horns or lacks horns 4

3a. Horns straight, not curved ....eland
3b. Horns curved ....sable

4a. Neck long and slender ....okapi
4b. Neck short and thick 5

5a. Lower back and rump of one color, without stripes ....takin
5b. Lower back and rump marked with stripes ....duiker

6a. Snout piglike 7
6b. Snout not piglike 8

7a. Ears greatly extended, like those of a jack-rabbit or donkey ....aardvark
7b. Ears shortened, not extended ....peccary

8a. Body covered by fur 9
8b. Body covered with horny scales ....pangolin

9a. Nose long and flexible ....coati
9b. Nose short, not flexible ....potto

TABLE 12-1. IDENTIFYING MAMMALS			
Unusual Mammal	Name	Unusual Mammal	Name
A		F	
B		G	
C		H	
D		I	
E		J	

Name ______________________ Date ______________

Hydrothermal-Vent Tube Worms

A little over 10 years ago, geologists on the research submarine *Alvin* discovered a system of hydrothermal vents at a spreading ridge on the floor of the Pacific Ocean. Although the scientists were not surprised to find the spreading ridge, a place where Earth's crust is spreading apart, they were surprised and puzzled by the completely unexpected discovery of a thriving community of unusual invertebrate species. These species included giant tube worms as much as 1 meter long, large white clams 30 centimeters in length, and clusters of mussels. They also discovered shrimp, crabs, and fish.

The presence of such a rich community of organisms at a depth of such high pressure, low temperature (2°C–4°C), and darkness was bewildering. Every ecosystem on Earth must have a source of energy and, for the majority of Earth's communities, sunlight is that source. Plants transform sunlight into energy that is available to other members of the ecosystem. Here, in the perpetual darkness, there must be another source of energy. Observations made over the last 6 years have shown that while the water is very warm around the vents, ranging from 10°C to 20°C, the heat cannot supply enough energy to account for life at such depths. Scientists have known for years that sulfide-rich environments, such as terrestrial hotsprings, support bacteria that derive their energy from hydrogen sulfide, rather than the sun. Further study of the vent environment has shown that sulfur bacteria are present around the vents as well, and they serve as "green plants," turning the energy in hydrogen sulfide and other carbon compounds (the equivalent of sunlight) into a form usable by the tube worms and other organisms. The sulfur bacteria provide energy and support life around the hydrothermal vents.

The anatomy and metabolism of the tube worm, *Riftia pachyptila,* dominant life form around the vent, provides a remarkable model of the relationship between an organism and these sulfur bacteria. *Riftia* is an unusual creature. It is essentially a closed sac, without a mouth or a digestive system. At its tip is a bright red, gill-like plume through which oxygen, carbon dioxide, and hydrogen sulfide are exchanged with seawater. Below the plume, there is a ring of muscle, the vestimentum, that anchors the worm in its white tube. Most of the rest of the animal consists of a thin-walled sac that contains the worm's internal organs. The largest of the organs is the trophosome, which occupies most of the body cavity.

Microscopic studies of the trophosome indicate that it contains vast numbers of sulfur bacteria. *Riftia* seems to take in carbon dioxide, oxygen, and hydrogen sulfide from the water, thus supplying the bacteria with the materials they need for their metabolism. These substances are absorbed by *Riftia's* plume and are transported to the bacteria by way of the worm's circulatory system. The bacteria, in turn, produce the reduced carbon compounds that *Riftia* requires as food.

Riftia has the unusual ability to take in and transport hydrogen sulfide without poisoning itself. Hydrogen sulfide is toxic to most life forms. Research has shown that *Riftia* has a higher amount of hemoglobin in its blood than other invertebrates. Hemoglobin serves to bind with oxygen and transports it throughout the tube worm's body. Hemoglobin in *Riftia* is not a typical form of hemoglobin. It binds with hydrogen sulfide as well as oxygen. It is through this binding action that hydrogen sulfide can be transported to the bacteria in the trophosome without poisoning *Riftia.*

Questions:

1. How can the dark, isolated ecosystem around the hydrothermal vents supply itself with energy? ______________________________

____

2. What are three unusual features of *Riftia*? ______________________________

____

____

Classification of Organisms

Kingdom	Animal	Animal	Animal	Animal
Phylum	Chordata	Chordata	Chordata	Chordata
Class	Mammalia	Mammalia	Mammalia	Mammalia
Order	Carnivora	Carnivora	Carnivora	Carnivora
Family	Felidae	Felidae	Felidae	Canidae
Genus	*Felis*	*Felis*	*Panthera*	*Canis*
Species	*F. domesticus*	*F. concolor*	*P. pardus*	*C. lupus*

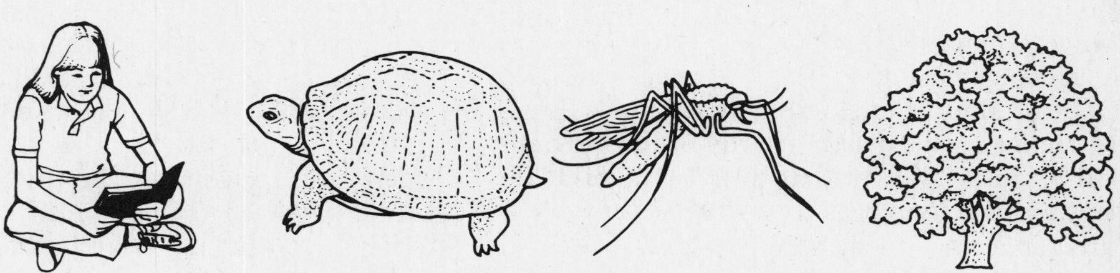

Kingdom	Animal	Animal	Animal	Plant
Phylum	Chordata	Chordata	Arthropoda	Tracheophyta
Class	Mammalia	Reptilia	Insecta	Angiospermae
Order	Primates	Chelonia	Diptera	Fagales
Family	Hominidae	Emydidae	Culicidae	Fagaceae
Genus	*Homo*	*Terrapene*	*Theobaldia*	*Quercus*
Species	*H. sapiens*	*T. carolina*	*T. anulata*	*Q. alba*

Name ______________________ Date ______________________

Problem: What information can be gained from classifying living organisms?

(text page 254)

Part B Answers:

TABLE 12-2. MATCHING SCIENTIFIC AND COMMON NAMES

I	II
______ *Beta vulgaris*	a. black pepper
______ *Salmo gairdneni*	b. perch
______ *Citrus limon*	c. rat
______ *Piper nigrum*	d. canary
______ *Ipomoea batatus*	e. penicillin
______ *Tarpor atlanticus*	f. herring
______ *Crocyodylus americanus*	g. beet
______ *Rattus norvegicus*	h. carrot
______ *Perca flavescens*	i. crocodile
______ *Daucus carota*	j. lemon
______ *Serinus canarius*	k. sweet potato
______ *Clupea harengus*	l. salmon
______ *Penicillium chrysogenum*	m. Atlantic tarpon

TABLE 12-3. MATCHING SCIENTIFIC AND COMMON NAMES

I	II
______ *Aralia quinquefolia*	a. dog
______ *Crotaphytus collaris*	b. seventeen-year locust
______ *Helianthus annus*	c. cat
______ *Eurycea bilineata*	d. paper birch
______ *Alytes obstetricans*	e. sea cucumber
______ *Urus horibilis*	f. sugar cane
______ *Magicicada septendecem*	g. collared lizard
______ *Betula papyrifera*	h. earthworm
______ *Secale cereale*	i. two-lined salamander
______ *Felis domesticus*	j. sunflower
______ *Saccharum officinarum*	k. midwife toad
______ *Lumbricus terrestris*	l. grizzly bear
______ *Cucumaria frondosa*	m. rye
______ *Canis familiaris*	n. five leaflet ginseng

Data and Observations:

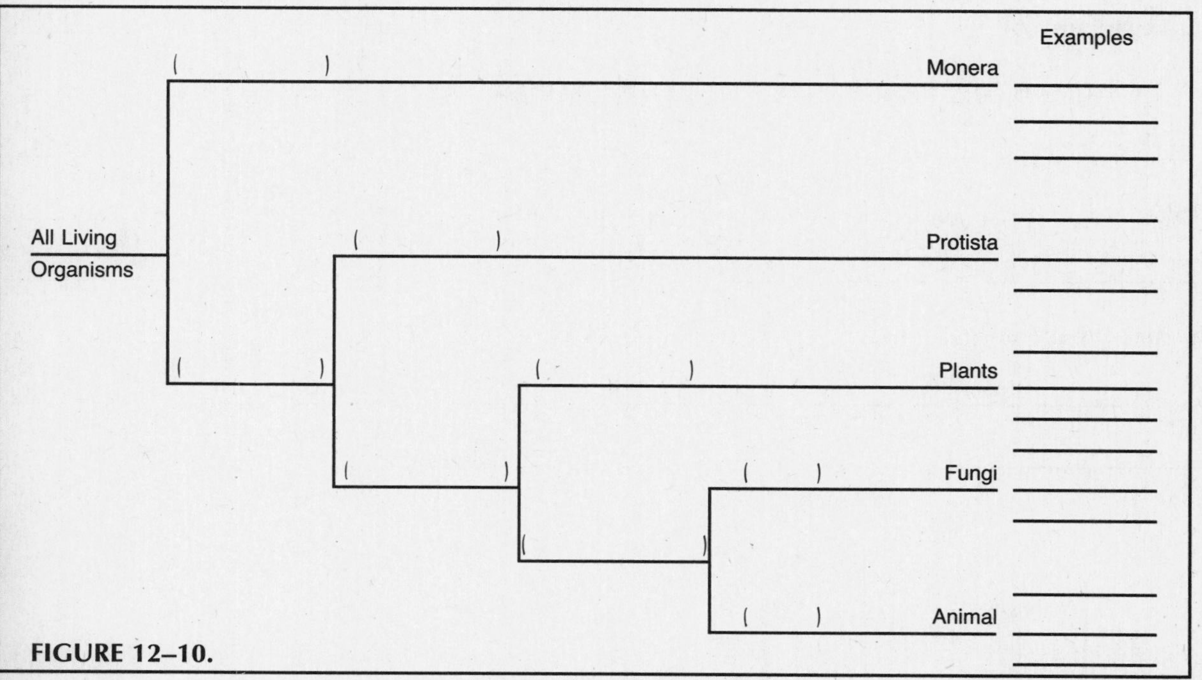

FIGURE 12–10.

Name ______________________ *Date* ______________

Questions and Conclusion:

1. Define: (a) binomial nomenclature (b) taxonomy (c) eukaryotic (d) prokaryotic (e) autotrophic (f) heterotrophic. ______________________
2. (a) What category of classification is used for the first term in a scientific name? (b) What category of classification is used for the second term in a scientific name? ______________
3. Describe three rules that are used in writing a scientific name. Do not use the information in question 2. ______________
4. An organism is found to be eukaryotic and ingests food. Using completed Figure 12–10: (a) name the kingdom to which this organism belongs (b) list two other traits of this organism.
5. An organism is found to be prokaryotic. Using completed Figure 12–10, name the kingdom that this organism belongs to. Explain. ______________
6. An organism belongs to the plant kingdom. Using completed Figure 12–10, list three traits that this organism will have. ______________
7. An organism belongs to the fungi kingdom. Using completed Figure 12–10, list three traits that this organism will have. ______________
8. List two reasons why there is a need for classifying organisms. ______________
9. Explain why the language of classification is based mainly on Latin. ______________

Conclusion: What information can be gained from classifying living organisms? ______________

PLANNING GUIDE	
TEXT	**UNIT 4 Diversity** **Chapter 13 Monerans, Protists, Fungi, and Viruses** **Investigation 13 What are the traits of organisms in the kingdoms Monera, Protista, and Fungi? p. 282**
TEACHER RESOURCE PACKAGE:	
READING AND STUDY GUIDE	Student Edition, p. 75 Teacher Edition, p. 21
RESOURCE MASTER BOOK	Student Master 13–1. Yeasts: New Research Tools, p. 13–2 Student Master 13–2. Is It a Plant or an Animal? p. 13–3 Teaching Master 13–1. Comparing Fungi, p. 13–4 Investigation Worksheet, p. 13–5
EVALUATION PROGRAM	Test Masters, p. 49 Alternate Test Masters, p. 167
LABORATORY BIOLOGY: INVESTIGATING LIVING SYSTEMS	33 A Comparison of Some Monerans and Protists, p. 129 34 Lichens, p. 133
PROBING LEVELS OF LIFE: A LABORATORY MANUAL	28 Morphology and Staining of Bacteria, p. 78 29 Size and Structure of Protozoa, p. 81 30 Morphology of Lichens, p. 83

Name ____________________ Date ____________________

Yeasts: New Research Tools

There are roughly 60 genera and 600 species of yeast. One species, *Saccharomyces cerevisiae,* better known as baker's yeast, is commonly used to swell bread, brew beer, and cause champagne to bubble. The bakers and brewers, however, are not the only people interested in this single-celled, colony-dwelling fungus. Biologists are also interested in *Saccharomyces cerevisiae.* Biologists are probing yeast cells to find out about the intimate details of genes, proteins, and the structure of living cells. Yeasts are helping biologists answer such questions as: How do you make a chromosome? What signals a cell that it is time to divide? What tells a cell to stop dividing?

Biologists apply to human cells what they learn from yeast because, in certain aspects, yeast cells and human cells are very similar. Like human cells, yeast cells have two genders and reproduce with cells similar to eggs and sperm; and each cell has a nucleus. A yeast cell has 17 pairs of chromosomes that behave remarkably like the 23 pairs of human chromosomes. During reproduction, the chromosomes in yeast cells can be involved in the same mistakes as those that cause genetic disorders such as Down Syndrome. Yeasts manufacture enzymes similar to those of humans and release and ferry them around in much the same way that the human pancreas, liver, and brain cells do. Yeast cells, like human cells, are vulnerable to mutagenic agents.

From a research standpoint, yeast cells have numerous advantages over cultured human or mouse cells. Yeast thrive in a petri dish. The cells divide about every two hours. Some mouse or human cells take 12 hours or more to divide. This means that experiments can be completed more quickly when using yeast cells. Since a yeast cell has about 10 000 genes and a human cell 40 000, yeast genes can be more easily mapped and analyzed than human genes. By exposing petri dishes of yeast cells to radiation or mutagenic chemicals, scientists can obtain a vast number of mutant strains of yeast. These strains can be studied for clues to the roles of genes in genetic defects.

Leland Hartwell, a geneticist at the University of Washington, has studied mutations in yeast cells. Some of the mutations did not allow yeast cells to divide. Hartwell wondered if a crucial gene controlling DNA synthesis could be involved. Some of the cells' buds would not separate from the mother cell. Over several years of research approximately 50 genes have been shown to control various stages of yeast cell division. It is thought that similar genes control cell division in human cells.

In 1985, Gerald Fink, a molecular biologist at the Whitehead Institute for Biomedical Research at Cambridge, Massachusetts, found in yeast something similar to the human AIDS virus. This virus does not make yeast immune-deficient, since there are no white blood cells for them to attack, but the virus is classified as a retrovirus, like the AIDS virus. A retrovirus carries its own nucleic acid to direct a cell's operations. It copies the genetic information it carries into the host cell's DNA. Fink hopes that understanding how the AIDS-like virus works in the yeast cell will lead to a better understanding of how the AIDS virus works in human cells.

Questions:

1. Why are scientists using yeast in order to better understand human cells?

____

2. What are some advantages of using yeast cells in research over human cells?

____

____

3. How have mutant genes in yeast helped scientists better understand cell division?

____

____

Name ______________________ Date ______________

Is It a Plant or An Animal?

Before the advent of high-powered microscopes, biologists had little difficulty in classifying the forms of life that were visible to their naked eye. In these earlier times there were only two kingdoms, Animalia and Plantae. If an organism had green color and the presence of leaves, stems, and roots it was considered a plant. In contrast, if an organism had eyes, teeth, and legs, it was considered an animal. Plants were thought of as simple organisms that were nonmotile, or that did not exhibit movement. Animals were motile and were obviously more complex than plants.

With the use of early microscopes, new organisms were discovered. The biologists at that time tried to follow the same thoughts in differentiating between microscopic green (chlorophyll-containing) algae and the colorless, unicellular animals, yeasts, protozoans, molds, and bacteria. All of the microscopic algae, fungi, and bacteria were assigned to the plant kingdom because they were not motile, they had simple, plant-like structures, and they did not capture and eat solid food like animals. The protozoans, on the other hand, were classified as animals because of their complex structure, motility, and their ability to capture and eat solid food.

This simple classification soon encountered difficulties. The advances in scientific technique and microscopes made it more and more difficult to classify some organisms as either plant or animal. For example, it was discovered that plant cells contain cellulose, a molecule that provides structural support, while many animals, such as insects and crustaceans, have a supporting structure of chitin. Yet, many fungi (classed as plants) have cell walls of chitin, and certain primitive animals, the sea squirts, have an outer covering of cellulose. There are types of bacteria that are photosynthetic, and there are algae that produce mobile reproductive cells that resemble protozoans. The lines of distinction between plants and animals have become blurred.

Euglena is an example of an organism that exhibits a combination of overlapping characteristics of plants and animals. Plants contain chlorophyll that enables them to use sunlight as a source of energy for making their own food. Typical animal cells and fungi do not contain chlorophyll and they must have an external source of food. *Euglena,* an algal-like microorganism, contains chlorophyll in chloroplasts but also has the ability to engulf solid food. When food is available it takes it in, but when food is scarce it makes its own food. It also possesses a flagellum that gives it mobility. Some species of *Euglena* lack chlorophyll and are animal-like, while others are nonmotile and are plant-like.

The challenge facing today's biologists is to learn more about these organisms and continue to improve the criteria and methods for classifying organisms.

Questions:

1. How did the invention and improvement of the microscope create problems in classification? ______________________

2. Why might *Euglena* be classified as a plant? As an animal? ______________________

____

3. Why are *Euglena* and some types of bacteria difficult to classify? ______________________

____

4. Why was the two-kingdom classification system (Animalia vs. Plantae) abandoned? ______________________

____

5. If scientists discover a new organism that clearly has characteristics of both fungi and protozoans (organisms, each in their own kingdom), how should the new organism be classified? ______________________

____

Comparing Fungi

STRUCTURE	FUNCTION
Cap	Reproduction
Gills	Reproduction
Annulus	Reproduction
Stipe	
Hyphae	Obtain nutrients

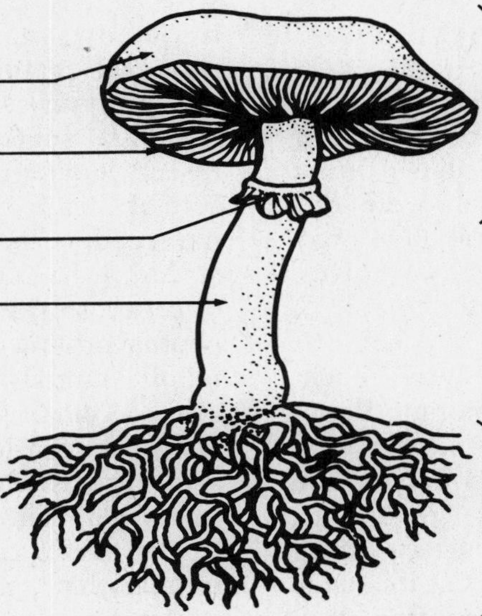

NAME: Mushroom PHYLUM: Basidiomycota (club fungi)

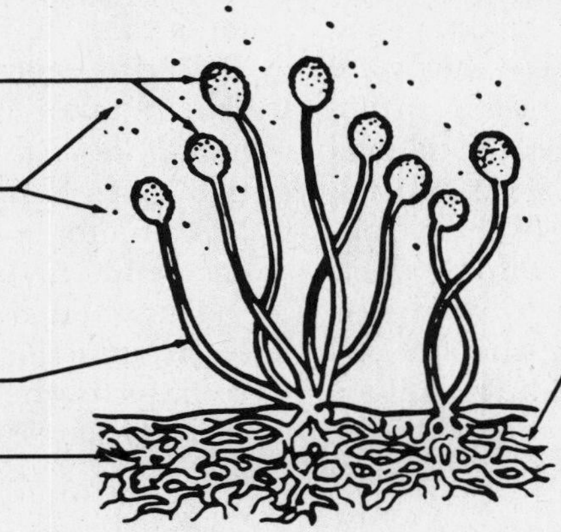

STRUCTURE	FUNCTION
Sporangia	Reproduction
Spores	Reproduction
Sporangiophore	
Rhizoids	Obtain nutrients

NAME: Rhizopus PHYLUM: Zygomycota (sporangium fungi)

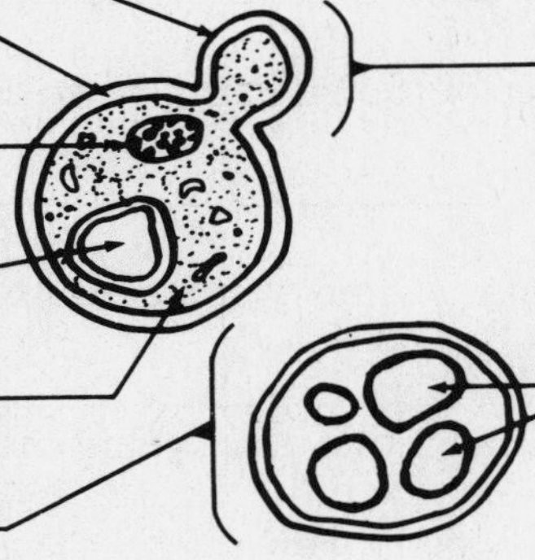

STRUCTURE	FUNCTION
Bud	Reproduction (bud)
Cell wall	
Nucleus	
Vacuole	
Cytoplasm	
Yeast cell with spores	Reproduction (spores)

NAME: Yeast PHYLUM: Ascomycota (sac fungi)

Name ______________________ Date ______________

Problem: What are the traits of organisms in the kingdoms Monera, Protista, and Fungi? (text page 282)

Data and Observations:

FIGURE 13–29.

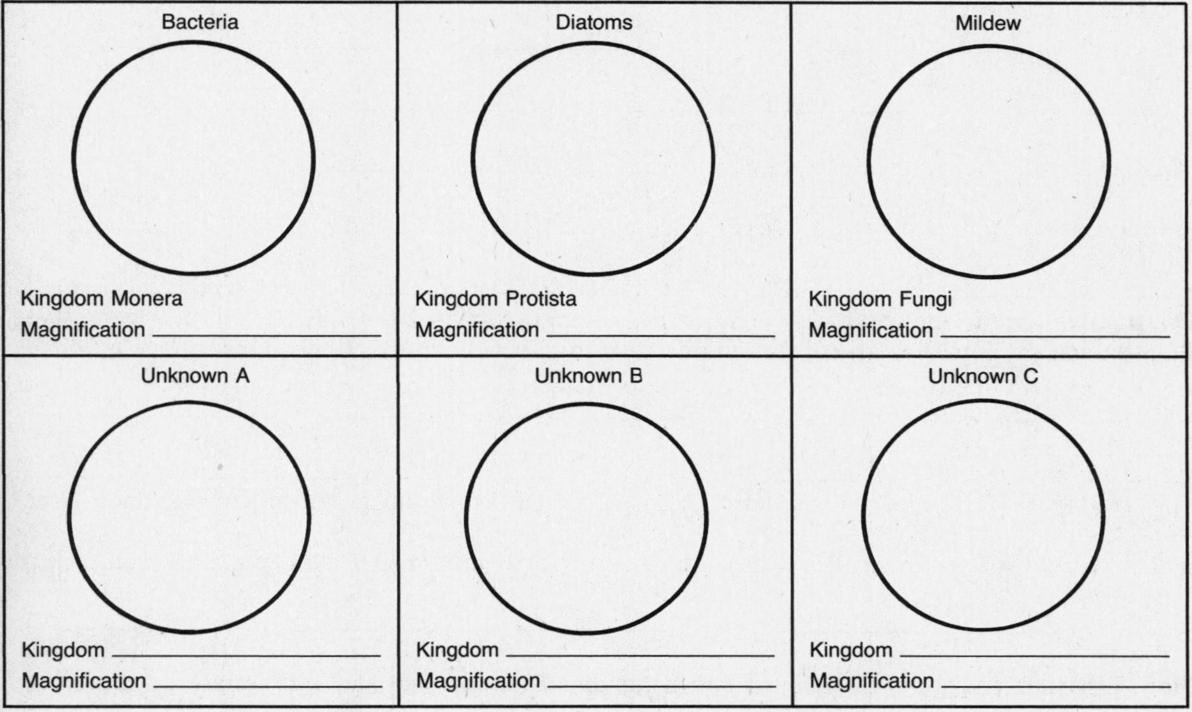

Questions and Conclusion:

1. List three traits of Kingdom Monera. ______________________

____

2. (a) Distinguish between the two main groups of Eubacteria in Kingdom Monera. (b) Based on your answer to 2(a), to what group does the organism observed in Part A belong? ______________

____

3. List three traits of Kingdom Protista. ______________________

____

Name ______________________ *Date* ______________

4. (a) Distinguish among the seven phyla in Kingdom Protista. (Omit slime molds.) (b) Based on your answer to 4(a), to what phylum does the organism observed in Part B belong? ______________

5. List three traits of Kingdom Fungi. ______________

6. (a) Distinguish among the three phyla in Kingdom Fungi. (Omit lichens.) (b) Based on your answer to 6(a), to what phylum does the organism observed in Part C belong? (HINT: This fungus produces asci.) ______________

7. List several traits that aided you in determining to which kingdom: (a) unknown organism A belonged (b) unknown organism B belonged (c) unknown organism C belonged. ______________

Conclusion: What are the traits of organisms in Kingdoms Monera, Protista, and Fungi? ______________

PLANNING GUIDE	
TEXT	**UNIT 4 Diversity** **Chapter 14 Plants** **Investigation 14 What are the characteristics of gymnosperms? p. 304**
TEACHER RESOURCE PACKAGE:	
READING AND STUDY GUIDE	Student Edition, p. 81 Teacher Edition, p. 23
RESOURCE MASTER BOOKLET	Student Master 14–1. Biotechnology: Growing Flavors in the Laboratory, p. 14–2 Student Master 14–2. The Expansion of Redwood National Park, p. 14–3 Teaching Master 14–1. Physical Features of Leaves, p. 14–4 Investigation Worksheet, p. 14–5
EVALUATION PROGRAM	Test Masters, p. 53 Alternate Test Masters, p. 169
LABORATORY BIOLOGY: INVESTIGATING LIVING SYSTEMS	35 Algal Plants, p. 135 36 Liverworts, Mosses, and Ferns, p. 139
PROBING LEVELS OF LIFE: A LABORATORY MANUAL	31 Morphology of Green Algae, p. 85 32 Mosses, Club Mosses, and Horsetails, p. 87 33 Ferns, Gymnosperms, and Angiosperms, p. 90

Name ______________________ Date ______________

Biotechnology: Growing Flavors in the Laboratory

At one time there were two flavors of ice cream from which to choose: vanilla and chocolate. Today we must make hard choices between common flavors like strawberry and unusual flavors like bubblegum. We must make the choice between the subtle, well-rounded natural flavor and its more intense, artificial, synthetically produced cousin.

Now we face other choices as biotechnology firms learn how to grow flavors in living plant cells. One California firm is harvesting vanilla flavor from cells that have been surgically removed from vanilla plants and cultured in a glass bioreactor. One of the key techniques of this technology is plant tissue culture, the growth of plant cells in the laboratory. For example, in order to make vanilla, scientists first remove cells from the vanilla plant and culture them in a laboratory dish. Various hormones are added to the cell culture to prevent the cells from differentiating into root or leaf cells. The cell culture is then submerged in a bath of nutrients that help the cells multiply. To turn on the cells' flavor-making factories, additional hormones are added. The cells are finally placed in a protected material and packed into a glass column through which more nutrients flow. Flavor that leaks out of the cells is collected.

The production of pure, natural vanilla flavoring is perhaps less complicated, but more expensive and time-consuming. The vanilla orchid grows primarily in the Malagasy Republic and Indonesia. Each flower of the orchid opens for only one day of the year and must be hand pollinated in order to produce the fruit, or bean. The vanilla bean is cured in a labor-intensive process that takes three to six months. Two kilograms of uncured beans produce approximately one-half kilogram of cured beans. The pure, natural vanilla flavoring extracted from the beans sells for around $2000 per kilogram.

Artificial vanilla flavoring is much less expensive than pure, natural vanilla. Artificial vanilla sells for $10 per kilogram and is made primarily of vanillin. Vanillin is an inexpensive by-product of the paper industry, extracted from wood pulp.

There is no question as to what is natural vanilla and what is artificial vanilla, but how do we treat the vanilla produced by vanilla plant cell cultures? Is it natural or artificial? The biotechnology firms claim that it is natural because it is produced by vanilla plant cells. The vanilla industry insists that it is artificial. They maintain that since pure, natural vanilla contains 150 constituents and the biotechnology firms product contains only eight or ten of these constituents, one of which is vanillin, it cannot be considered natural vanilla flavor. By 1990, the California biotechnology firms expect to produce several hundred thousand kilograms of vanilla flavor a year. This is about the same amount of vanilla that is currently produced by the vanilla bean industry.

Vanilla is not the only flavor that can be produced by plant cell tissue cultures. Similar techniques can be used to produce strawberry, raspberry, grape, and nearly any other fruit flavor. In the future, when you say "I'll take vanilla," what kind of flavor will you get?

Questions:

1. How are flavors produced through plant cell culture similar to natural flavors? ______________

2. Which type of vanilla flavoring would you prefer—natural, artificial, or that produced through biotechnology? Explain your reasoning. ______________

3. If the laboratory-produced vanilla flavoring is accepted and approved for sale, what effect might this product have on the vanilla bean industry in the Malagasy Republic? (The cost of the laboratory-produced vanilla would be less expensive than pure, natural vanilla but slightly more than artificial vanilla.) ______________

Name ______________________ Date ______________

The Expansion of Redwood National Park

The sequoias, or coastal redwoods, have existed on Earth for approximately 160 million years. Today, these trees grow nowhere else but in the northwestern United States. At one time, the redwood forests covered approximately 808 000 hectares (1 hectare = 10 000 m^2) of land. These forests remained untouched until the 1850s, when logging began. By 1925 more than one-third of the trees had been removed. Redwood is resistant to fire and decay and is especially suited for decks, walkways, fences, picnic tables, and construction beams. The United States lumber industry currently cuts about 4000 hectares of redwood per year.

In 1968, the Redwood National Park was established to protect the trees, many of which were hundreds of years old and nearly a hundred meters tall. But while protecting some trees, the establishment of the park has created controversy. The redwood lumber industry and conservationists have been at odds with one another.

By 1978, conservation groups had lobbied Congress and the park increased to 88 000 hectares. Of this total, 30 300 hectares were virgin forest, untouched by logging, and 57 700 hectares were a combination of stumps and saplings that eventually will grow into new forest. According to the Save-the-Redwoods League, only 8 percent of the original 808 000 hectares remained. Further expansion of the park became a priority.

The logging industry opposed expansion of the park in 1978 and logger was pitted against conservationist. The battle was portrayed as saving jobs or saving trees. Logging jobs were, however, already becoming threatened by the indiscriminate cutting of redwoods. The industry often cut areas of trees without replanting them and was essentially endangering its loggers' livelihoods by failing to provide growth for future harvest. In the spirit of compromise, the law that provides for the expansion of the park requires that only selected trees can be cut where logging is permitted. The law also provides funds for job training and relocation of loggers who might suffer from loss of work resulting from the diminished logging of park lands.

Concern for the magnificent trees has not, however, ended. Conservationists believe that in order to assure the survival of the redwoods, another 40 400 hectares must be added to the park, so the purchasing of parcels of land from the logging industry continues. These conservationists may not live to enjoy the full-sized park or see the trees that today are mere sprouts, but they gain a satisfaction in knowing that the redwoods will be saved for generations to come.

Questions:

1. Were the conservationists justified in lobbying Congress for park expansion? Explain.
2. Were the loggers justified in expressing their concerns about the possible loss of jobs? Explain.
3. Would you purchase a product, such as a picnic table, made from redwood? Why? Why not?
4. Is there likely to be a shortage of products made from redwood in the future? Why? Why not?
5. Are you aware of any living resources that, in the past, have become endangered or extinct?
6. Are you aware of any other resources (living or otherwise) that are endangered today?

Physical Features of Leaves

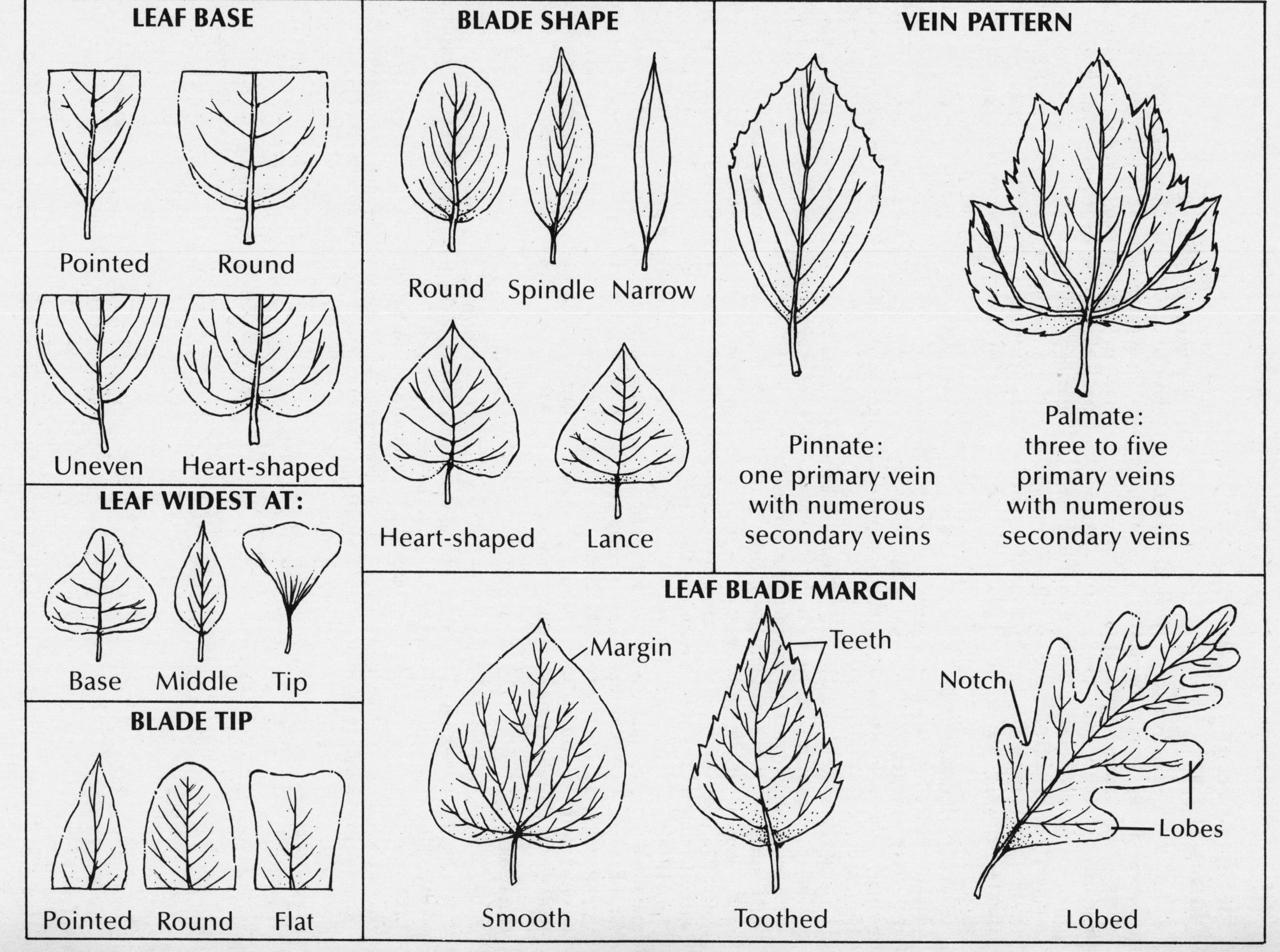

External Structure of Stems and Leaves

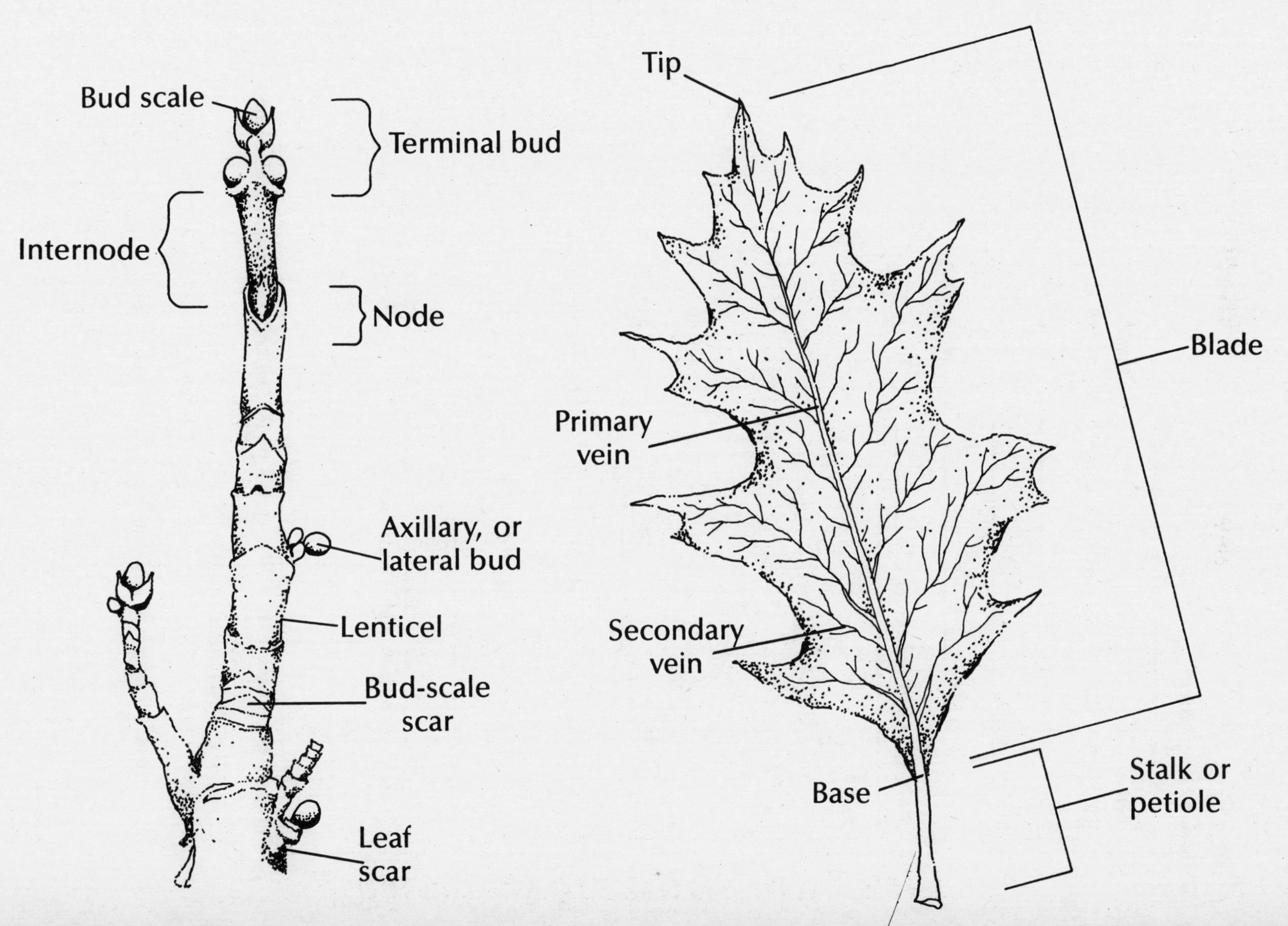

Investigation Worksheet — Chapter 14

Name ______________________ Date ______________

Problem: What are the characteristics of gymnosperms? (text page 304)

Data and Observations:

Part A.

(a) general leaf shape ______________

(b) number of leaves per bundle ______________

____

(c) color of leaf ______________

(d) presence or absence of cutin ______________

Part B.

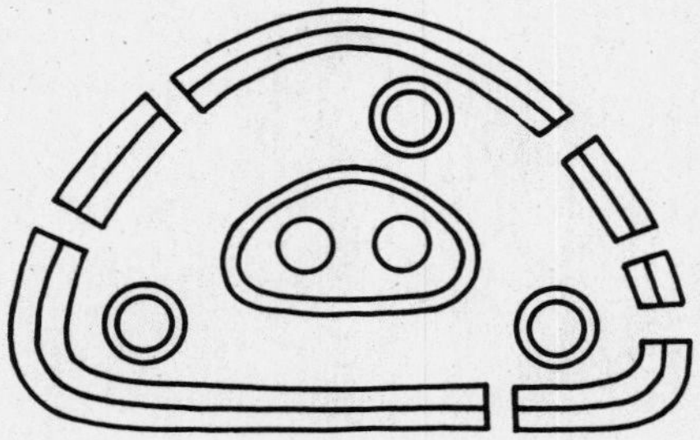

Part C.

(a) Which cone type is larger? ______________

(b) Which cone type is smaller? ______________

(c) Which cone type appears singly? ______________

(d) Which cone type appears in groups? ______________

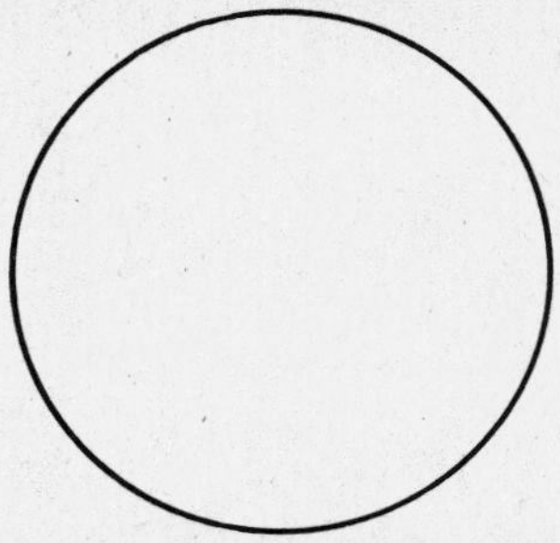

(e) estimate of number of pollen cells ______________

____

(f) number of egg cells ______________

Questions and Conclusion:

1. Define: (a) gymnosperm (b) pollen grain (c) cone. ______________
2. Refer to Appendix A and determine the kingdom, phylum, subphylum, and class for a pine tree. ______________
3. Compare the number of pollen grains (male sex cells) on one scale to the number of egg cells (female sex cells) on one scale. ______________
4. Pollen cells are carried by the wind to female cones where fertilization of egg cells occurs. Explain the adaptive advantage of air bladders on the pollen grains. ______________

Conclusion: What are the characteristics of gymnosperms? ______________

PLANNING GUIDE	
TEXT	**UNIT 4 Diversity** **Chapter 15 Animals: Sponges Through Mollusks** **Investigation 15 What does the pork worm *Trichinella spiralis* look like and what is its life cycle? p. 324**
TEACHER RESOURCE PACKAGE:	
READING AND STUDY GUIDE	Student Edition, p. 87 Teacher Edition, p. 24
RESOURCE MASTER BOOK	Student Master 15–1. Medicinal Leeches, p. 15–2 Student Master 15–2. Coral Reefs, p. 15–3 Teaching Master 15–1. Annelid Anatomy: Earthworm, p. 15–4 Teaching Master 15–2. Mollusk Anatomy: Clam and Snail, p. 15–5 Teaching Master 15–3. Coelenterate Anatomy: Hydra, p. 19 Investigation Worksheet, p. 15–6
EVALUATION PROGRAM	Test Masters, p. 57 Alternate Test Masters, p. 171
LABORATORY BIOLOGY: INVESTIGATING LIVING SYSTEMS	37 A Survey of Some Animal Phyla, p. 143 38 Earthworm Anatomy, p. 147
PROBING LEVELS OF LIFE: A LABORATORY MANUAL	34 Diversity of Lower Invertebrates, p. 93 35 Constructing a Key to the Lower Invertebrates, p. 95

Name ______________________ Date ______________

Medicinal Leeches

To scientists a leech is an annelid and a close relative of the earthworm. It is also a hermaphrodite, having both male and female sex organs. To many of us, however, a leech is a repulsive, slimy creature with a notorious past. We relate leeches to the outdated medical practice of "leeching." The use of leeches for medicinal purposes was based on the belief that disease was caused by an excess of "bad" blood or by an imbalance in body humors (fluids). The medicinal leech, *Hirudo medicinalis,* was used to withdraw the bad blood or to readjust the body humors.

Leeching was most popular from 1820 to 1850, when the enthusiasm for leeching bordered on madness. A French doctor, Francois Broussais, once treated his own indigestion with 15 applications of 50 to 60 leeches over an 18-day period. Leeches were applied, up to 50 at a time, to patients having every disorder from nosebleeds to obesity.

Today, there is a resurgence in the medicinal use of leeches. It has promising potential for yielding new knowledge and new medical therapies. One such therapy was used in 1985 to save a reattached ear.

On August 16, 1985 in Medford, Massachusetts, a dog attacked a five-year-old boy and bit off his right ear. In a previous operation, an adult's ear had been reattached by surgeons. A child's ear, however, never had been. Not only did the ear have to be reattached, but the artery and veins that would supply blood to the ear had to be reconnected. Dr. Joseph Upton, who performed the operation, worked for 10 hours while looking through a surgical microscope. Artery reconnection is relatively easy, but reattachment of the smaller veins is more difficult: it takes a period of time before the veins are healed well enough to return blood from the ear. During this time, the tissues are subject to damage and infection. Within a few days, the boy's ear began to discolor. It first turned blue and then purple as blood pooled in the ear. Dr. Upton searched for a way to relieve the blood congestion in the ear while the veins healed, and he chose to return to the practice of leeching. He found the medicinal leech to be unavailable in the United States, but a series of phone calls led him to a company called Biopharm in Swansea, Wales. The firm sent a package of 30 medicinal leeches. Upon application, the first leech fastened itself to the upper part of the boy's ear and began to pulse slightly, the sign that bloodsucking had begun. Eight leeches and a few days later, the boy was released from the hospital and returned home with an intact, healthy ear. The leeches had given the ear time to heal itself.

Leeches have also become a model for research. The medicinal leech has large and accessible nerve cells. With a leech, one can pick out a particular neuron under the microscope and study it in detail. Scientists are interested in several biochemicals that have evolved in the leech as a means of obtaining blood. Scientists hope that these biochemicals may one day be used to treat circulatory problems and other disorders. One substance is an anticoagulant, a substance that prevents blood from clotting. Another biochemical secreted by the leech dilates the veins. Still another chemical, called a spreading factor, breaks down the cement that binds cells together. These biochemicals helped keep the boy's ear clear of congested blood until the veins could heal.

The giant Amazon leech secretes an anticoagulant that also may be used in medicine. Roy Sawyer and Andrei Budzynski discovered this biochemical and named it hemetin. Sawyer is a research scientist and owner of Biopharm. Budzynski is a biochemistry professor at Temple University. Hemetin is unusual in that it not only prevents coagulation, but also dissolves blood clots after they form. It is hoped that hemetin can one day be used to dissolve blood clots.

Questions:

1. What is leeching? ______________________
2. How were leeches recently used to help save a reattached ear?

____

3. Why are leeches of interest to medical scientists today? ______________________

____

____

Name ______________________ Date ______________

Coral Reefs

Coral reefs are unique underwater ecosystems. Submerged in tropical, shallow water, coral reefs are enormous limestone structures that are inhabited by strange forms of life. The reefs are homes for many exotic creatures. Animals that resemble fans or flowering plants gently wave back and forth in the ocean current. Brightly colored fish dart in and out of hiding places. Worms that live in tubes and snails that kill with a deadly poison are all inhabitants.

One of the inhabitants of the coral reef is so small that it could easily be overlooked, yet this tiny animal, the coral polyp, is the principal architect of the reef ecosystem. The coral polyp is a very simple animal that has few body parts. A polyp's body consists of a tube made of a jelly-like tissue with an opening, or mouth, at one end. Food is taken in and waste is expelled through this opening. The mouth is surrounded by a number of flexible tentacles. The tentacles capture food and carry it to the polyp's mouth. One of the most significant abilities of a coral polyp is its ability to produce hard limestone to protect its soft body.

Limestone is a material made up of a chemical called calcium carbonate. Coral polyps are able to extract this calcium carbonate from ocean water. A polyp deposits layers of calcium carbonate around the lower half of its body so that it forms a kind of cup. The limestone cup, or corallite, serves as a shelter for the polyp. The polyp can withdraw its body, tentacles and all, into its protective corallite.

Coral polyps that form corallites are called stony corals. They are the primary builders of a coral reef. The Great Barrier Reef, located off the northeastern coast of Australia, is the world's largest coral reef. It extends for more than 1920 kilometers and, at its widest part, stretches to more than 241 kilometers. The process by which the tiny coral polyps create such large reefs is remarkable and complex.

Although coral polyps are quite resilient under normal conditions, they are vulnerable to the results of human carelessness. Polyps absorb vital nutrients from passing water currents, but those same currents can also bring them poisonous substances. Waste materials pumped into the ocean by factories and ships can prove to be devastating. Like a giant sponge, the coral reef can quickly absorb harmful pollutants, killing the polyps and eventually the entire aquatic community. Fertilizers that flow from the land are also detrimental to the reefs. As fertilizer mixes with ocean water, the nitrogen content of the water increases, encouraging the growth of algae. Algae can quickly cover and smother the coral polyp. Soil erosion that results from shoreline development introduces great amounts of silt into ocean currents. If silt settles upon a coral reef, the blanketlike covering chokes and kills the delicate coral polyps. Today, the world's coral reefs are threatened in many ways.

Questions:

1. Studies have indicated that fertilizers used by farmers in Australia are entering the ocean water in the runoff from the land. Should any measures be taken to avoid fertilizer runoff? Why?
2. How might an oil spill affect a coral reef?
3. Although coral reefs are found in relatively shallow water where large oil tankers cannot travel, should oil tankers be required to travel a certain distance from coral reefs? Why?
4. Should coral reefs be protected by designating them national parks? Why?
5. Crown-of-thorns sea stars are natural predators of coral polyps. Population explosions of crown-of-thorns have occurred in several coral reefs, causing severe damage to the reefs. Some scientists believe that these population explosions are part of a natural cycle. Other scientists disagree. They believe that the increase in population is due to overcollecting of a large marine snail, the triton, a natural predator of the crown-of-thorns. Some scientists believe that the reduction in the number of tritons has lead to an increase in the crown-of-thorns. When a population explosion of crown-of-thorns occurs, should people interfere by automatically reducing the crown-of-thorns population before it damages the coral reef? Explain.

Annelid Anatomy: Earthworm

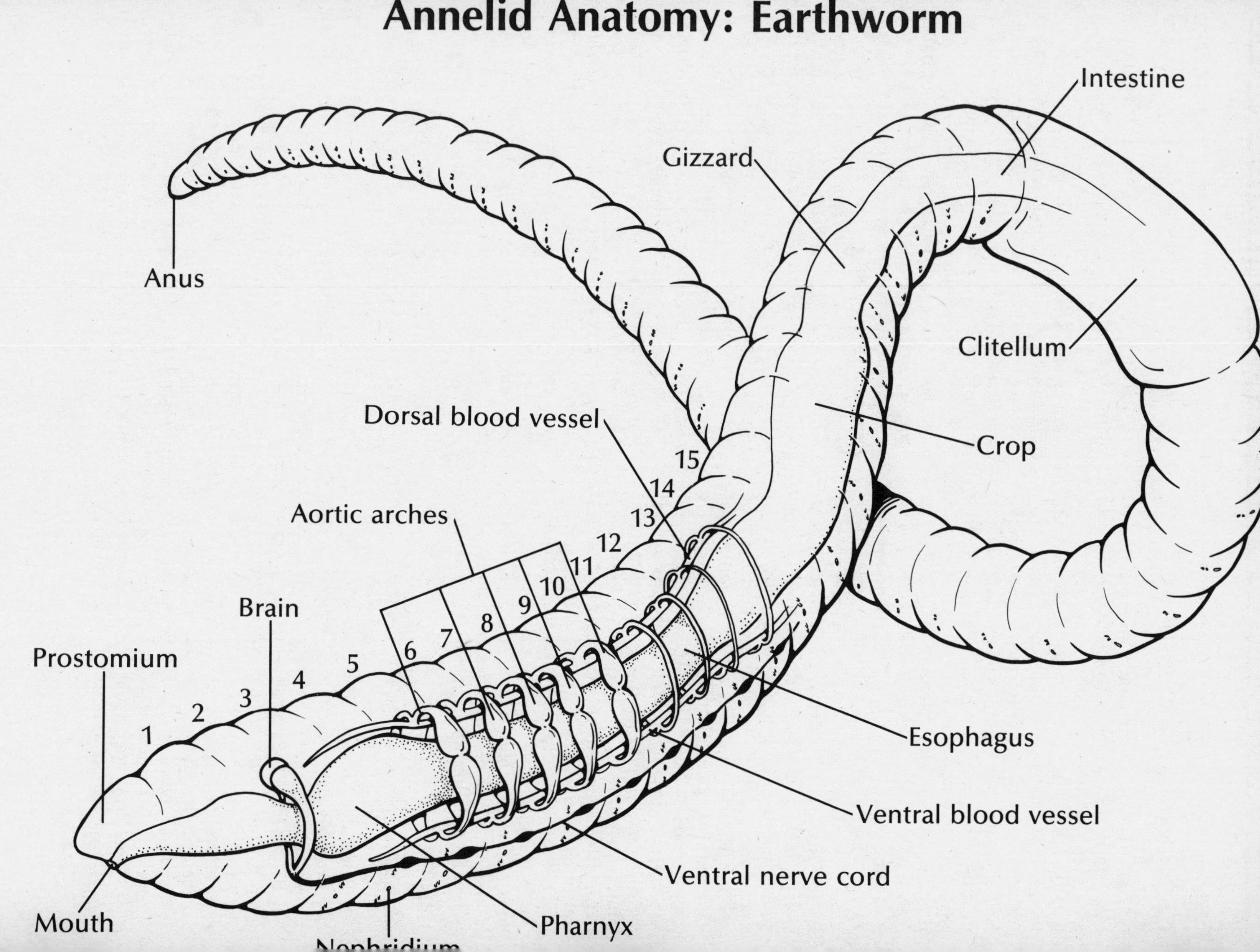

Mollusk Anatomy: Clam and Snail

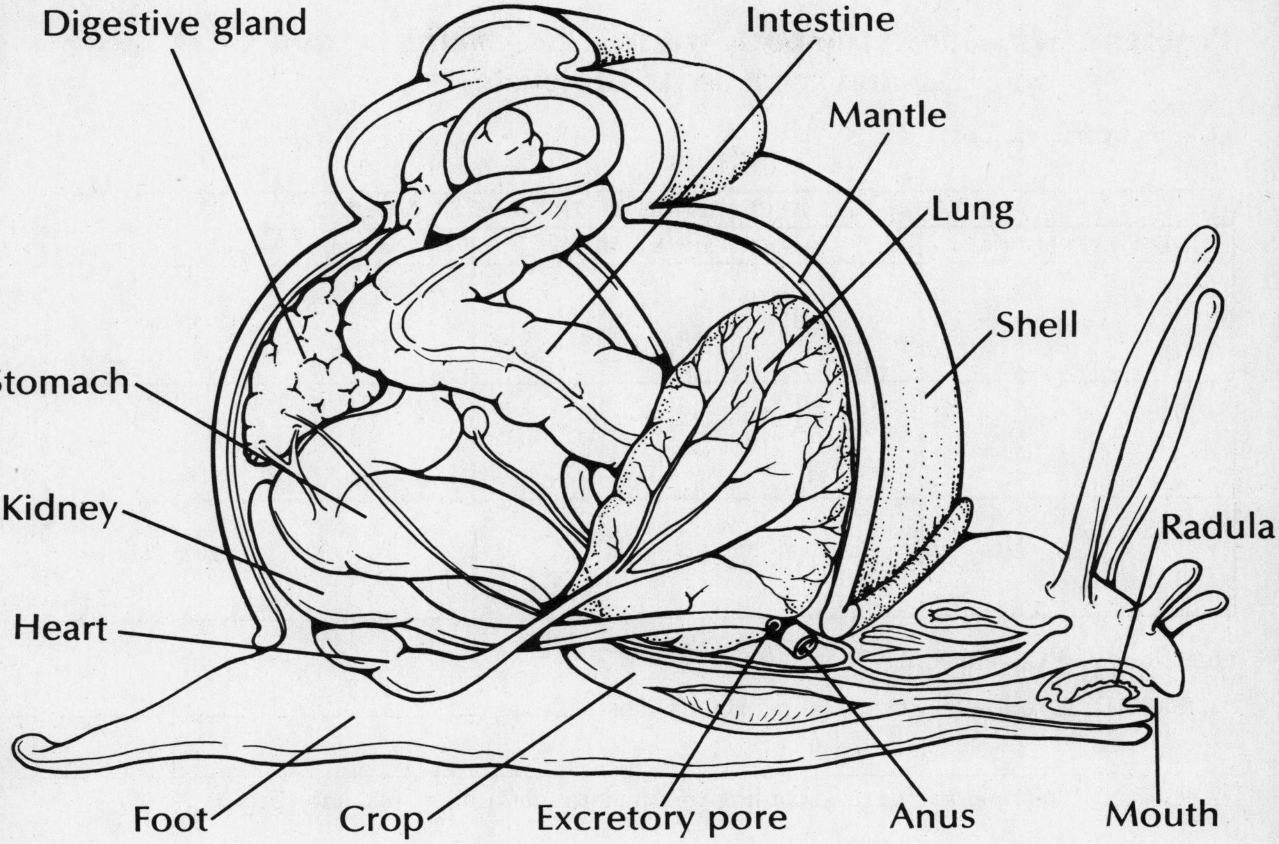

Digestive gland
Intestine
Mantle
Lung
Shell
Stomach
Kidney
Heart
Radula
Foot
Crop
Excretory pore
Anus
Mouth

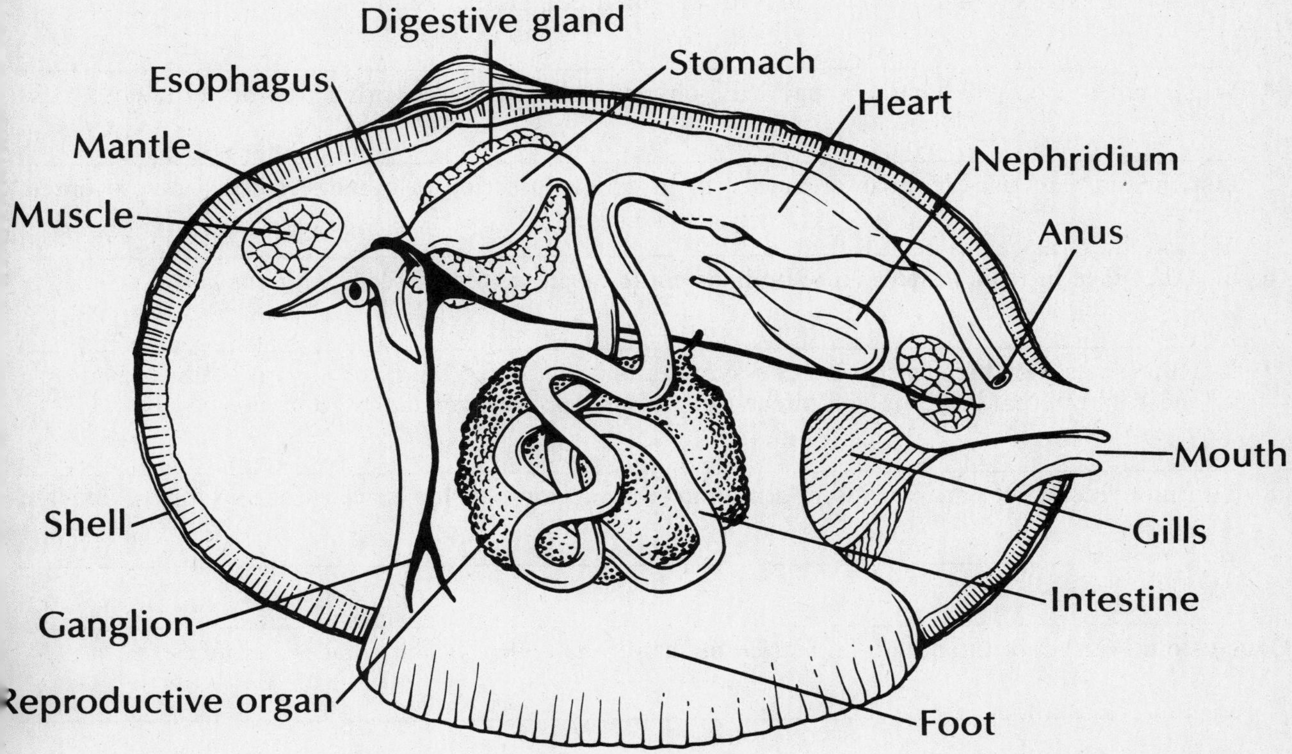

Digestive gland
Esophagus
Stomach
Heart
Mantle
Nephridium
Muscle
Anus
Mouth
Shell
Gills
Intestine
Ganglion
Reproductive organ
Foot

Name ______________________ Date ______________

Problem: What does the pork worm *Trichinella spiralis* look like and what is its life cycle? (text page 324)

Data and Observations:

TABLE 15-2. APPEARANCE OF *TRICHINELLA SPIRALIS*		
Trichinella spiralis	Diagram of life-size worms	Diagram of magnified worms
Female	______ mm	______ X
Male	______ mm	______ X
Larva and Cyst		______ X Estimated length: ______ mm

Questions and Conclusion:

1. Define the following terms: (a) parasite (b) host. ______________________
2. Classify *Trichinella spiralis* according to kingdom, phylum, genus, and species.
3. List several characteristics for the phylum to which this animal belongs.
4. What evidence do you have to support the observation that these worms are not hermaphrodites?
5. List the stage in the life cycle of the worm in which infection of other pigs could be prevented. Explain your answer. ______________________
6. List the stage in which infection of humans could be prevented. Explain your answer.
7. List the stage at which each of these symptoms may occur: (a) extreme weakness and muscle soreness (b) internal bleeding and infections (c) diarrhea, abdominal pain, and nausea.
8. To find evidence of pork worms in a human, would you look for larval or adult worms? Explain your answer. ______________________

Conclusion: What does the pork worm *Trichinella spiralis* look like and what is its life cycle?

PLANNING GUIDE

TEXT	**UNIT 4 Diversity** **Chapter 16 Animals: Arthropods Through Vertebrates** **Investigation 16 How do poisonous and nonpoisonous snakes compare? p. 352**
TEACHER RESOURCE PACKAGE:	
READING AND STUDY GUIDE	Student Edition, p. 93 Teacher Edition, p. 26
RESOURCE MASTER BOOK	Student Master 16–1. A Comparison of a Crustacean and an Insect, p. 16–2 Student Master 16–2. The Horseshoe Crab, p. 16–3 Teaching Master 16–1. Arthropod Anatomy: Crayfish, p. 16–4 Teaching Master 16–2. Vertebrate Anatomy: Fish, p. 16–5 Teaching Master 16–3. Arthropod Anatomy: Grasshopper, p. 20 Teaching Master 16–4. Echinoderm Anatomy: Starfish, p. 21 Teaching Master 16–5. Vertebrate Anatomy: Rat, p. 22 Investigation Worksheet, p. 16–6, p. 10
EVALUATION PROGRAM	Test Masters, p. 61 Alternate Test Masters, p. 173
LABORATORY BIOLOGY: INVESTIGATING LIVING SYSTEMS	39 Arthropods, p. 153 40 Starfish, p. 157
PROBING LEVELS OF LIFE: A LABORATORY MANUAL	36 Identification of Aquatic Insect Larvae and Juveniles, p. 96 37 Diversity of Vertebrates, p. 98

Name ______________________ Date ______________________

A Comparison of a Crustacean and an Insect

One characteristic that crustaceans and insects share, along with all other arthropods, is an exoskeleton, or external skeleton. The exoskeleton is composed of a substance called chitin. It may seem strange to find the skeleton on the outside of an animal's body, but whether the skeleton is internal or external, it serves the same functions. The skeleton gives the body form, protects delicate internal organs, and aids movement by serving as a place of attachment for muscles. The nature of the exoskeleton, however, limits the size and affects the development of an organism. The exoskeleton required to support a large insect would be very heavy, much more so than an internal skeleton supporting the same weight. It would make movement on land cumbersome. That is why most insects are relatively small. Flying would be even more difficult, although the fossil record reveals that at one time dragonflies with three-foot wingspans were common. The growth in size of an organism is also somewhat limited by an exoskeleton. Once the exoskeleton of an organism forms, it does not increase in size. Further growth of the organism depends upon molting, which is the splitting, shedding, and regrowth of the exoskeleton. The organism is vulnerable to predation during this molting process.

The exoskeleton is only one external characteristic that all arthropods share. Another is the segmented body. In addition to the external similarities, arthropods also share some internal features. You will discover several of these characteristics by studying the diagrams of a lobster and a grasshopper in Figure 16–1.

Questions:

1. Locate and label the cephalothorax and the abdomen on the lobster diagram.
2. Locate and label the head, the thorax, and the abdomen on the grasshopper diagram.
3. What types of internal parts do the lobster and the grasshopper share? ______________________

____

4. How does the digestive system of the lobster differ from that of the grasshopper?

____

____

5. The location of the heart in all arthropods is the same. Locate the heart in the lobster and in the grasshopper. Write a statement about where the heart is located with respect to the digestive system. (HINT: *Dorsal* means located near or on the back of an animal; *ventral* means located on the lower, or anterior, surface of an animal.) ______________________

____

FIGURE 16–1.

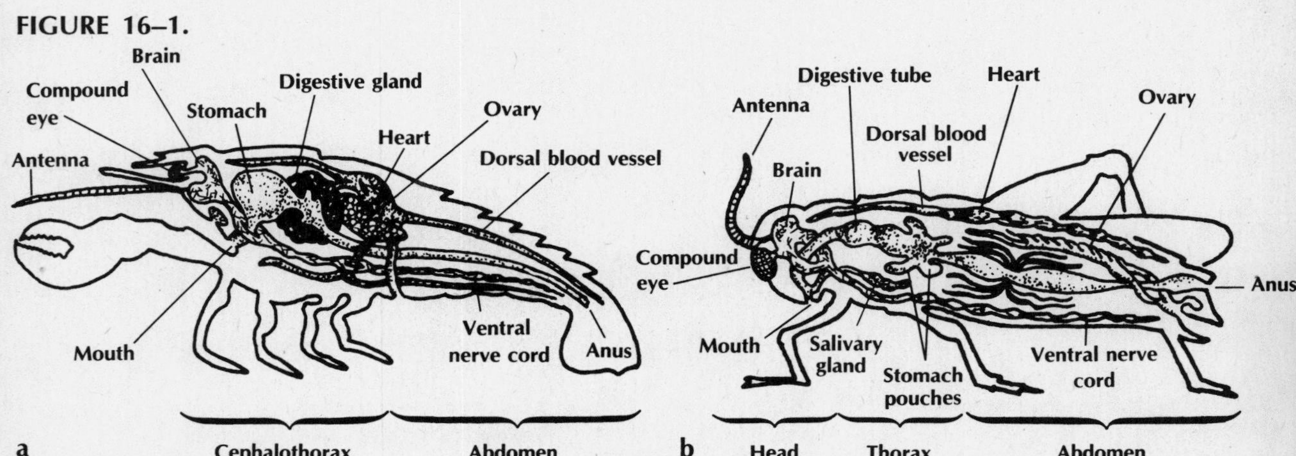

Name ______________________ Date ______________

The Horseshoe Crab

Despite its name, the horseshoe crab is not a crab at all. It is an arthropod, but it is related to spiders and scorpions. All species of horseshoe crabs belong to the class Merostomata. The best known species of horseshoe crab, *Limulus polyphemus,* can be found from Maine to the Yucatan peninsula.

The remarkable, tanklike horseshoe crab is a hardy creature. It has existed on Earth for over 300 million years. Its anatomical structure enables it to walk the ocean floor, drift in the ocean waters, and burrow into the sand. The horseshoe crab has an exoskeleton that is tough but flexible. The exoskeleton, also called the shell, ranges in color from dark to light brown with subtle hues of green or yellow. A horseshoe crab can grow as large as 0.6 meter long and can have a mass of over 4.5 kilograms. In the adult crab, two compound eyes are located on the upper part of the shell. Scientists believe that the eyes can perceive movement, but not images.

Five pairs of legs are located on the underside of the horseshoe crab. Each leg has a clawlike pincer. The last pair of legs also have a fanlike structure that is used for burrowing into the sand. The other four pairs of legs are used for walking and for handling prey.

In the center of the legs, on the underside, is the mouth. It has a powerful gizzard with small teeth for grinding food. Near the mouth are two small pincers, called chelicerae. These are used for feeding. Directly above the mouth is the brain. The elongated heart is located along the back.

Toward the rear of the horseshoe crab is the abdomen. The abdomen is followed by the telson, or long, spikelike tail. The telson is used to help the horseshoe crab burrow into the sand. Burrowing is very important if the horseshoe crab is stranded by a tide. By burrowing into the sand, the horseshoe crab keeps moist until the next tide. The telson is also used to upright the horseshoe crab should it become inverted.

In the spring, usually in late May or June, an unusual phenomenon takes place. Thousands of horseshoe crabs converge on the beaches along Delaware Bay to mate. This mating episode always takes place at the new or full moon. At these times, the spring tide is at a high level. This enables the horseshoe crab to deposit its eggs high up on the beach.

During the mating episode, the large females crawl out of the water. Each female has a smaller male attached to her. The male holds onto the female with his first pair of walking legs. Once on the beach, the female digs 10 to 15 holes in the sand. She deposits from 200 to several thousand pearl-like eggs in each hole. The male is dragged across the eggs and emits sperm over them. After 24 hours, the horseshoe crabs cover their eggs and slip back into the ocean.

For 2 to 10 weeks, the fertilized eggs develop in the sand. The waves of the next high tide filter through and stir the sand, helping the newly hatched larvae reach the surface. The larvae then float out with the tide. A young horseshoe crab grows and molts several times a year for the first 2 to 3 years. At 10 to 12 years it becomes a sexually mature adult, and it may live for another 7 years.

The population of horseshoe crabs on the east coast of the United States has dwindled since 1900. The decrease in population can be attributed to fishermen who have, historically, destroyed the horseshoe crab because it eats clams. The horseshoe crab also has been harvested for fertilizer and eel bait. More recently, the horseshoe crab has been harvested for the processing of foods and for medical research. If the decline in the horseshoe crab population continues, we may see the disappearance of one of the world's last-remaining living fossils.

Questions:

1. What might happen to a horseshoe crab that has no telson and has been left inverted on the beach? ______________________
2. What might signal the horseshoe crab that it is time to mate? ______________________
3. Why does the female horseshoe crab lay so many eggs? ______________________
4. For what reasons is the horseshoe crab harvested today? Which reasons are acceptable to you? Why? ______________________

Arthropod Anatomy: Crayfish

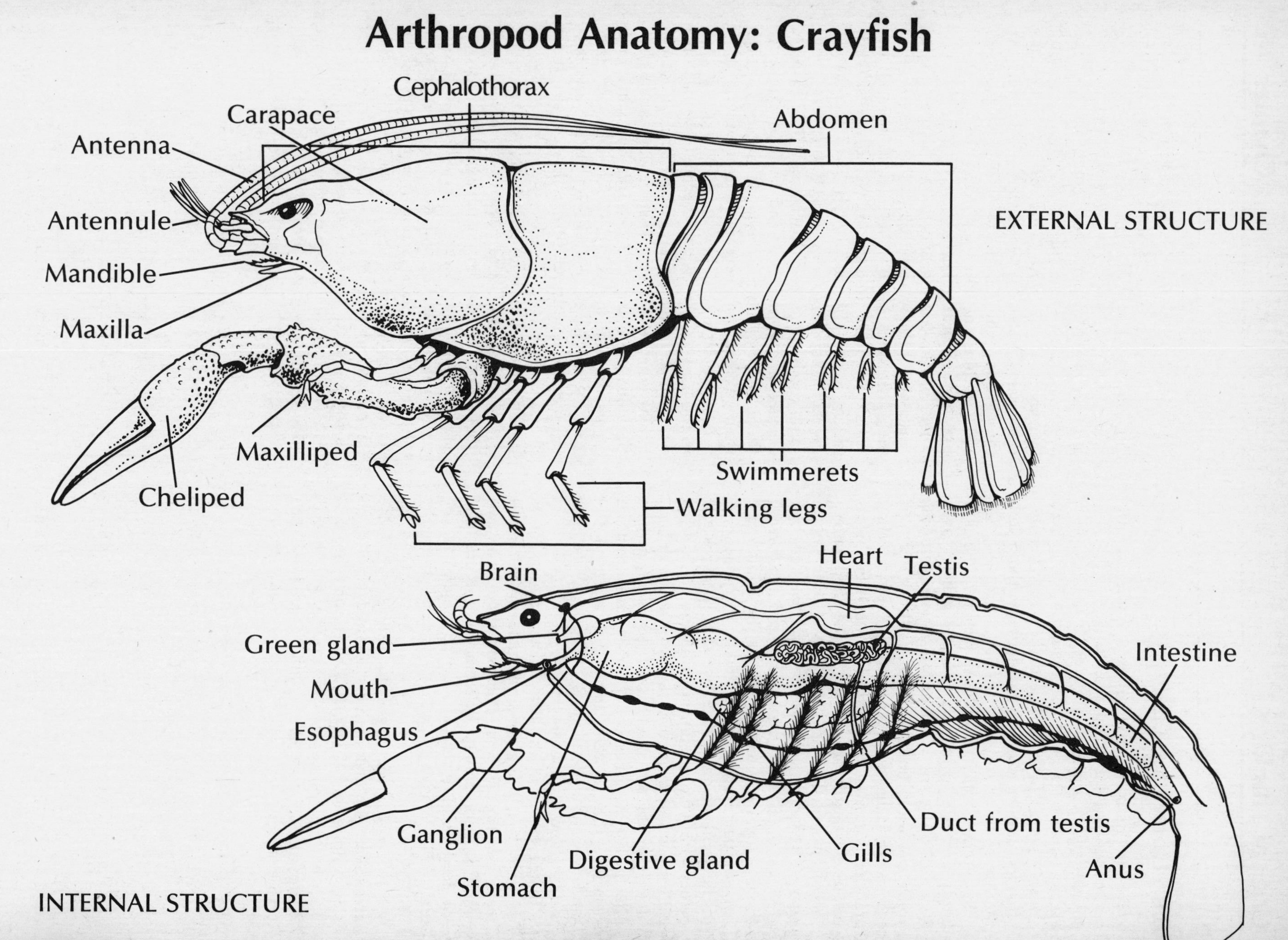

Vertebrate Anatomy: Fish

EXTERNAL STRUCTURE

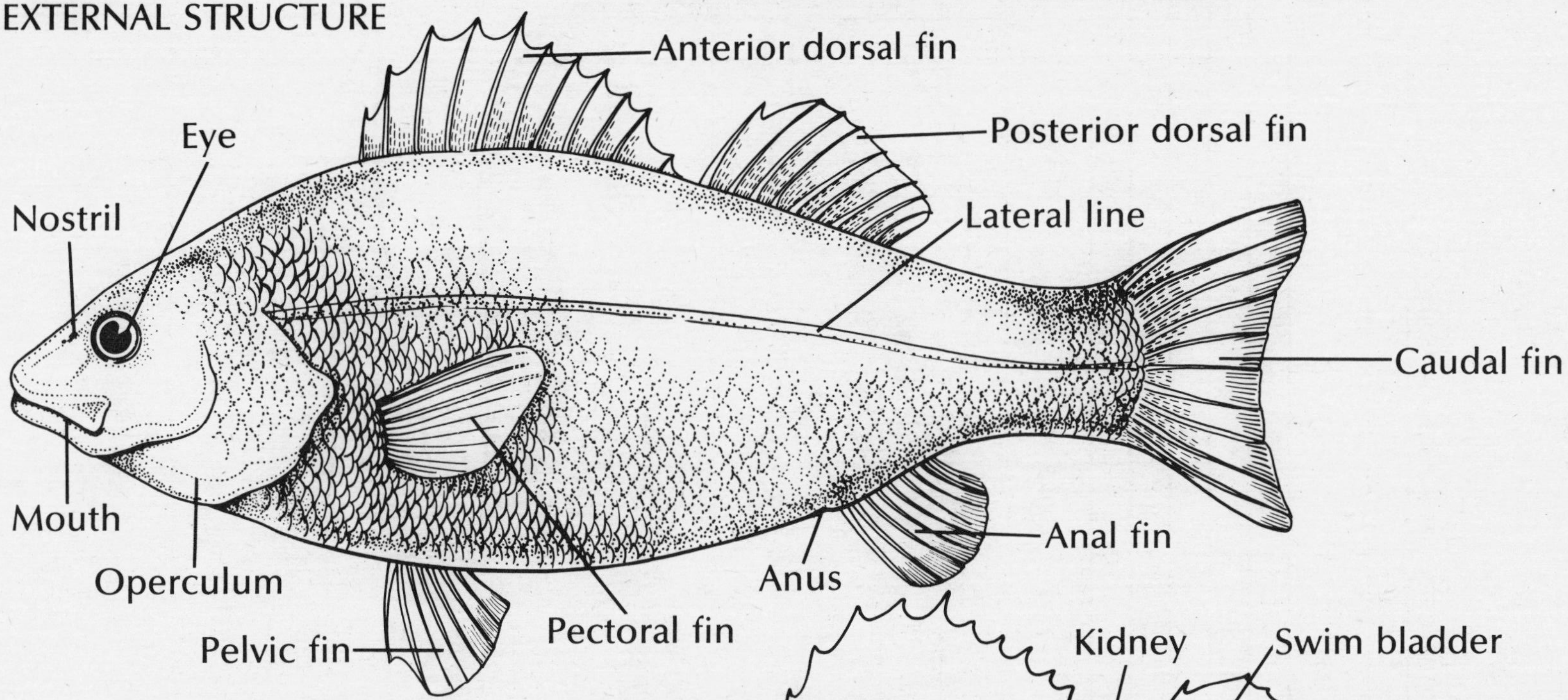

Anterior dorsal fin
Eye
Posterior dorsal fin
Nostril
Lateral line
Caudal fin
Mouth
Anal fin
Operculum
Anus
Pectoral fin
Pelvic fin

INTERNAL STRUCTURE

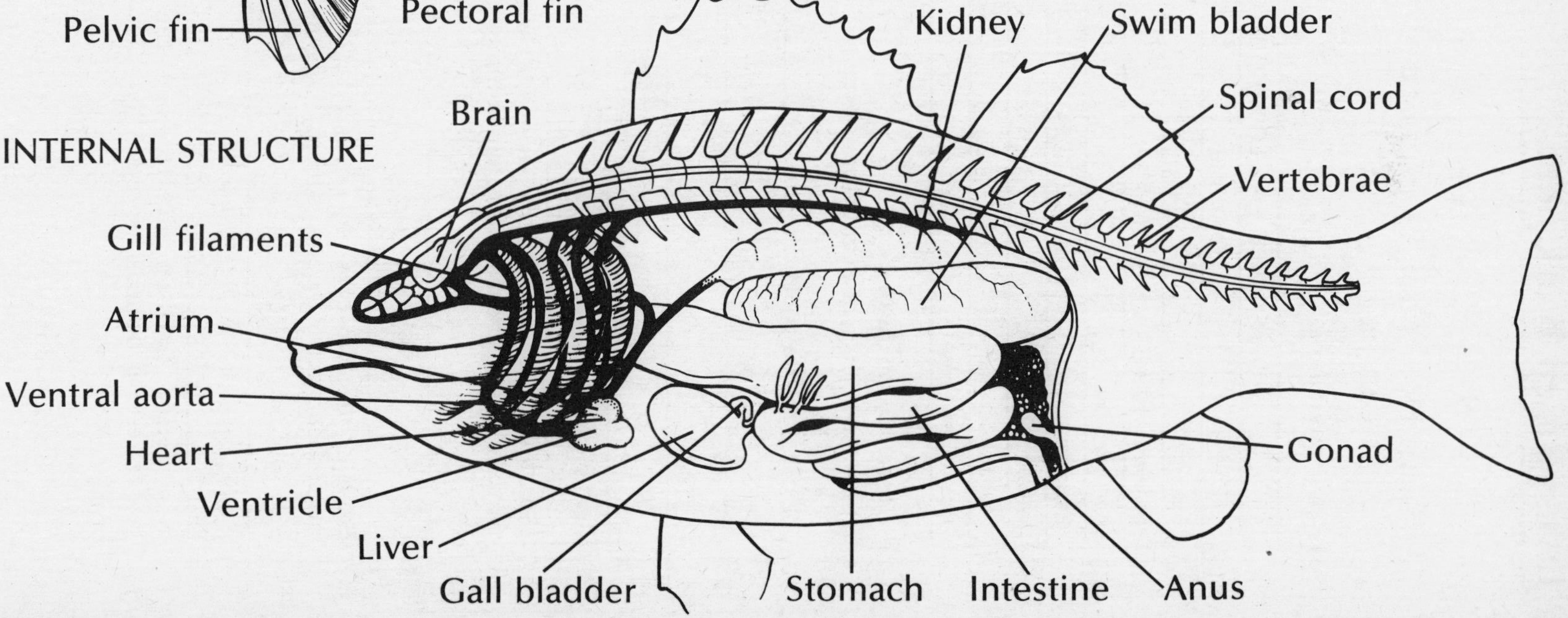

Kidney
Swim bladder
Brain
Spinal cord
Vertebrae
Gill filaments
Atrium
Ventral aorta
Heart
Gonad
Ventricle
Liver
Gall bladder
Stomach
Intestine
Anus

Name ____________________ Date ____________________

Problem: How do poisonous and nonpoisonous snakes compare?

(text page 352)

Data and Observations:

TABLE 16-4. LOCATIONS OF SOME POISONOUS SNAKES					
	Your State	California	Florida	Maine	Texas
Eastern coral					
Southern copperhead					
Northern copperhead					
Eastern cottonmouth					
Western cottonmouth					
Eastern massasauga					
Western rattlesnake					

Questions and Conclusion:

1. (a) List five traits of Subphylum Vertebrata.

   (b) List three traits of all reptiles. ____________________

2. List three ways that most poisonous snakes may be distinguished from nonpoisonous snakes. ____________________

3. Explain how the coral snake may be distinguished from nonpoisonous snakes.

4. Which states listed in Table 16-4 have the: (a) fewest poisonous species (b) most poisonous species? ____________________

Conclusion: How do poisonous and nonpoisonous snakes compare? ____________________

FIGURE 16–27.

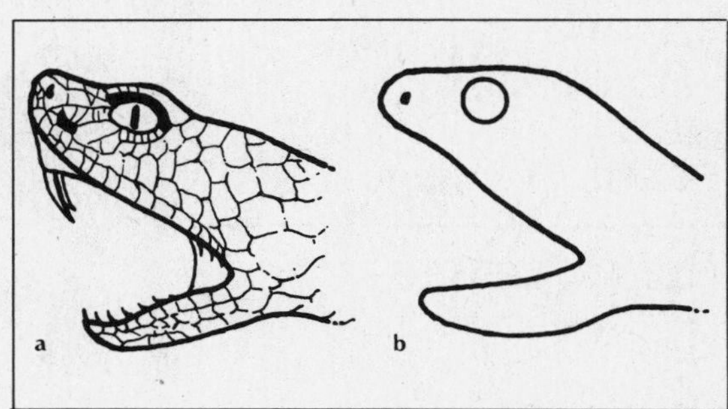

FIGURE 16–28.

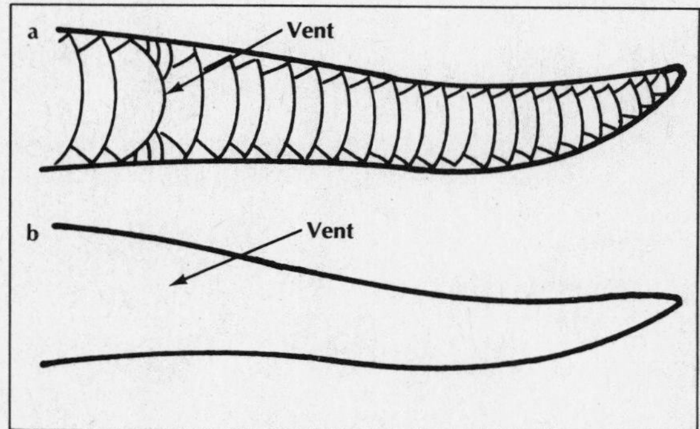

FIGURE 16–29.

Fang puncture marks

a b

PLANNING GUIDE	
TEXT	**UNIT 5 Simple Organisms** **Chapter 17 Simple Organisms: Reproduction** **Investigation 17 How do different organisms reproduce asexually? p. 370**
TEACHER RESOURCE PACKAGE:	
READING AND STUDY GUIDE	Student Edition, p. 99 Teacher Edition, p. 27
RESOURCE MASTER BOOK	Student Master 17–1. Four Types of Sexual Spores, p. 17–2 Student Master 17–2. Polio Vaccine—Dead or Alive? p. 17–3 Teaching Master 17–1. Bacteriophage Life Cycle, p. 17–4 Investigation Worksheet, p. 17–5
EVALUATION PROGRAM	Test Masters, p. 65 Alternate Test Masters, p. 175
LABORATORY BIOLOGY: INVESTIGATING LIVING SYSTEMS	41 How Common Are Bacteria and How Quickly Do They Reproduce? p. 161 42 Reproduction in Fungi, p. 163
PROBING LEVELS OF LIFE: A LABORATORY MANUAL	38 Reproduction in Yeasts, p. 100 39 Growth and Reproduction of Fungi, p. 102 40 Assay of Bacteriophage, p. 104

Name ______________________ Date ______________

Four Types of Sexual Spores

Fungi usually exhibit two different phases of growth. One phase is asexual and involves the growing, vegetative part of the fungi. The other phase is the sexual, or reproducing, phase. During the sexual phase, nuclei fuse or two gametes join together to produce spores. Different types of sexual spores are produced by fungi. The types of sexual spores formed are used to help differentiate the major groups of Eumycotina, the true fungi.

One type of sexual spore is called a *zygospore.* It is produced by a simple process in which there is a chance contact of the tips of two hyphae. Once in contact, the ends of the two hyphae swell and form two gametangia. A gametangium is a structure that forms gametes. The gametes are similar in appearance and structure and are not easily distinguishable as either male or female. The walls of the gametangia that make contact dissolve, permitting the protoplasts to fuse. The zygote that results from this union is called a zygospore. One fungus that reproduces sexually by zygospores is *Rhizopus stolonifer,* the common bread mold.

A second type of sexual spore is the *oospore.* This type of spore is formed by the fusion of two unlike gametes. The gametes are formed at the ends of hyphae. In *Saprolegnia,* an aquatic mold, a structure called an oogonium forms at the end of the hyphae. Within each oogonium, several female gametes, or eggs, form. Also formed at the end of other hyphae are structures called antheridia. Male gametes, or sperm, form within each antheridium. One antheridium presses close to the wall of an oogonium. A fertilization tube forms and penetrates the wall of the oogonium until it reaches an egg. Fertilization results from the fusion of sperm and egg. The fertilized egg that results is called an oospore.

Sexual spores that are enclosed in a sac, or ascus, form a third type of spore. These spores are called *ascospores.* In forming ascospores, the tips of certain hyphae form reproductive structures that contain similar gametes. Because these gametes are so similar and they cannot be identified as sperm or egg, they are referred to simply as + and −. When the two reproductive structures meet, the cell walls between them dissolve. The nucleus of each + hypha passes into a − hypha. Pairs of + and − nuclei fuse. Meiosis then occurs, followed by mitosis. In the process, each nucleus receives some of the cytoplasm of the original − hypha and surrounds itself with a thick wall, forming an ascospore. All of the ascospores that are formed are enclosed in the same sac, or ascus. Among the familiar molds that produce ascospores are those species that are sky-blue or green in color and are commonly seen on old bread, cheese, and oranges. These species of mold belong to the genus *Penicillium.*

The class Basidiomycetes is familiar to almost everyone as mushrooms, rusts, smuts, and shelf, or bracket, fungi. A distinctive feature of this class is that members develop spores called basidiospores. During a common form of reproduction, two cells of any two hyphae come together, after which the walls between them dissolve. The nucleus from one cell passes into the other cell. The cell now contains two nuclei and is said to be dikaryotic. Fusion of the two nuclei, followed by meiosis, takes place in special cells called basidia. The basidia are often club-shaped. The spores formed by these basidia are called *basidiospores.* The basidiospores are not enclosed in any structure, such as an ascus. Rather, the basidiospores are attached to each basidium by short stalks, each called a sterigma. Most basidia have four sterigmata.

Questions:

Label the parts of the various sexual spores in Figure 17–1.

FIGURE 17–1.

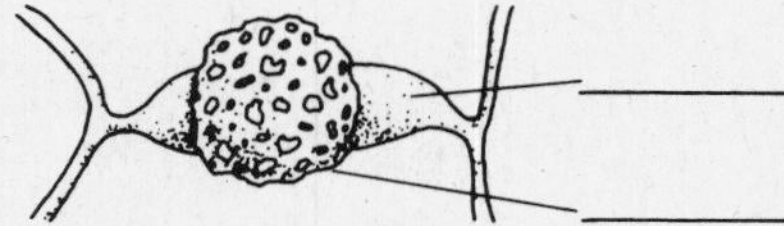

a Formation of zygospore

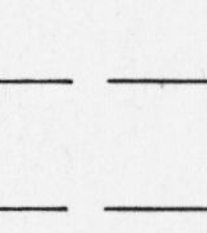

b Formation of oospore

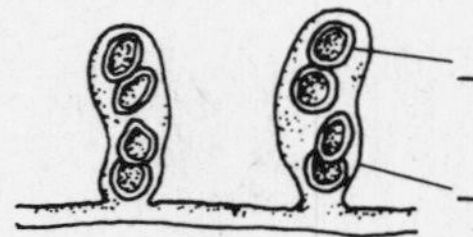

c Formation of ascospore

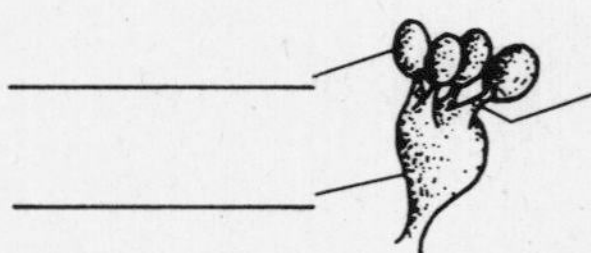

d Formation of basidiospore

Name ______________________ Date ______________________

Polio Vaccine—Dead or Alive?

Before the polio vaccine, each year about 16 000 people in the United States contracted paralytic polio. That ended in 1955 with the general use of a killed-virus vaccine developed by Dr. Jonas Salk. Very quickly, the posters of crippled children and images of polio victims lying in iron lungs became a thing of the past. By 1961, the number of cases of paralytic polio dropped by more than 90 percent.

Although the killed-virus vaccine is effective in immunizing people against polio, it has its drawbacks. The vaccine does not cause antibodies to form in the intestine. Because the polio virus can colonize the intestine, the vaccinated person can still carry the virus and pass it on to a person who has not been vaccinated. The early batches of the vaccine were also relatively weak, requiring booster shots. For the individual this might have meant several shots. For the physician, it meant that it would be difficult to immunize everyone, especially when people would not return for the booster shots.

In 1961, the U.S. Department of Health and Human Services approved a live-virus vaccine that had been developed by Dr. Albert Sabin. The live-virus vaccine is taken orally and travels to the intestine where it stimulates intestinal tissues to develop antibodies. This not only protects the vaccinated person against polio but it also makes him or her unable to be a carrier of the disease. In addition, it is possible that some of the virus in the vaccine may be excreted and passed on to a nonvaccinated person, thus immunizing him or her. For these reasons, the live-virus vaccine has become the vaccine of choice. As a matter of fact, by the late 1960s it was almost impossible to get anything but the live-virus vaccine in the United States.

This, however, is not the entire story of the live-virus vaccine. In rare instances, the virus mutates to a pathogenic, or disease-causing, state as it passes through the body. The pathogenic virus that is excreted may be picked up by others and cause polio. According to the Centers for Disease Control, the live-virus vaccine was the *only* cause of polio cases in 1982 and 1983. The killed vaccine cannot give people the disease.

The issue the polio vaccine raises is not whether or not people should be vaccinated. After all, the polio vaccine has prevented about five million cases of polio worldwide. The issue, rather, is whether the killed-virus vaccine or the live-virus vaccine should be used.

Countries using the killed-virus vaccine have not had polio problems. Both Sweden and Finland use the killed-virus vaccine. There had been no cases of polio in Finland since 1964; however, in 1984, five Finns came down with the disease. People supporting use of the live-virus vaccine claimed that the polio cases reported in Finland were not unexpected because people inoculated with the killed-virus vaccine could still be carriers of the disease. People supporting use of the killed-virus vaccine also claimed the results were not unexpected, but for a different reason. They maintained that the vaccine used was not highly effective against the type of polio found in Finland.

The controversy over the killed-virus and the live-virus vaccines continues today. Taiwan, a country that routinely uses the live-virus vaccine, experienced a polio epidemic in 1982. It occurred in a subpopulation that had been poorly vaccinated. The epidemic seemed to show that the live-virus vaccine is effective in preventing polio in vaccinated people but that the immunity did not spread to the unvaccinated as hoped.

The issue is sure to be raised again as another killed-virus vaccine awaits approval by the U.S. Food and Drug Administration. This vaccine is produced by Institut Merieux of France. Tests of the vaccine have shown that there is no difference in the abilities of the new vaccine and the existing live-virus vaccine to produce immunity. A preliminary report on the vaccine concludes that only two doses of the vaccine in the first year of life will be sufficient for full immunization. The new killed-virus vaccine is more potent than the one used during the 1950s.

Questions:

1. How has the polio vaccine been beneficial?
2. In the United States, all states require that children entering school be vaccinated against measles, rubella, diphtheria, and polio. Do you support this legislation? Why?
3. What are the major drawbacks to use of the killed-virus and live-virus vaccines?
4. Should people be made aware of the advantages and disadvantages of both kinds of polio vaccines? Why?
5. Should people have a choice as to the type of polio vaccine they receive? Explain.

Bacteriophage Life Cycles

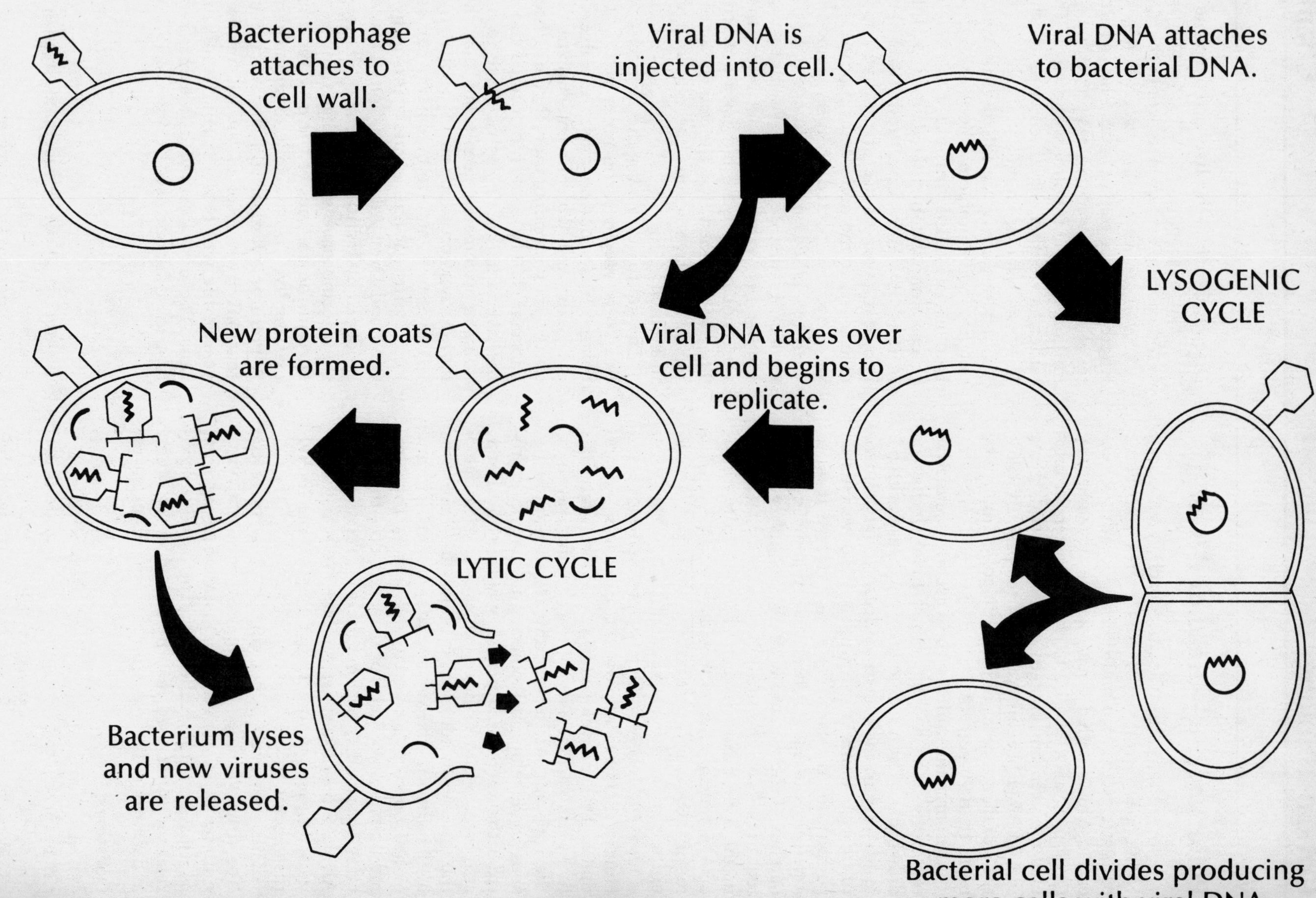

Name ______________________ Date ______________

Problem: How do different organisms reproduce asexually? (text page 370)

Data and Observations:

TABLE 17-1. OBSERVATIONS OF ASEXUALLY REPRODUCING ORGANISMS		
Organism	Single Organism	Organism Reproducing
Paramecium		
Yeast		
Oscillatoria		
Rhizopus nigricans		

Questions and Conclusion:

1. Define: asexual reproduction, fission, budding, fragmentation, spore. ______________________

Name ______________________ Date ______________

2. Explain why the four types of reproduction studied are asexual and not sexual. Include features such as parent number and type of cell reproduction. ______________________

3. To which kingdom does each of the following organisms belong: paramecium, yeast, *Oscillatoria, Rhizopus nigricans*? ______________________

4. Explain how the cells formed during budding differ from those formed during fission. ______________________

5. How do the number of cells formed by budding or fission compare to the number of spores formed by *Rhizopus nigricans*? ______________________

6. How may the number of spores formed be important to the survival of the bread mold? ______________________

7. (a) How do offspring formed during asexual reproduction compare to the parent? (b) How may this be helpful to the offspring? ______________________

Conclusion: How do different organisms reproduce asexually? ______________________

PLANNING GUIDE	
TEXT	**UNIT 5 Simple Organisms** **Chapter 18 Simple Organisms: Other Life Functions** **Investigation 18 How can you measure respiration rate in yeast? p. 384**
TEACHER RESOURCE PACKAGE:	
READING AND STUDY GUIDE	Student Edition, p. 105 Teacher Edition, p. 29
RESOURCE MASTER BOOK	Student Master 18–1. Bacterial Flagella, p. 18–2 Student Master 18–2. Termites and Protozoans, p. 18–3 Teaching Master 18–1. Structures of *Euglena,* p. 18–4 Investigation Worksheet, p. 18–5
EVALUATION PROGRAM	Test Masters, p. 69 Alternate Test Masters, p. 177
LABORATORY BIOLOGY: INVESTIGATING LIVING SYSTEMS	43 Gas Exchange in Microorganisms, p. 167 44 Fungal Nutrition, p. 171
PROBING LEVELS OF LIFE: A LABORATORY MANUAL	41 Ingestion and Digestion in Protists, p. 107 42 Locomotion in Protists, p. 109 43 Response of Protists to Chemical and Physical Stimuli, p. 113

Name ______________________ Date ______________

Bacterial Flagella

Some, but not all, species of bacteria move by means of flagella. The flagellum of a bacterium has no definite covering membrane and it consists of a single, small filament. This filament is made up of three or more longitudinal fibers. In some cases, the fibers are parallel to one another. In other cases, the fibers are intertwined. Some flagella, and perhaps all, appear to be attached to a structure called the hook. The hook is attached to a structure called the basal body. Flagella move with a wavelike motion that propels the bacterium.

Chemical analyses of flagella show that they are made up of a single protein. This protein has been named flagellin. Although all flagella are composed of flagellin, bacterial flagella take many forms. These forms include coiled, curly, wavy, and straight. Several forms can be found in a single cell. The flagella also may be arranged in various ways on bacterial cells. If only one flagellum is located on one end of the cell, the flagellation is said to be *monotrichous*. The flagellation is said to be *lophotrichous* if several flagella are located at one end. *Amphitrichous* flagellation describes the condition when at least one flagellum is located at each end. The flagellation is said to be *peritrichous* when the flagella protrude from all parts of the bacterial surface. It should come as no surprise that bacteria have been classified based on their flagellation.

In addition to flagella, some bacteria have very fine appendages that extend outward from the surface of the cell. These appendages are called fimbriae, or pili. Like flagella, the pili are made up of a single protein. This protein is different from flagellin and is called *pilin*. Each pilus is made of a single rigid filament. Unlike the flagella, the pili are small, short, and very numerous. Pili are also rigid and immobile. The function of pili is not well understood. It is known that bacteria with pili have a strong tendency to adhere to one another and to various other particles, such as animal cells (including red blood cells), plant cells, and yeast cells. It has been suggested that the ability to adhere to particles may be important for the bacteria in terms of fixing themselves to tissues from which they can obtain nutrients.

Questions:

1. Write the type of flagellation on the blank below each figure.

FIGURE 18–1.

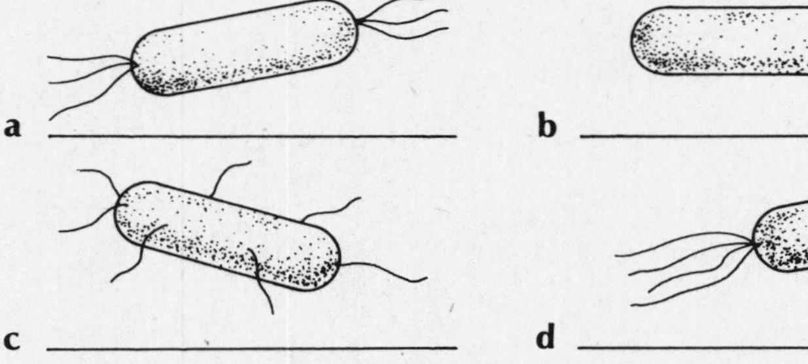

2. How are flagella and pili similar? ______________________

3. How do flagella and pili differ? ______________________

____

4. Figure 18–2 is a drawing of *Escherichia coli*. Identify the flagellum and a pilus.

FIGURE 18–2.

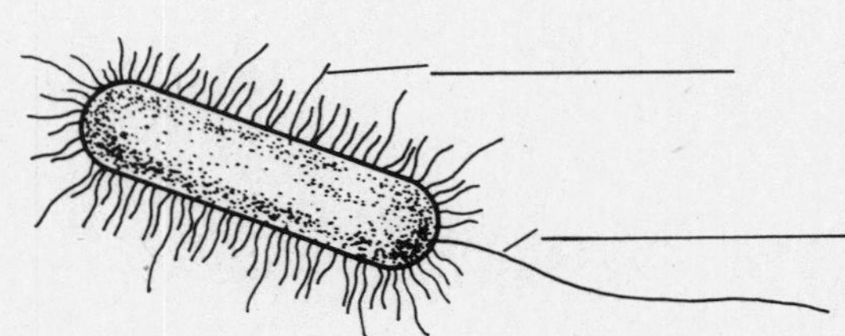

Name ______________________ *Date* ______________

Termites and Protozoans

Termites live in colonies that range in size from a few hundred to several million individuals. This insect society consists of several castes, including the winged and sighted queen and king and the wingless and usually blind workers and soldiers. The termites have a social structure similar to that of ants. They not only feed, groom, and protect one another, but the offspring of one generation assist the parents in raising the next generation. This behavior is remarkable since termites evolved much earlier than, and quite independently from ants.

Termites belong to the only order of insects that have the general ability to digest cellulose. Like their close relatives the cockroaches, termites harbor protozoans in their gut. The protozoans produce the enzymes that termites need to digest cellulose, the main chemical constituent of all plants. Most of the protozoans live in a vesicular appendix of the termite's gut. Ingested wood, ground up in the termite's proventriculus, or gizzard, is broken down into a sugar called dextrose. Dextrose is the same kind of sugar found in grapes. The termites also digest a great many of the rapidly multiplying protozoans, thereby obtaining protein. The protozoans, in turn, have a place to live and a steady supply of food.

The presence of protozoans in the gut, as in the primitive Darwin termite, is a characteristic of all primitive termites. Most primitive termites feed on dead wood, making them especially dreaded by people whose homes are made of wood. Termites not only destroy the supportive structure of homes, but also eat wood furniture, books, packing cases, leather, cloth, and crops that include fruit trees, stem crops such as sugarcane, and a wide variety of underground crops such as potatoes and yams.

The advanced termites lack special gut protozoa. They do, however, maintain a sophisticated association with bacteria and/or fungi. In three of the four subfamilies of advanced termites, large cultures of bacteria grow in the hindgut. The bacteria help ferment plant material, thus making nutrients available to the termites.

Both advanced and primitive termites, except those belonging to the fungus-growing subfamily, also have bacteria in their gut that can fix atmospheric nitrogen. These bacteria can take nitrogen from the air and incororate it into amino acids, the building blocks of proteins. The only other insect known to harbor such bacteria is the brown-hooded cockroach.

Most termites prefer to eat dead plant material that has been attacked by fungi. The fungi break down the plant cells and release nutrients. In the savannah regions of Asia and Africa, the long dry seasons slow the activities of the fungi. This often results in a food shortage for the termites. One group of termites, however, has solved this food-shortage problem. The fungus-growing subfamily, Macrotermitinae, has developed a unique relationship with the fungi of genus *Termitomyces.* As a matter of fact, this fungus is found nowhere else except in the nest of termites. The termites cultivate the fungus on fungus combs. These combs are made by the termites from their own feces. The fungus feeds on and breaks down the feces, releasing nutrients the termites can then consume. The fungus-growing termites are of great ecological importance. Their activities account for most of the decomposition process in the hot, dry savannahs.

Questions:

1. Termites have a general ability to digest cellulose. How are they able to do so? ______________

____

2. How are the primitive and advanced termites similar? ______________

____

____

3. In what way is *Termitomyces* important to termites? ______________

____

Structures of *Euglena*

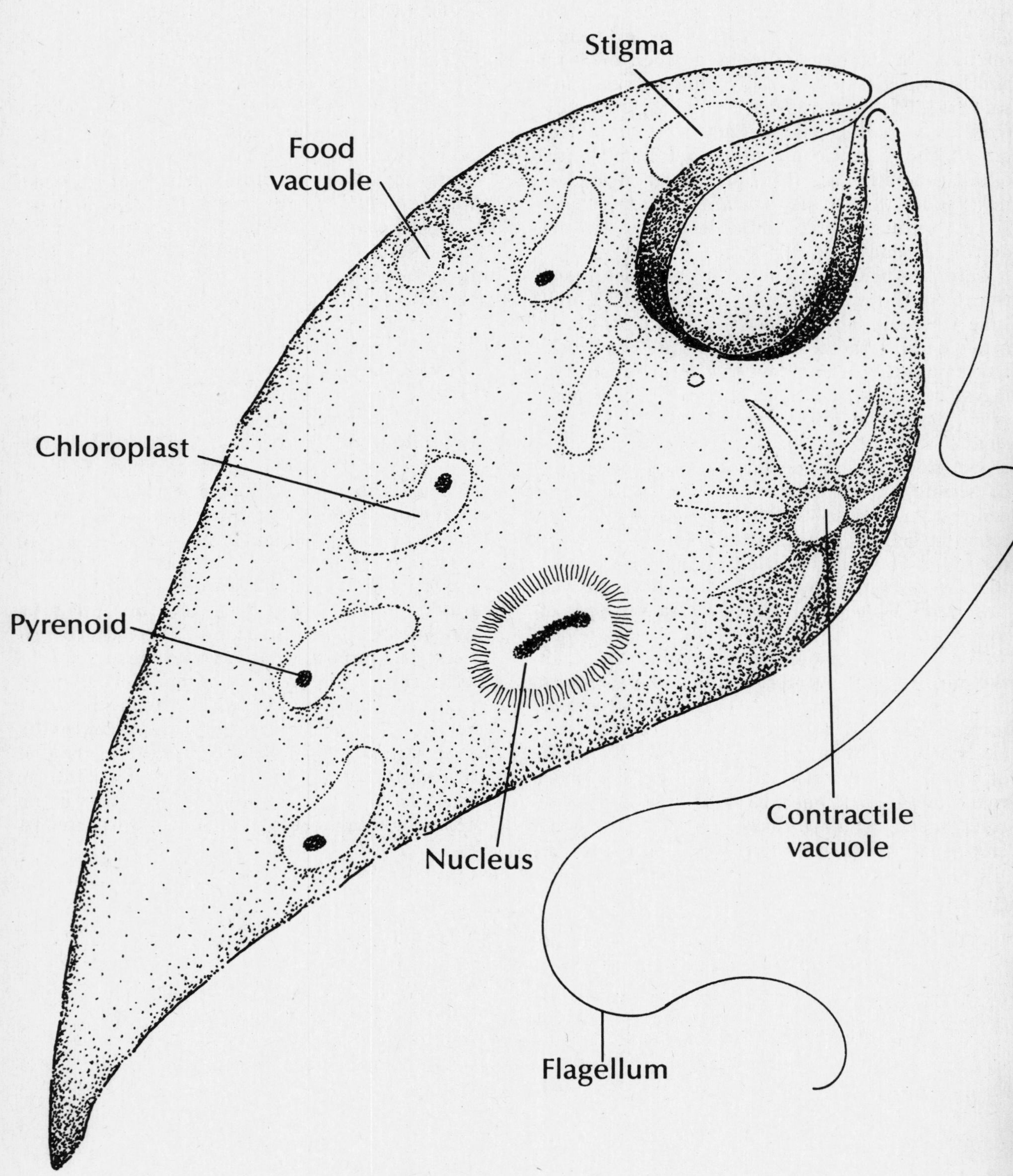

Name ______________________ Date ______________

Problem: How can you measure respiration rate in yeast?

(text page 384)

Data and Observations:

TABLE 18-2. READINGS OF HEIGHT OF LIQUID IN TUBES

	Starting Height	Height After 5 Minutes	Height After 10 Minutes	Height After 15 Minutes	Height After 20 Minutes	Total Distance Liquid Moved
Tube 1						
Tube 2						
Tube 3						
Tube 4						

Questions and Conclusion:

1. Define cellular respiration. ______________________

2. (a) What gas is released by yeast cells as they carry out cellular respiration? (b) What is the role of sucrose in the experiment? ______________________
3. As the yeast cells released gas, pressure within the test tube increased. This pressure forced the liquid within the test tube to rise into the glass tube. (a) Which tubes showed evidence of gas release? (b) How were the contents of those tubes alike? ______________________

4. What experimental evidence do you have that: (a) yeast without food does not carry out cellular respiration (b) food itself is not responsible for gas release? ______________________
5. Yeast is used in several baking processes. Dough rises due to the trapping of gas within the dough. (a) What gas is trapped within the dough? (b) Where does this gas come from? ______________________

Name ______________________ Date ______________________

6. Unleavened bread is made without yeast and is usually very flat. Explain why. ______________________

7. (a) What chemical produced by yeast cells is used in the production of beer and wine? (b) Why do yeast cells produce this chemical? ______________________

8. Design an experiment to test these hypotheses: (a) Temperature influences the respiration rate of yeast cells. (b) The pH of a liquid influences the respiration rate of yeast cells. ______________________

Conclusion: How can you measure respiration rate in yeast? ______________________

PLANNING GUIDE	
TEXT	**UNIT 5 Simple Organisms** **Chapter 19 Simple Organisms and Disease** **Investigation 19 What are certain traits of bacteria? p. 406**
TEACHER RESOURCE PACKAGE:	
READING AND STUDY GUIDE	Student Edition, p. 111 Teacher Edition, p. 30
RESOURCE MASTER BOOK	Student Master 19–1. Bone Marrow—Where Immunity Begins, p. 19–2 Student Master 19–2. PNI—Psychoneuroimmunology, p. 19–3 Teaching Master 19–1. Life Cycle of *Plasmodium malariae,* p. 19–4 Investigation Worksheet, p. 19–5
EVALUATION PROGRAM	Test Masters, p. 73 Alternate Test Masters, p. 179
LABORATORY BIOLOGY: INVESTIGATING LIVING SYSTEMS	45 Control of Disease-Causing Bacteria, p. 173 46 Using Antibiotics to Stop Bacterial Growth, p. 175
PROBING LEVELS OF LIFE: A LABORATORY MANUAL	44 Controlling Microbial Growth, p. 116 45 The Regional Spread of a Disease-Causing Protozoa, p. 118

Name ______________________ Date ______________________

Bone Marrow—Where Immunity Begins

Bone marrow can be thought of as a massive factory that makes the materials the body needs to defend itself from foreign invaders. The bone marrow is one of the largest and most active tissues in the body. For example, the average half-life of a white blood cell called a neutrophil is about 6 hours. To maintain a normal level of neutrophils it is necessary that the bone marrow produce over 100 billion neutrophils a day. In addition, the bone marrow forms red blood cells (erythrocytes), platelets, and various other white blood cells (leukocytes).

The production of cells begins with a pluripotent stem cell. This stem cell differentiates into a myeloid stem cell or a lymphoid stem cell. The myeloid stem cell goes through a preliminary process that prepares it for becoming a red blood cell, a megakaryocyte, a myeloblast, or a monocyte. Red blood cells help supply oxygen to all the body's tissues. Megakaryocytes break apart to form platelets. Platelets work with blood proteins to help in blood clot formation. The myeloblast develops into an eosinophil, basophil, or neutrophil, all of which are white blood cells. Eosinophils help combat allergies and chronic parasitic infections and possibly detoxify foreign proteins to which the person is allergic. The basophils contain heparin, an anticoagulant. But the role of basophils in maintaining a balance between the clotting and anticlotting systems is uncertain. Neutrophils seek out, ingest, and destroy bacteria and have been referred to as the body's first line of defense against bacterial infections.

Monocytes, which are another type of white blood cell, often follow neutrophils into an infected area of the body. The monocytes ingest bacteria, other foreign matter, and dead cells. Monocytes make up a second line of defense. After monocytes circulate in the blood for about 24 hours, they enter tissue and become macrophages. Macrophages ingest foreign invaders and work with special lymphocytes to fight infections and cancer.

Lymphoid stem cells are responsible for the formation of certain lymphocytes. Lymphocytes are formed in the bone marrow, lymph nodes, thymus, and spleen. Lymphocytes include B cells and three kinds of T cells: K cells, or killer T cells, helper T cells, and suppressor T cells. B cells are primarily responsible for humoral immunity, or immunity due to circulating antibodies. B cells create antibodies that bind to bacteria and viruses. The antibodies either neutralize these foreign objects or make them vulnerable to attack by other immune cells. B cells often complete their formation in the spleen. Cellular immunity is directed by T cells. Cellular immunity is responsible for delayed allergic reactions, rejection of transplanted foreign tissue, and the breaking apart of tumor cells. T cells also attack viruses, fungi, and bacteria. T cells often complete their development in the thymus.

Questions:

Complete the chart, which shows how various blood cells are formed from bone marrow.

FIGURE 19–1.

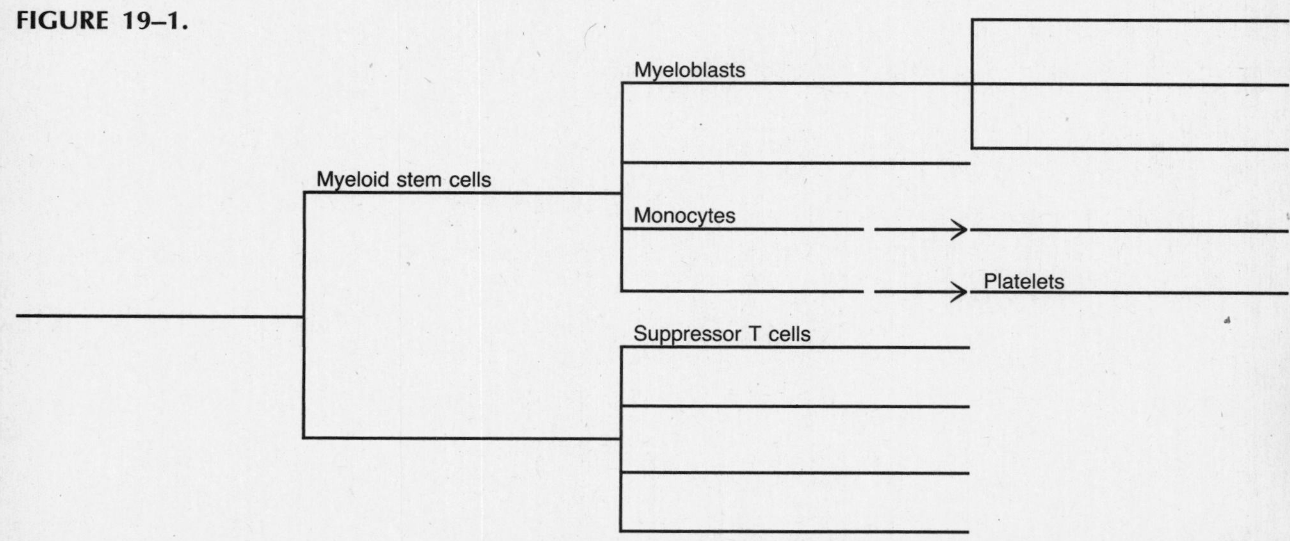

Name ______________________ Date ______________

PNI—Psychoneuroimmunology

Is it coincidence that people have fewer colds when they are content with their lives than when they are under stress? A theme of folklore and literature hints that the mind can influence the body's vulnerability to infection and disease. Just 10 years ago, most specialists in communicable disease would have scoffed at such a suggestion. But today, research by immunologists and neurologists is giving credibility to such ideas. The idea that the mind can influence the body's immune system has developed into a new discipline—psychoneuroimmunology, or more simply, PNI.

There is overwhelming evidence for chemical and anatomical links between the brain and the immune system. First, there is evidence that neurotransmitters, chemicals released by nerves, bind to immune cells. The neurotransmitters then alter the immune cell's ability to multiply and kill foreign invaders. Second, there are reports that hormones, which are regulated by the brain, could affect the immune cell's ability to fight disease. Hormones known as hematologic growth factors stimulate immune cell production. Finally, there is evidence that nerve fibers in immunological organs, such as the thymus, bone marrow, and lymph nodes, are associated with lymphocytes. Together, the nerves and hormones that carry messages to the immune system activate the immune system by turning it on and off.

Further research shows that neuropeptides, small proteinlike chemicals made by brain cells, can possibly latch onto macrophages and change the speed or direction of their movement. Macrophages are large ameboid white blood cells that gather at the sight of an infection. They rebuild damaged tissues and devour bacteria, viruses, and other foreign particles.

Candace Pert and Michael Ruff, both of the National Institute of Mental Health, have carried out a study concerning neuropeptides and macrophages. In this study, they showed that when people felt helpless, their macrophages moved more sluggishly than usual. The sluggishness was probably caused by changes in neuropeptides. This finding suggests why seriously ill patients who give up hope often fare worse than those who remain optimistic.

With growing evidence that the brain and immune system are linked, Gérard Renoux of the University of Tours in France decided to find out which areas of the brain were responsible for controlling the immune system. Renoux found that if he damaged the left side of the cortex in a mouse, the structure and activity of the mouse's immune system would change. The number of white blood cells in the spleen dropped and the ones that remained became less efficient at killing tumors and responding to foreign cells. Renoux concluded that the right side of the cortex must be responsible for the slowing of the immune system. When Renoux damaged the right side of the cortex, the immune cells acted differently. The cells became slightly more active. Renoux concluded from his studies that the left side of the cortex stimulates the immune system and the right side suppresses it.

Renoux's theory provides a clue as to how emotions and mental imagery may help fight disease. Since formation of images seems to be controlled by the right side of the brain, it is possible that exercises involving imagery somehow keep the right side of the brain from suppressing the immune system. It also has been suggested that the left side of the brain processes emotions such as excitement, sense of control, and hope. Thus, the sense of control and hope experienced by optimistic patients might stimulate their brains to bolster their immune systems.

Questions:

1. Through which substances does the brain seem to affect the immune system? ______________

____

2. How does the left side of the brain affect the immune system? ______________

____

3. How does the right side of the brain affect the immune system? ______________

____

Life Cycle of *Plasmodium malariae*

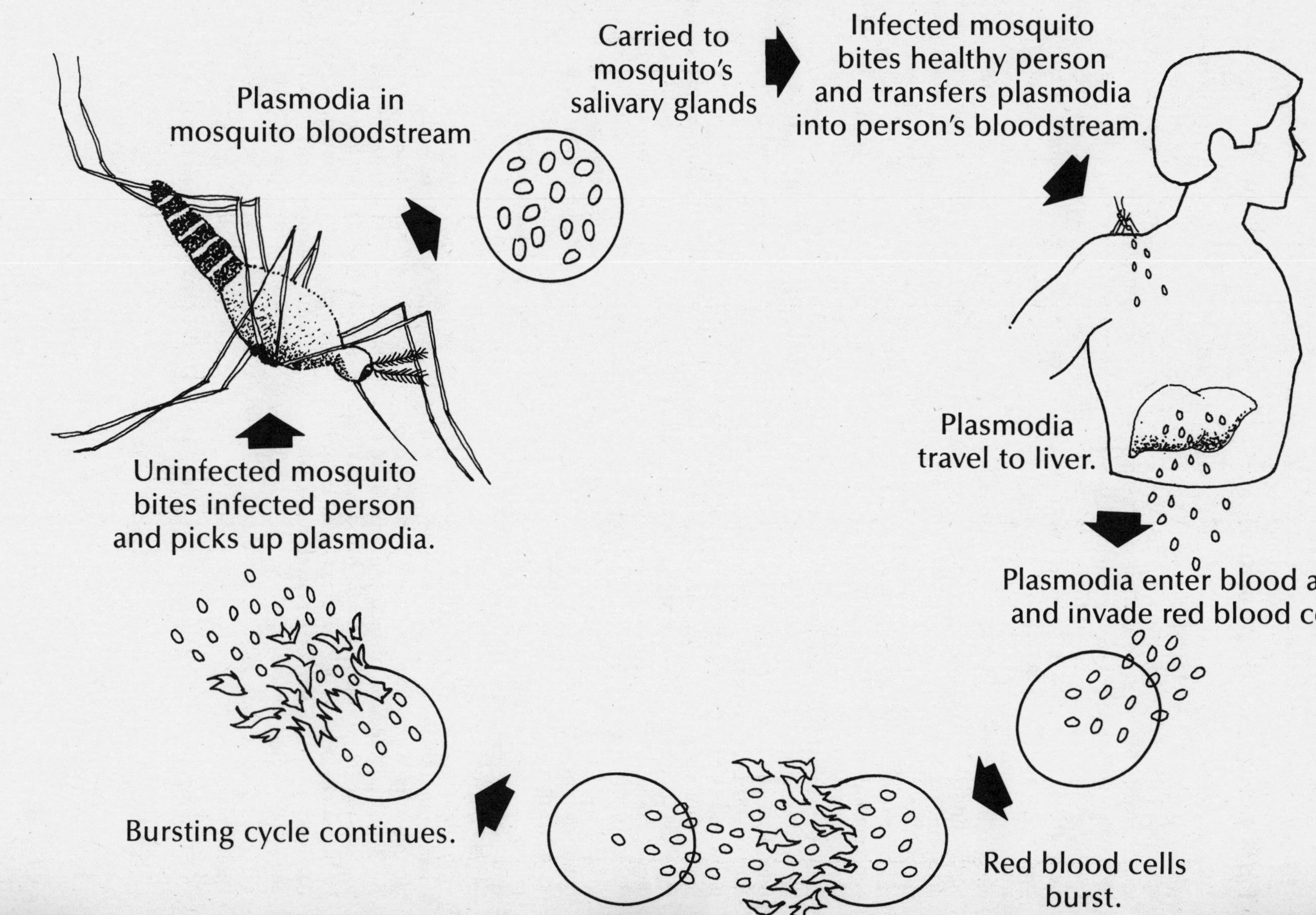

Name ______________________ Date ______________

Problem: What are certain traits of bacteria? (text page 406)

Data and Observations:

TABLE 19-1. TRAITS OF BACTERIA		
Part	Observations	
	Species name	Shape
A. Shape	______	______
	______	______
B. Pattern	Pattern 1 ______	Pattern 6 ______
	Pattern 2 ______	Pattern 7 ______
	Pattern 3 ______	Pattern 8 ______
	Pattern 4 ______	Pattern 9 ______
	Pattern 5 ______	Pattern 10 ______
	Sample	Motile (yes or no)
C. Motility	______	______
	______	______
	______	______

Questions and Conclusion:

1. Define bacteria, flagellum, motility. ______________________________

2. Analyze the scientific names and descriptions of the following bacteria. Diagram and label these species of bacteria on a separate sheet of paper: (a) *Staphylococcus aureus*—nonmotile, causes infection of any body organ (b) *Streptococcus pyogenes*—nonmotile, causes sore throat, scarlet fever (c) *Clostridium tetani*—motile, bacillus, occurs in pairs and in chains, causes tetanus.

____

Conclusion: What are certain traits of bacteria? ______________________________

____

____

PLANNING GUIDE	
TEXT	**UNIT 6 Plants** **Chapter 20 Plant Reproduction and Development** **Investigation 20 How can you tell if a seed is still alive? p. 428**
TEACHER RESOURCE PACKAGE:	
READING AND STUDY GUIDE	Student Edition, p. 117 Teacher Edition, p. 32
RESOURCE MASTER BOOK	Student Master 20–1. Simple Fruits, p. 20–2 Student Master 20–2. Endangered Plants, p. 20–3 Teaching Master 20–1. Parts of a Flower, p. 20–4 Teaching Master 20–2. Life Cycle of Flowering Plants, p. 20–5 Investigation Worksheet, p. 20–6
EVALUATION PROGRAM	Test Masters, p. 77 Alternate Test Masters, p. 181
LABORATORY BIOLOGY: INVESTIGATING LIVING SYSTEMS	47 Flower Anatomy, p. 179 48 Fruit and Seeds, p. 183 49 Moss Plants and Alternation of Generations, p. 187
PROBING LEVELS OF LIFE: A LABORATORY MANUAL	46 Classification of Fruits, p. 120 47 Development of Seeds, p. 122 48 Vegetative Reproduction in Duckweed, p. 124

Name ______________________ Date ______________

Simple Fruits

The old question "Is it a fruit or a vegetable?" raises few problems, botanically. A fruit has its origins in the flower. By definition a fruit is a mature ovary that contains seeds. Botanically speaking then, a string bean, a kernel of corn, and a tomato are as much fruits as is a peach or a strawberry. The term vegetable is a nontechnical term and is rarely used by botanists.

The form, texture, and structure of fruits vary. Some fruits are fleshy, some are dry, some have many seeds, some have few or one. These and other characteristics help botanists classify fruits. Various types of simple fruits are discussed below.

Legume (or pod). This type of fruit is characteristic of nearly all members of the pea family, Leguminosae. The shell of this type of dry fruit generally splits in half revealing and releasing the seeds. Beans, peas (in their shell), and peanuts (in their shell) are all examples of legumes.

Achene. Buckwheat, the "seeds" on the surface of the strawberry, and sunflower "seeds" (shell and all) are parts of this group. All members of the sunflower family, the Compositae, produce achenes. These fruits are dry and since they are usually very small and contain only one seed, they are commonly called seeds. The seed in an achene can be separated easily from its shell. Unlike legumes, achenes do not split open.

Caryopsis (or grain). This fruit is found in members of the grass family, the Gramineae. This family includes important plants such as wheat, oats, barley, rye, corn, and rice. Like the achene, the caryopsis is a dry, one-seeded fruit that does not split open. Unlike the achene, the shell of the caryopsis is united all the way around and it is difficult to separate the shell (the fruit wall) from the seed except by a special milling process.

Nut. The term nut is often applied to a number of hard-shelled fruits and seeds. Botanically, a nut is a one-seeded, dry fruit that does not split open. The fruit wall is hard or stony. Chestnuts, walnuts, and acorns are all nuts.

Drupe. This is a fleshy fruit produced by some members of the rose family, the Rosaceae. Plums, cherries, almonds, peaches, and apricots are all drupes. The drupe usually is one-seeded and the seed is surrounded by a hard, stony structure, called the *pit.* Surrounding the pit is the edible flesh. Both the pit and the fleshy part of a drupe are parts of the ovary wall. In almond fruits, the seed is surrounded by a fleshy part of the ovary wall that becomes hard and dry and forms the hull as the seed develops.

Berry. Like the drupe, a berry is a fleshy fruit. But unlike the drupe, it contains many seeds and many compartments, or locules. A tomato is a common type of berry. Citrus fruits, such as lemons and limes, are a type of berry called a *hesperidium.* A hesperidium has a thick leathery fruit wall with oil glands, and many seeds surrounded by an edible flesh. Another berrylike fruit is the *pepo.* In this type of fruit, the fruit wall is a rind that surrounds a fleshy material. Pepos are produced by members of the Cucurbitaceae, the cucumber or pumpkin family. Watermelons, squashes, pumpkins, cantaloupes, and cucumbers are all types of pepos.

Pome. This fruit is characteristic of members of one subfamily of the Rosaceae that includes the apple and quince. Most of the ovary portion of the apple is found in the core. The fleshy part of the apple is a combination of part of the ovary wall and other floral tissues.

Aggregate Fruit. An aggregate fruit is formed from many ovaries of a single flower. Each one of these ovaries matures into an individual fruit which, individually, may be a small drupe *(drupelet),* achene, or a number of other kinds of simple fruits. The raspberry and the blackberry are aggregates of drupelets. The strawberry, an aggregate of achenes, is made up of many small achenes that are attached to a large, fleshy receptacle. The receptacle is the base structure to which the flower parts are attached.

Questions:

Provide the technical term that applies to each of the following fruits. One has been done for you.

1. honeydew melon berry/pepo
2. zucchini squash ______________
3. popcorn ______________
4. nectarine ______________
5. lima bean ______________
6. pecan ______________
7. grapefruit ______________
8. strawberry ______________

Name ______________________ Date ______________________

Endangered Plants

The plight of endangered animals, such as the blue whale and the whooping crane, is well known. It is less well known and less appreciated that about 25 000 of the world's plant species face extinction.

An independent organization, the International Union for the Conservation of Nature and Natural Resources (IUCN), appealed to botanists around the world to supply accurate information about endangered plant species in their countries. A special committee of the IUCN, the Threatened Plant Committee, assembled the information and chose about 250 of the thousands of species of plants submitted by botanists to appear in the publication. This publication is called the *Plant Red Data Book.* The species chosen to appear in the book are those that are in greatest danger of becoming extinct or are those that are particularly spectacular, useful, or interesting.

Certain plants have become endangered for a number of reasons. Some of these reasons include overgrazing by wild and domestic animals, herbicide spraying, and destruction of habitats by fire, cutting for lumber, and forest clearing. Collecting by plant fanciers has also caused some species of plants to become threatened. A few species of endangered plants are discussed below.

Furbish's lousewort. This plant is a member of the snapdragon family and was named for Kate Furbish, a turn-of-the-century American botanical artist. About a thousand of these plants were located growing along a 190-kilometer stretch of the St. John River in northern Maine and a much shorter stretch along the same river in New Brunswick. The Furbish's lousewort has caused a considerable amount of debate. The debate arose when the proposed site for a hydroelectric plant's dam proved to be the very area that these plants, labeled as endangered, grew. The dam would flood the habitat of the Furbish's lousewort and doom the species in the United States. Environmental groups demanded that the dam project be abandoned, while many of the dam's proponents argued that since the plant was already thought to be extinct, there should be no problem if the plant were to drown under the water impounded by the dam. The controversy stirred much debate with the result that the dam for the hydroelectric plant was built, but with special conservation measures to protect the Furbish's lousewort.

African violet. The African violet is a popular houseplant. In its native habitat, the damp cliffsides of eastern Tanzania, it is extremely rare. The continued existence of the native African violet is threatened by the removal of the trees that provide the shade under which the African violet grows.

Rafflesia. A rare parasitic plant, *Rafflesia arnoldi,* grows on the rain forest floor, attached to the roots of tropical grapevines. This flower is the largest in the world, stretching to a width of one meter. Its habitat is dangerously near Japanese timber operations in Sumatra. *Rafflesia* also suffers another threat, trampling by curiosity seekers.

Ginseng. A brew using ginseng root has long been believed to restore flagging spirits and cure diseases. Recently there has been an increase in its use and its price. In 1977, the United States exported 170 000 kilograms of ginseng at a value of $26.5 million. About half of this amount came from farms in Wisconsin. The other half came from the wild, where the plant has now become depleted.

Besides ginseng, other plants have been used for their therapeutic values. The popularity of herbs and other plants has had a twofold effect. First, the demand for herbs, especially in parts of Africa and Asia, has brought some plants near extinction. Second, there is growing scientific evidence that some kinds of herbal remedies do have medicinal value. As scientists learn more about plants and their possible hidden cures, it becomes more important that no plant species be destroyed without careful analysis of its chemical constituents and their therapeutic uses.

Questions:

1. Should endangered plants be given the same recognition and priorities as endangered animals? Why?
2. What might you do to make people more aware of endangered plants?
3. The National Seed Storage Laboratory is located in Fort Collins, Colorado. It houses more than 100 000 samples of all sorts of seeds. What purpose does this seed bank now play? What purpose will it play in the future?

Parts of a Flower

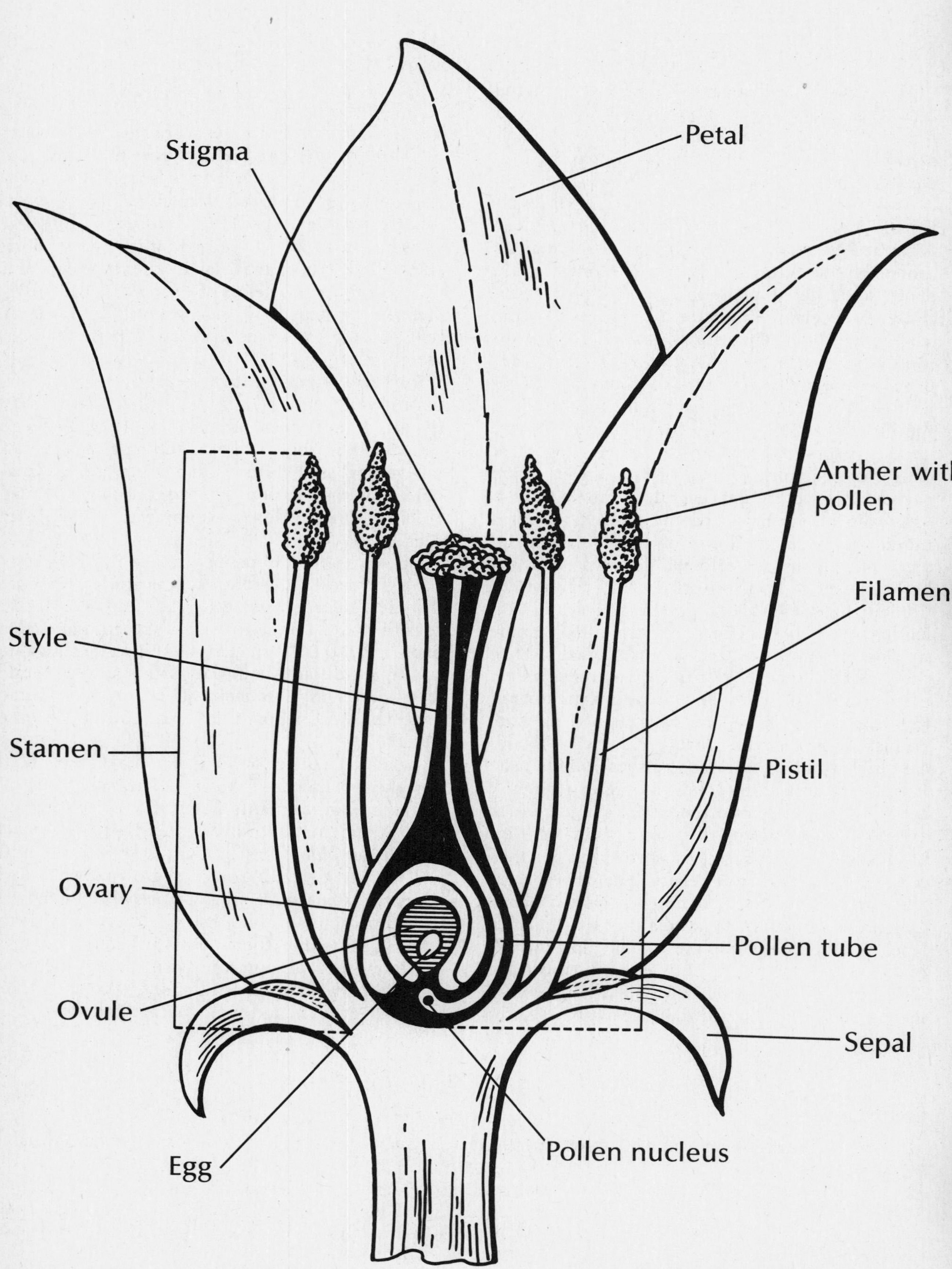

ife Cycle of Flowering Plants

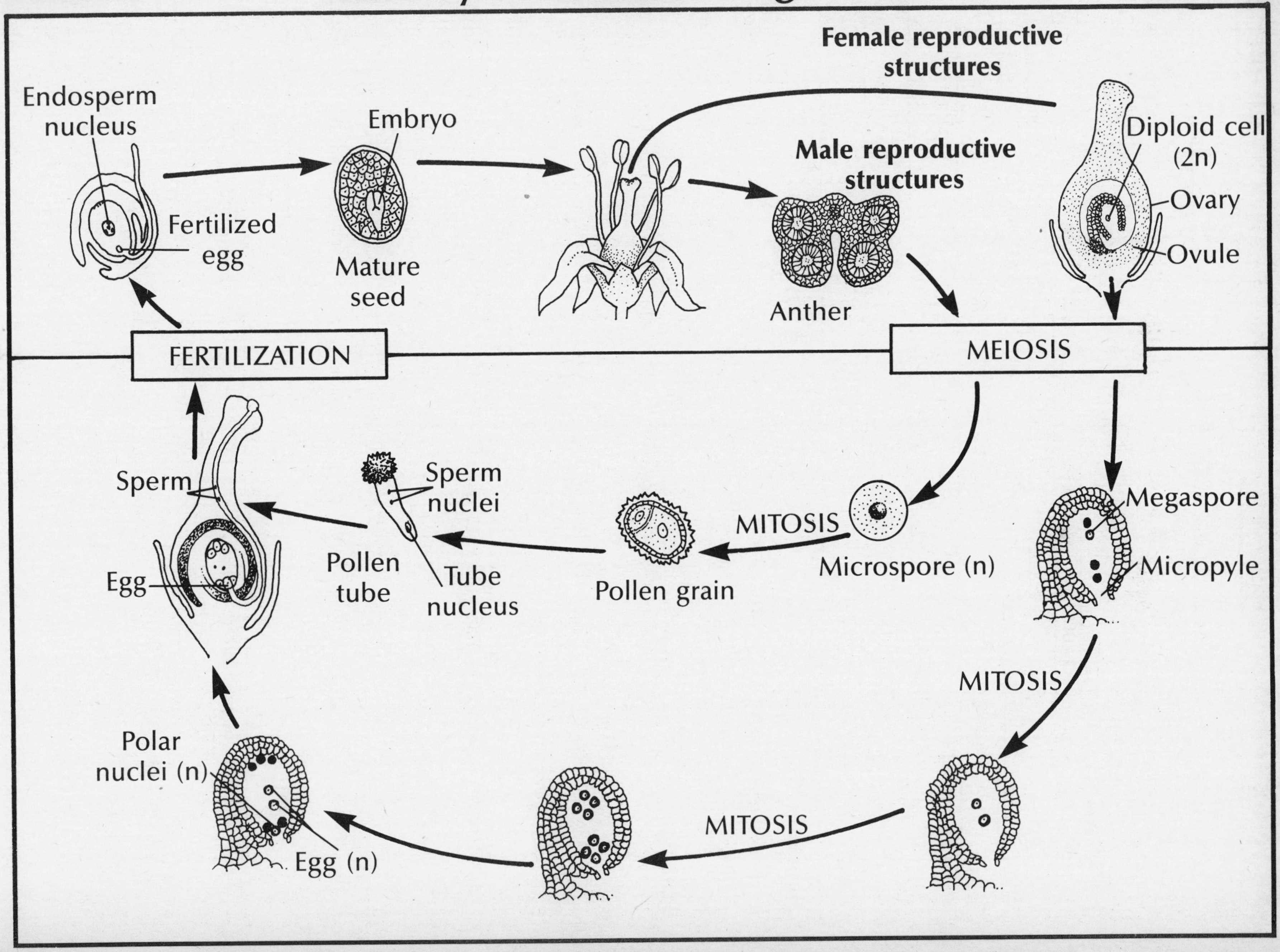

Female reproductive structures

Diploid cell (2n)

Ovary

Ovule

Male reproductive structures

Anther

MEIOSIS

Megaspore

Micropyle

Microspore (n)

MITOSIS

Pollen grain

MITOSIS

MITOSIS

Sperm nuclei

Pollen tube

Tube nucleus

Polar nuclei (n)

Egg (n)

Sperm

Egg

FERTILIZATION

Endosperm nucleus

Fertilized egg

Embryo

Mature seed

Name ______________________ Date ______________

Problem: How can you tell if a seed is still alive?

(text page 428)

Data and Observations:

TABLE 20-1. PERCENTAGE OF SEEDS WITH LIVING TISSUE				
	Your Results		Class Results	
	Boiled	Unboiled	Boiled	Unboiled
Total number of seeds				
Number of seeds with living tissue				
Number of seeds with no living tissue				
Percentage of seeds with living tissue				

Questions and Conclusion:

1. Define: (a) seed embryo (b) endosperm (c) cellular respiration. ______________________
2. Which area of the seed turned blue when iodine was added? What does this tell you about that area within the seed? ______________________
3. In which area of the seed did the pink color of tetrazolium concentrate? What does this tell you about that area within the seed? ______________________
4. How do the class percentages of living tissue for boiled and unboiled seeds compare? What process was halted as a result of the boiling? ______________________
5. Explain why the presence of living tissue is an indication of which seeds will germinate. ______________________
6. How might the tetrazolium test be of value to farmers before they plant large batches of seeds? ______________________

Conclusion: How can you tell if a seed is still alive? ______________________

PLANNING GUIDE	
TEXT	**UNIT 6 Plants** **Chapter 21 Plant Nutrition** **Investigation 21 How can you estimate the number of stomata on a leaf? p. 444**
TEACHER RESOURCE PACKAGE:	
READING AND STUDY GUIDE	Student Edition, p. 123 Teacher Edition, p. 33
RESOURCE MASTER BOOK	Student Master 21–1. Variations on Photosynthesis, p. 21–2 Student Master 21–2. Hydroponics, p. 21–3 Teaching Master 21–1. Leaf Structure, p. 21–4 Investigation Worksheet, p. 21–5
EVALUATION PROGRAM	Test Masters, p. 81 Alternate Test Masters, p. 183
LABORATORY BIOLOGY: INVESTIGATING LIVING SYSTEMS	50 Influencing the Rate of Photosynthesis, p. 191 51 Chloroplast Pigment Analysis, p. 195 52 Leaf Anatomy, p. 199
PROBING LEVELS OF LIFE: A LABORATORY MANUAL	49 Leaf Structure and Function, p. 126 50 Analysis of Plant Pigments, p. 129 51 Some Aspects of Photosynthesis, p. 131

Name ______________________ Date ______________

Variations on Photosynthesis

Most plants carry out the process of photosynthesis. In this process, light energy is used to combine carbon, oxygen, and hydrogen to form glucose. There are two phases of photosynthesis, the light reactions and the dark reactions. In the light reactions, energy absorbed by the chlorophyll molecule is used to produce two different energy molecules: ATP and $NADPH_2^+$. During the light reactions water also is split into hydrogen and oxygen. In the dark reactions, the energy molecules produced by the light reactions and CO_2 are used to drive reactions that form glucose.

The light reactions of photosynthesis are similar for all higher land plants; but, over the course of millions of years, three major variations of the dark reactions have evolved.

The most common variation is called C_3 photosynthesis. In C_3 plants, the first compound formed from CO_2 during the dark reactions is PGA, phosphoglycerate. This PGA then reacts to eventually form glucose.

A second variation, characteristic primarily of tropical plants, is called C_4 photosynthesis. In plants such as corn and sugarcane, the first molecule to be formed from CO_2 is oxalacetic acid, a four-carbon compound. This molecule then undergoes several changes to form PGA. The rest of the dark reactions continue as in C_3 plants. C_4 plants are able to carry out photosynthesis under conditions that are unfavorable for C_3 photosynthesis: high light intensity, high temperature, little available water, and low concentrations of carbon dioxide.

A third variation of photosynthesis has evolved in plants such as the cactuses, the jade plant, kalanchoe, and most succulents that inhabit hot, dry regions. In order to take in CO_2, these plants, called CAM plants, open their stomates at night. This enables them to conserve water. During the night, CAM plants use the CO_2 to form various acids, most commonly malic acid. The malic acid is stored until the daytime when it is converted to oxalacetic acid. Photosynthesis then continues in a way similar to that of C_4 plants. The acronym CAM stands for Crassulacean Acid Metabolism and was first identified among members of the Crassulaceae, the sedum family.

Questions:

1. How does photosynthesis in C_4 plants differ from that of C_3 plants? ______________________

____

2. How does photosynthesis in CAM plants differ from that of C_4 plants? ______________________

____

3. Crabgrass is considered a weed and can withstand droughts, intense light, and high temperatures. Which variation of photosynthesis would you expect this plant to have? ______________________
4. "Living stones" are succulents that grow naturally in the arid regions of South Africa. Which type of photosynthesis would you expect these plants to have? ______________________

Name ______________________ Date ______________________

Hydroponics

Originally, the Aztecs of Mexico were a nomadic tribe. They roamed the valleys of what is now central Mexico in search of a place to settle. Eventually they settled on the shores of Lake Tenochtitlan and set about the task of building a great city.

The land around their settlement could not provide enough food for their growing population and they had to turn to the lake to solve this problem. Demonstrating their flair for invention, the Aztecs lashed together rushes and reeds to make rafts. Then they covered the rafts with soil and created giant floating islands on which they grew vegetables, flowers, and even trees. The plants' roots would grow through the bottom of the rafts into the water. These rafts, called *chinampas,* were the first hydroponic gardens. The plants thrived, as did the city that later became the Aztec capital. Today we know it as Mexico City, the capital of Mexico.

Hydroponics is a method of growing plants in a nutrient-rich water without soil. A solid substance, such as sand, gravel, or vermiculite, is sometimes used to physically support the plants, but there is no soil. Though the technique is not new, it has grown in popularity as agronomists seek new ways to grow food in areas with poor soil or other unfavorable growing conditions.

It was not until the nineteenth century that scientists discovered the role of soil in plant growth. Along with its ability to hold gases and water, the soil stores nutrients that are eventually carried in water to the roots of plants. Scientists began growing plants in water by adding the necessary nutrients to a water solution. Dr. W. F. Gericke at the University of California named this method "hydroponics," using Greek root words that meant "water working." During the late 1930s, the media became aware of hydroponics and touted the technique as the wave of the future that would make traditional agriculture obsolete. Thousands of small hydroponic greenhouses were built, but World War II shifted most people's minds to other things and use of the technique suffered.

In the late 1970s, hydroponics was revived by agricultural scientists. It is no replacement for conventional agricultural techniques, but it does have certain advantages. Insects, weeds, and diseases can be kept to a minimum because many insects and disease-causing organisms need soil in order to breed. As a result, fewer herbicides and pesticides are needed in hydroponics than in traditional farming. The abundantly available nutrient solution also reduces competition among plants and allows the plants to be grown at greater densities. Unlike traditional farming, there is no waste of fertilizer by means of land runoff because only the amount of nutrients needed by the plants are added to the water solution.

There are, however, some major disadvantages to hydroponics. It has not been used successfully to grow grain crops, the primary sources of food on Earth. Hydroponics requires a great deal of water. The technique is more efficient for small-scale production than for large-scale farming. When compared to organic farming, hydroponics uses more chemical fertilizers and pesticides, but less than the amounts normally used in traditional farming methods.

The success of hydroponics seems certain, but its future applications remain unclear. It may prove most useful for growing specific fruits and vegetables in areas where they otherwise cannot be grown. This practice will aid local food supplies and help to avoid the high food costs and energy consumption that result from energy-expensive, long-distance transportation. Once considered only science fiction, hydroponics is expected to provide the food that will be required for space travel over great distances.

Questions:

1. How would you define hydroponics?
2. What are the advantages of hydroponics over conventional farming? The disadvantages?
3. A goal of organic gardening is to produce fruits and vegetables that have not been contaminated by chemical herbicides, pesticides, and fertilizers. What difficulty would face an organic gardener who wanted to grow plants hydroponically?
4. Suppose that you are concerned about the use of chemical pesticides in traditional farming. In the grocery store, you notice that there are tomatoes that have been grown both hydroponically and by traditional methods. Which tomatoes would you choose? Why?
5. How might hydroponics be useful in an area that has hot, dry weather?

Leaf Structure

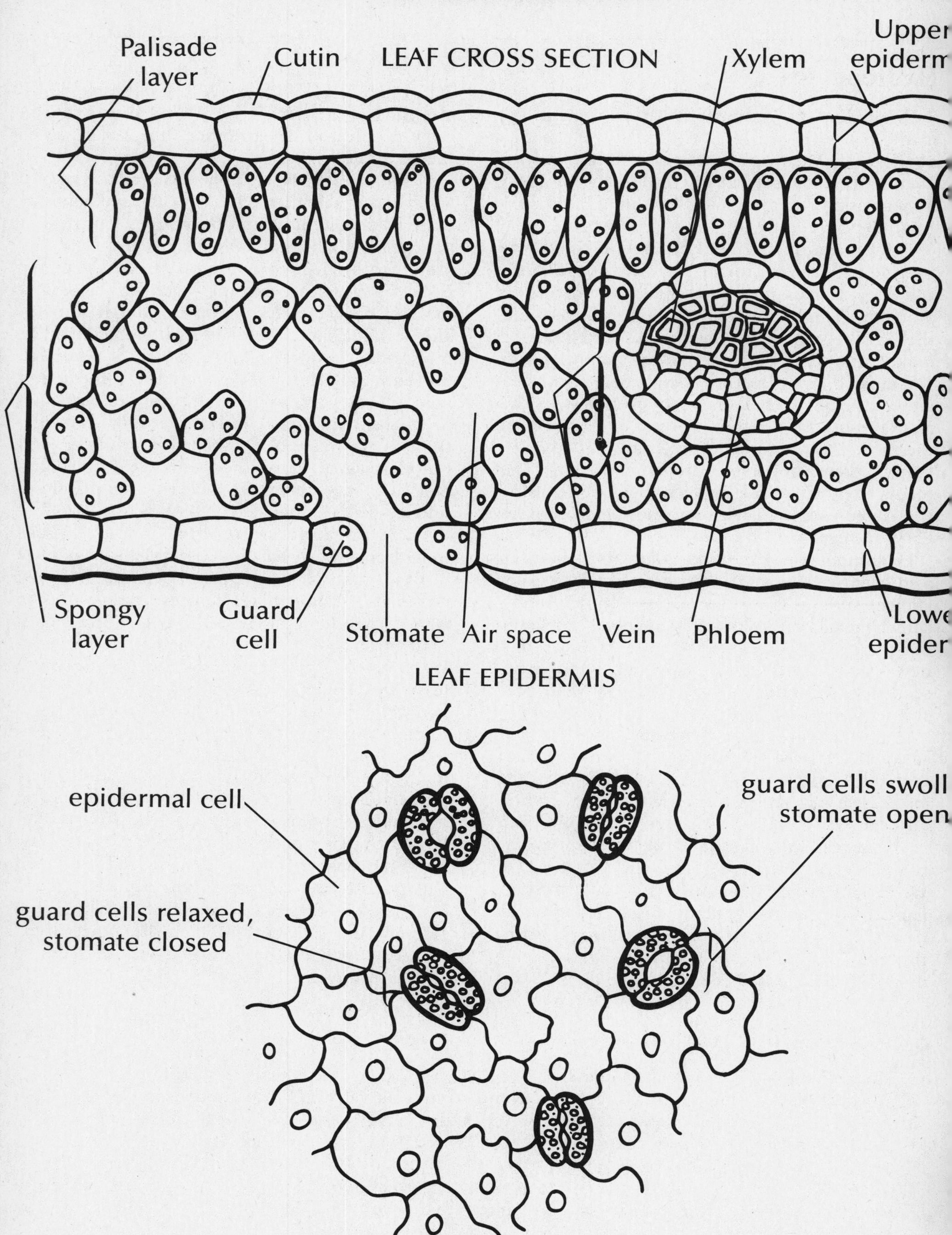

Name ______________________ *Date* ______________

Problem: How can you estimate the number of stomata on a leaf?

(text page 444)

Data and Observations:

TABLE 21-2. ESTIMATION OF NUMBER OF STOMATA ON A LEAF		
	Sample Data	Your Data
Length and width of leaf	length = 140 mm width = 10 mm	
Total area of leaf (length × width)	140 mm × 10 mm = 1400 mm^2	
Number of stomata observed in: Area 1	4	
Area 2	6	
Area 3	3	
Area 4	5	
Area 5	2	
Total	20	
Average number of stomata observed	$\frac{20}{5} = 4$	
Number of high power fields of view on entire leaf (total area ÷ area of high power field of view – 0.07 mm^2)	$\frac{1400\ mm^2}{0.07\ mm^2} = 20\ 000$	
Number of stomata on entire leaf (number of stomata in one high power field of view × number of high power fields of view on entire leaf)	20 000 × 4 = 80 000	

Questions and Conclusion:

1. Define (a) guard cell (b) stoma (c) leaf epidermis. ______________________

2. (a) Name the gases that enter and leave a leaf by way of the stomata. (b) Where do these gases originate or come from? (c) How are these gases related to photosynthesis? ______________________

Name ______________________ *Date* ______________

3. Explain the relationship between stoma size and the action of guard cells. ______________________

4. Name two places in the procedure in which the accuracy of your final count of stomata for the entire leaf could be improved. ______________________

5. A student estimated the number of stomata on three different kinds of leaves. The data are shown here:

	Upper epidermis	Lower epidermis
A.	0 stomata/mm^2	214 stomata/mm^2
B.	27 stomata/mm^2	31 stomata/mm^2
C.	350 stomata/mm^2	0 stomata/mm^2

Use the following plant types to match with plant A, B, or C: water lily, cactus, oak tree. Explain your choices. ______________________

Conclusion: How can you estimate the number of stomata on a leaf? ______________________

PLANNING GUIDE	
TEXT	**UNIT 6 Plants** **Chapter 22 Plants: Other Life Functions** **Investigation 22 How do different environmental conditions alter transpiration rate? p. 466**
TEACHER RESOURCE PACKAGE:	
READING AND STUDY GUIDE	Student Edition, p. 129 Teacher Edition, p. 35
RESOURCE MASTER BOOK	Student Master 22–1. Stems as Reproductive Structures, p. 22–2 Student Master 22–2. Plant Movements, p. 22–3 Teaching Master 22–1. Roots, p. 22–4 Teaching Master 22–2. Stems, p. 22–5 Investigation Worksheet, p. 22–6
EVALUATION PROGRAM	Test Masters, p. 85 Alternate Test Masters, p. 185
LABORATORY BIOLOGY: INVESTIGATING LIVING SYSTEMS	53 Comparing Dormant and Germinating Seeds, p. 203 54 Roots and Stems, p. 207 55 Influence of Hormones on Plant Growth, p. 213
PROBING LEVELS OF LIFE: A LABORATORY MANUAL	52 Root Anatomy, p. 134 53 Stem Anatomy, p. 136 54 Transpiration in Plants, p. 138

Name ______________________ Date ______________

Stems as Reproductive Structures

In plants, reproduction that does not involve the sexual process is called vegetative reproduction. Leaves, stems, and roots all may be involved in helping a plant reproduce vegetatively. Stems, however, are more often involved in vegetative reproduction than either leaves or roots.

Most plants derived through vegetative reproduction are genetically identical to the parent plant and are called clones. Sometimes mutations can occur during vegetative reproduction and the mutated individuals that result can be different from the parent.

There are five main kinds of stems that frequently carry out vegetative reproduction. These stems include the stolon, the rhizome, the tuber, the corm, and the bulb.

Stolon. Some plants, such as Bermuda grass, have above-ground, horizontal stems called stolons, or runners. The stolon, like a normal, erect stem, has nodes and internodes and usually leaves. The stolon of Bermuda grass has shoots and roots that arise at each node. The strawberry also produces stolons, however, shoots and roots arise from every other node.

Rhizome. A horizontal, below-ground stem is called a rhizome. Like the stolon, it has nodes and internodes at regular intervals. Shoots and roots may arise from each node. Rhizomes may be long and slender, as in Kentucky bluegrass, or they may be thick and fleshy as in the iris.

Tuber. Some slender rhizomes have thickened, fleshy segments, especially at the tip. These thickened parts are called tubers. The potato is a common type of tuber. On the potato tuber there are buds which are called "eyes." These eyes represent groups of buds at the nodes of the stem and have the potential to develop into shoots.

Corm. A corm is a thickened, food-storing underground stem that develops in preparation for a plant's dormant period. The corm remains alive in the soil while the above-ground portions of the plant dies. At the beginning of a new growing season, the corm sprouts roots and the terminal bud grows, eventually forming a flowering stem. During the growing season, axillary buds develop into new corms and it is these new corms that survive the dormant period. The crocus is a common plant that produces corms.

Bulb. A bulb is an underground, modified stem in which food is stored in thickened leaves that surround a short, erect stem. The stem has at least one central terminal bud that will produce a single, upright, leafy stem and flower. There is usually at least one axillary bud that has the potential to develop into a new bulb. The onion is a commercially valuable bulb.

Questions:

1. How do stolons differ from long, slender rhizomes? ______________________

____

2. How are corms and bulbs similar? ______________________

3. What is the relationship between rhizomes and tubers? ______________________

____

Name ______________________ Date ______________

Plant Movements

Plants seem so changeless and still, yet they are in continuous motion. Time-lapse photography shows that stems actively twist and turn, and flowers and leaves often repeat a series of movements like a well-rehearsed, stately dance.

Most movements of plants can be classified according to the mechanism involved. Two different types are growth movements and turgor movements. Growth movements result from the differential growth of cells. That is, cells in one part of the plant grow faster than those in another part of the plant. Turgor movements of plant parts result from the differential changes in turgor of some cells. In this type of movement, water moves in or out of cells, causing cells to either swell and become turgid or to shrink and collapse. Turgor movements are readily reversible while growth movements are irreversible.

A tropism is a type of growth movement that results from an external stimulus. The stimulus must come from a single direction, and it affects the direction of growth of a plant. Two familiar tropic movements are geotropism (response to gravity) and phototropism (response to light). Others include thigmotropism (response to touch), chemotropism (response to chemicals), and hydrotropism (response to water).

Tropisms can be either positive or negative, and a plant's response to the same stimulus may differ from plant part to plant part. For example, the primary root is usually positively geotropic, growing in the direction of gravity. The stem, however, is negatively geotropic, growing away from the pull of gravity. A plant's geotropic movements enable a seed that is planted "upside down," with root end pointing upward, to germinate and grow normally. The stem tip will turn as it grows so that it points upward and the root tip will turn and grow deeper into the soil.

Phototropic responses occur in most plants. Commonly, the stems are positively phototropic, bending toward the light as they grow. The stems of some plants, such as English ivy, are negatively phototropic. This negative response can be observed if a pot of English ivy is placed in a sunny window. The stems of the English ivy turn and grow away from the light and into the room.

Different intensities of light may evoke opposite phototropic responses. The stems of Bermuda grass and a few other plants are negatively phototropic at low-light intensities. Such plants grow close to and along the ground when they grow in open places with full sun exposure. These same plants exhibit a positively phototropic response when they grow in the shade. They grow more erect, or away from the ground.

The most familiar examples of positive thigmotropism are shown by the tendrils or stems of some climbing vines. A slightly rough or uneven surface providing two or more sources of stimuli is needed. The immediate reaction of the tendrils or stems to the surface is probably due to changes in turgor, but the changes are irreversible and followed by growth so that the tendril or stem wraps around the supporting object.

An example of chemotropism is found in angiosperms. The chemotropism involves the pollen tube. The pollen tube, in response to chemical stimuli, grows unerringly downward through the style into the embryo sac in the ovule. Hydrotropism may be thought of as a special type of chemotropism, since water is a chemical substance. Curvature of roots in response to water is observed in several kinds of plants. However, hydrotropism is not as common as was once believed. The evident hydrotropism of roots is due to the more rapid growth that takes place in roots in moist soil and not to the curvature of existing roots toward water.

Questions:

1. Liverworts usually grow close to the ground. However, they can be observed growing at an angle in a terrarium that is exposed to little light. What type of growth does the liverwort exhibit?

____

2. Just after germinating, vines in tropical forests grow toward darker places, usually the shadows of large trees. Once they make contact with the tree they grow up the trunk toward the canopy of the forest. What tropisms are involved? Explain and identify each tropism as either negative or positive. ____

____

Roots

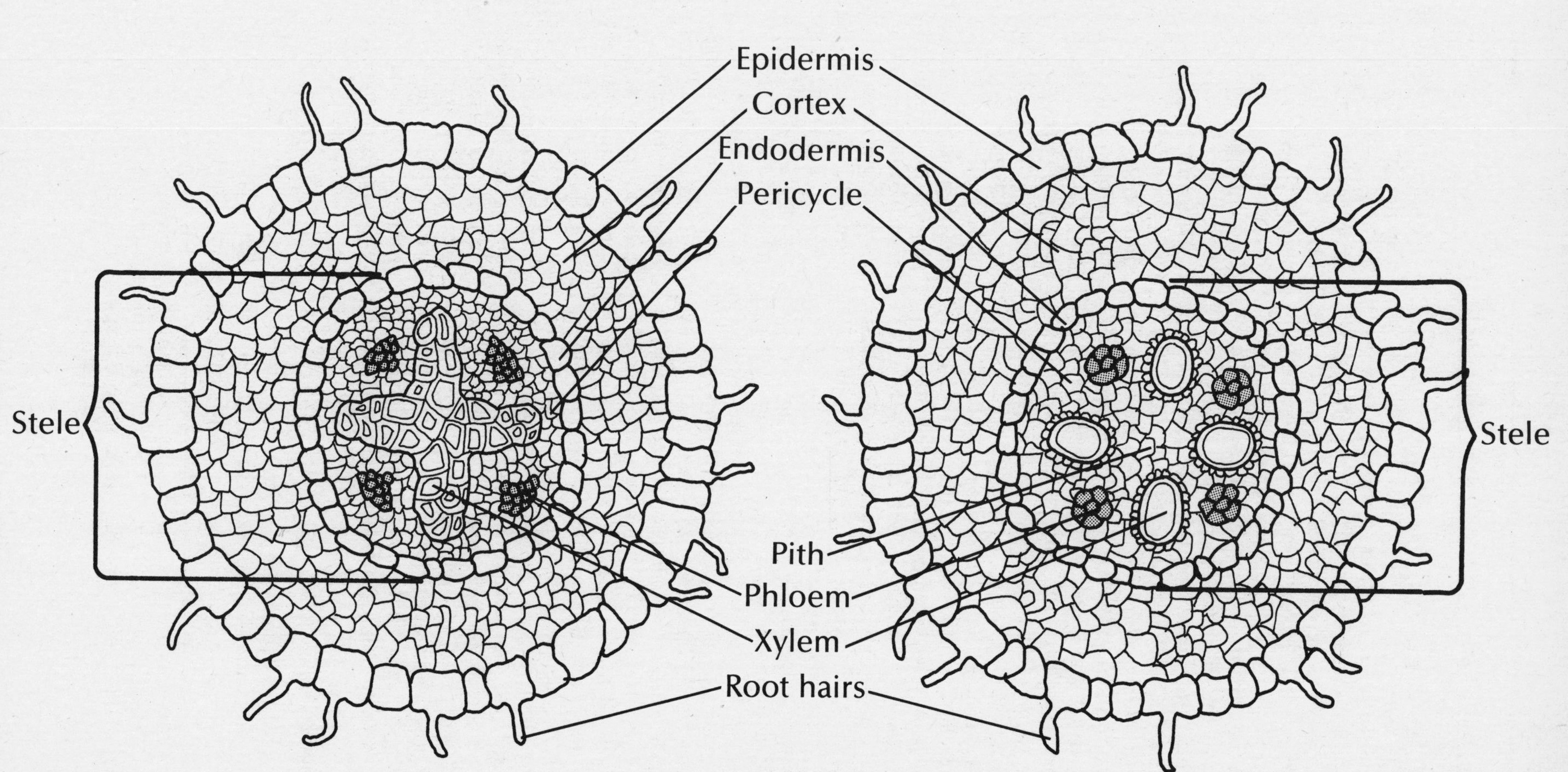
DICOT ROOT
MONOCOT ROOT
Epidermis
Cortex
Endodermis
Pericycle
Stele
Stele
Pith
Phloem
Xylem
Root hairs

Stems

MONOCOT STEM

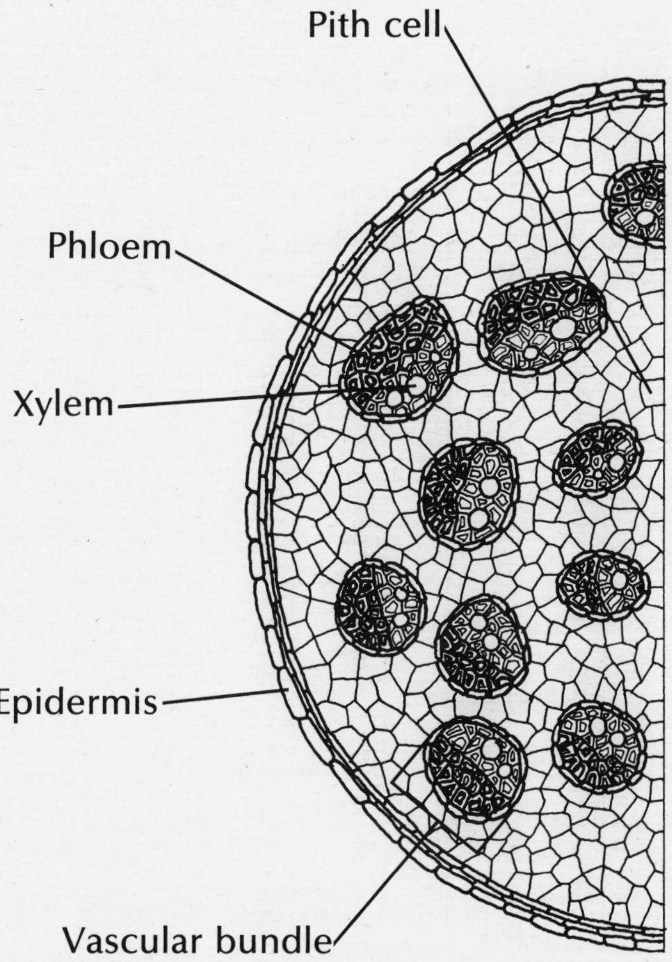

DICOT STEM

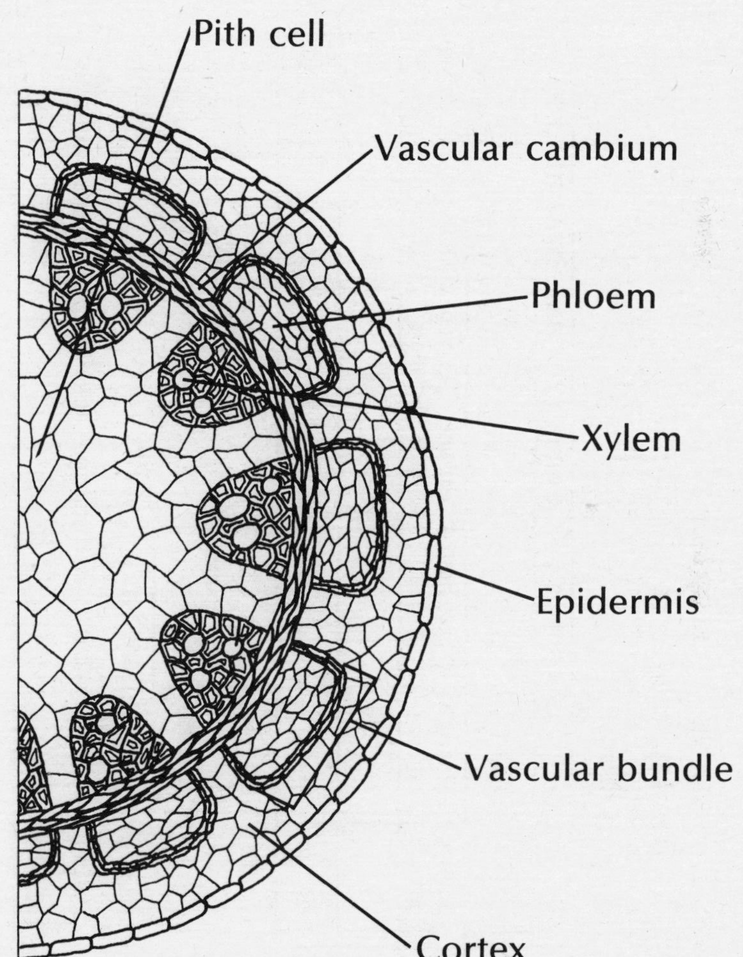

Investigation Worksheet — Chapter 22

Name ______________________ Date ______________

Problem: How do different environmental conditions alter transpiration rate? (text page 466)

Data and Observations:

TABLE 22-1. MEASURING THE RATE OF WATER LOSS

	Normal Conditions			High Humidity (Plastic Bag over Plant)			Low Humidity (Cool Air Blowing over Plant)		
Trial	Starting mark	Ending mark	Distance moved	Starting mark	Ending mark	Distance moved	Starting mark	Ending mark	Distance moved
1									
2									
		Total			Total			Total	
		Average			Average			Average	

Questions and Conclusion:

1. (a) Define xylem. (b) What is its function? (c) Where are xylem cells located in this experiment?

2. (a) Define stomata. (b) What is their function? (c) Where in your experiment were stomata found?

3. (a) Define transpiration. (b) Explain how xylem and stomata are related to the process of transpiration.

4. How was the transpiration rate measured in your experiment?

5. What three different conditions were used to influence transpiration rate?

6. (a) Using specific numbers from your data table, explain how each condition influenced transpiration rate. (b) Make a hypothesis about why transpiration rate is influenced by the changed conditions.

Conclusion: How do different environmental conditions alter transpiration rate?

PLANNING GUIDE	
TEXT	**UNIT 7 Animals** **Chapter 23 Animal Reproduction** **Investigation 23 How does *Obelia* show sexual and asexual reproduction? p. 484**
TEACHER RESOURCE PACKAGE:	
READING AND STUDY GUIDE	Student Edition, p. 135 Teacher Edition, p. 36
RESOURCE MASTER BOOK	Student Master 23–1. The Life Cycle of the Spadefoot Toad, p. 23–2 Student Master 23–2. Cryopreservation, p. 23–3 Teaching Master 23–1. Human Reproductive System, p. 23–4 Investigation Worksheet, p. 23–5, p. 11
EVALUATION PROGRAM	Test Masters, p. 89 Alternate Test Masters, p. 187
LABORATORY BIOLOGY: INVESTIGATING LIVING SYSTEMS	56 Regeneration: A Form of Asexual Reproduction, p. 219 57 The Menstrual Cycle, p. 221
PROBING LEVELS OF LIFE: A LABORATORY MANUAL	55 Regeneration in Planarians, p. 141 56 The Human Menstrual Cycle, p. 143

Name ______________________ Date ______________________

The Life Cycle of the Spadefoot Toad

It is late June in the Sonoran Desert of Arizona. The ground is parched because there has been little rain since March. The midafternoon temperature on bare ground reaches 65°C. Rumbling storms herald the arrival of moist air. The inevitable summer monsoon is about to begin.

The summer monsoon is made up of small thunderstorms—usually about five kilometers in diameter—that sweep across the desert. The thunderstorms, although small, make their appearance known. They occur almost daily and can yield as much as 2½ cm of rain in an hour.

Each living thing in the desert waits for the rain in its own way. Perhaps one of the most amazing is the spadefoot toad. To escape the hot, dry desert environment, this toad lives in a dormant state deep in the desert soil—about one meter underground. A membrane covers the toad's skin and enables it to absorb moisture while preventing any moisture loss. Its very large stomach enables it to eat half its body weight. This amount of food provides enough energy and nutrients to sustain life for an entire year or two. The spadefoot toad is called into action by the summer monsoon. Within the limits of this short season—about three months—it must find a mate, reproduce, and eat.

On the evening of the first flooding rains, tens of thousands of spadefoot toads dig themselves out of their burrows. The males assemble at newly formed ponds, singing their mating songs. Breeding must take place on the first night that the spadefoot toads emerge from their burrows to give the tadpoles a chance to complete metamorphosis before the ponds dry up.

In Tucson, Arizona, there are two species of spadefoot toads—the southern spadefoot *(Scaphiopus multiplicatus)* and the larger Couch spadefoot *(Scaphiopus couchii)*. The males of each species have unique mating calls that the females recognize. When the male encounters a female of his own species, he climbs onto her back and grasps her around the middle. This position is called amplexus. As the female moves through the water, she lays as many as 4000 eggs, which the male fertilizes. After mating, the toads leave the pond and dig shallow burrows in the moist soil. While the rains last, they emerge every night from their burrows to feed.

Depending on the temperature of the pond water, the eggs hatch into tadpoles in 13 to 48 hours. At first, they are blind and helpless. They are sustained by a small amount of yolk in their gut. After about one day, their eyes and mouths are fully developed. They become small eating machines, eating almost anything in sight—from bacteria to other tadpoles. Because the ponds are temporary, the tadpoles must undergo metamorphosis quickly. The Couch spadefoot has a brief larval life—as few as 8 days from egg to immature toad. The cost of this quick development is an extremely small and vulnerable toad. Several of them can sit on a quarter.

The southern spadefoot develops slower, taking about 21 days to become an immature toad. Although the southern spadefoot reaches a larger size than the Couch spadefoot, there may be a price to pay for slower development. If the rains do not continue, the ponds will not last for 21 days, and all the tadpoles will die.

There are other dangers faced by the spadefoot tadpoles. Several species of beetles and dragonflies also lay their eggs in the ponds. The larvae of these insects feed on tadpoles. Horsefly larvae that live in the mud at the bottom of the pond feed on the newly metamorphosed toads.

If a tadpole is able to find food, escape predators, and reach maturity, it still faces life in the desert. The young toads spend the rest of the summer struggling to capture enough food to triple or quadruple in size so that they can survive underground until the next summer rains. If the young spadefoot toads reach adulthood, they will be able to participate in mating activities in two or three years.

Questions:

1. Why is metamorphosis so short in the spadefoot toad?

____

2. What are some difficulties that face the spadefoot tadpole?

____

3. What is amplexus? ______________________

Name ______________________ Date ______________

Cryopreservation

Physicians can correct many cases of infertility using methods such as hormone injections, microsurgery, and artificial insemination with concentrated sperm. In spite of the successes of these methods, there are hundreds of thousands of couples in the United States who still are not able to have children. For these couples, *in vitro* fertilization offers a ray of hope.

In traditional *in vitro* fertilization, hormones are used to stimulate ovulation. A surgeon removes two to six eggs, which are then incubated for 3 to 30 hours before being placed into a culture dish containing sperm. After a few days, the fertilized eggs—about two-thirds of the eggs collected—are transferred to the woman's uterus with the hope that at least one fertilized egg, or embryo, will implant itself and develop into a normal fetus. The expected pregnancy rate is about 20 percent if one fertilized egg is inserted, 28 percent with two fertilized eggs, and 38 percent with three fertilized eggs.

A new step that promises to improve the success rate of *in vitro* fertilization has been developed at an Australian clinic. This step, cryopreservation, involves freezing the fertilized eggs. In traditional *in vitro* fertilization, all of the viable embryos are transferred to the uterus. But transferring more than three or four embryos greatly increases the chances of multiple births. Multiple births can complicate a pregnancy and possibly endanger the mother and her prospective children. With cryopreservation, this risk is avoided. No more than three embryos are inserted at a time, and the remaining embryos are frozen for possible future attempts.

Cryopreservation has yet other benefits. If the first attempt at inserting the embryos does not work, a second transfer procedure can be attempted without further surgery.

Cryopreservation raises several legal and ethical questions. Do people have the right to expose an embryo to a procedure that could kill it? Frozen embryos can possibly exist for an indefinite period of time. To whom do the frozen embryos belong? Would they belong to the living parents, to the estate of the deceased parents, to the storage facility that maintains them, or to the state?

The United States does not have a clear ethical or legal framework by which to regulate cryopreservation, or any other *in vitro* technique. Traditional *in vitro* fertilization raises its own set of ethical questions. If physicians could tell the difference between embryos that are most likely to implant and those that are not, should the embryos that look promising be implanted and the rest discarded? Should experiments be allowed on any remaining embryos? Should any remaining embryos be frozen and donated to another couple?

The American Fertility Society has issued guidelines to address some of these questions. The guidelines state that experimentation on embryos are ethical until the 14th day. At that time, the primitive streak, the forerunner of the neural tube, appears. Before the 14th day, the embryo is essentially a hollow ball of cells about the size of the period at the end of this sentence. Under these guidelines, it also is acceptable to discard embryos up to the 14th day. The guidelines state that cryopreservation should be done only under strict rules that spell out ahead of time the fate of the frozen embryos.

Questions:

1. What is an advantage to *in vitro* fertilization?
2. What advantages does cryopreservation offer to the traditional *in vitro* fertilization process?
3. What are some disadvantages to cryopreservation?
4. Because some ethical questions surround *in vitro* fertilization, should the procedure be totally abandoned? Explain.
5. What do you feel should be done with any frozen embryos that may be left over?

Human Reproductive System

MALE

SIDE VIEW (cut away)

Urinary bladder
Ureter
Vas deferens
Urethra
Penis
Testis
Scrotum

FRONT VIEW

Vas deferens
Seminal vesicle
Prostate gland
Cowper's gland
Penis
Urethra
Testis
Epididymis
Scrotum
Seminiferous tubules

FEMALE

SIDE VIEW (cut away) / FRONT VIEW

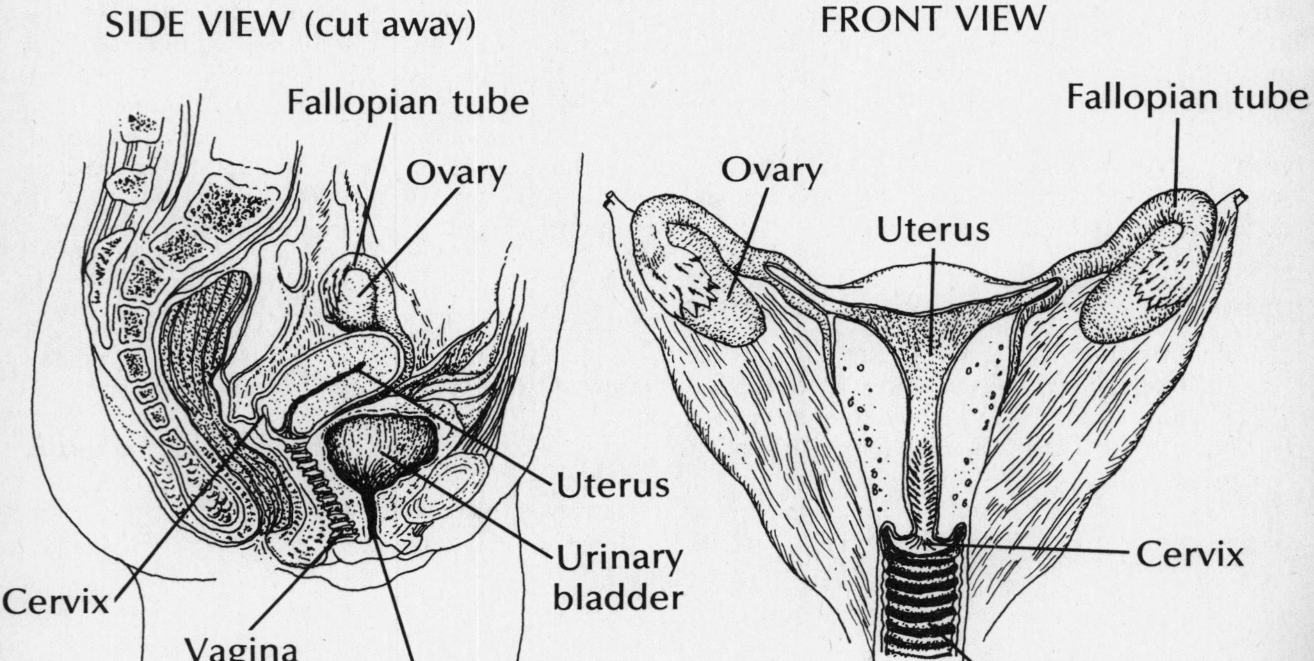

Name ______________________ Date ______________

Problem: How does *Obelia* show sexual and asexual reproduction?

(text page 484)

Data and Observations:

TABLE 23–1. COMPARISON OF SEXUAL AND ASEXUAL PHASES IN *OBELIA*		
Letter	Structure	Sexual or Asexual Phase?
Figure 23–13 Parts		
A		
B		
C		
D		
E		
F		
G		
Figure 23–14 Parts		
H		
I		
J		
K		
Figure 23–15 Parts		
L		
M		
N		
O		
P		
Q		
R		
S		
T		
U		
V		
W		

Name ______________________ *Date* ______________

Questions and Conclusion:

1. Define: (a) asexual reproduction (b) sexual reproduction. ______________________

2. Explain why (a) the colony form of *Obelia* is the asexual phase of the life cycle and (b) the medusae of *Obelia* are the sexual phase. ______________________

3. (a) To what phylum does *Obelia* belong? (b) List several characteristics for this phylum that are shown by *Obelia*. ______________________

Conclusion: How does *Obelia* show sexual and asexual reproduction? ______________________

PLANNING GUIDE	
TEXT	**UNIT 7 Animals** **Chapter 24 Animal Development** **Investigation 24 How does sea urchin egg development compare to human egg development? p. 510**
TEACHER RESOURCE PACKAGE:	
READING AND STUDY GUIDE	Student Edition, p. 141 Teacher Edition, p. 38
RESOURCE MASTER BOOK	Student Master 24–1. Reunited Twins, p. 24–2 Student Master 24–2. Drug Abuse During Pregnancy, p. 24–3 Teaching Master 24–1. Insect Metamorphosis, p. 24–4 Teaching Master 24–2. Frog Egg Development, p. 24–5 Investigation Worksheet, p. 24–6
EVALUATION PROGRAM	Test Masters, p. 93 Alternate Test Masters, p. 189
LABORATORY BIOLOGY: INVESTIGATING LIVING SYSTEMS	58 Chick Development, p. 227 59 Fruit Fly Development, p. 231
PROBING LEVELS OF LIFE: A LABORATORY MANUAL	57 Effects of Salt Concentration on Development of Brine Shrimp, p. 145 58 Development of a Chicken Embryo, p. 147

Name ______________________ Date ______________

Reunited Twins

The reuniting of twins can produce fascinating results. In one such case, twins who did not know one another were reunited as adults. When they were brought together, many similarities were discovered. Both were firefighters, both had moustaches, sideburns, and the same glasses. Both drank the same kind of beer and held the bottle in the same way. Both were bachelors and were good humored. When reunited, they kept making the same remarks at the same time and using the same gestures.

Though the twins saw their similarities as wondrous curiosities, the scientific community sees things very differently. Behavioral researchers grapple with the old question as to whether it is our environments or our heredities that make us what we are. To these researchers, identical twins that have different upbringings are a rare opportunity to study this question.

A research group headed by psychologist Thomas Bouchard, Jr. is studying reunited twins. What this group hopes to discover is the heritability of certain human traits. Heritability is the degree to which a trait is influenced by genes, expressed in percentages.

The heritability of a specific characteristic, for example height, can be judged by looking at identical twins that were raised apart. Since these twins share 100 percent of their genetic material, any difference in height must be due to environment. By comparing twins, the researchers found that within the population, 90 percent of the variation in height is influenced by genetic factors. The remaining 10 percent is influenced by environment.

The researchers also found that one's ability to ward off illness is heritable. Identical twins reared apart appear to have similar immune systems. The researchers looked for nine key antibodies. They found that the twins usually had at least seven in common. Fraternal twins and nontwin siblings shared only four key antibodies on average.

Genes also seem to play a role in susceptibility to heart and lung disease. More remarkable is the fact that the timing of the onset of a disease is genetically encoded. Identical twins have developed glaucoma, diabetes, and heart attacks within a short time of one another.

Researchers stress, however, that identical twins inherit predispositions to diseases and that health habits influence those predispositions. For example, a nonsmoking twin with a family history of lung cancer will have a better chance of staying healthy than his or her identical twin who smokes a pack of cigarettes a day.

Research on twin psychology has not yielded substantial results. However, there is some evidence that identical twins reared apart have very similar brainwave patterns, react alike to stimuli, and process information at a similar speed. Identical twins also perform similarly on tests of verbal fluency and IQ. Results of IQ tests show that identical twins reared in the same family have IQ scores that correspond 86 percent of the time. Fraternal twins reared in the same family have IQ scores that correspond 60 percent of the time. But identical twins reared apart are generally much more similar than the fraternal twins, showing a 72 percent match in IQ scores. By contrast, nontwin siblings had similar IQ scores about 47 percent of the time.

Questions:

1. Why do you think identical twins that are reared apart are more similar in physical structure than in IQ? ______________________
2. Two identical twins were raised apart. When they met, they were identical in height, although one was several pounds heavier than the other. Do you think the difference in weight is influenced by genes or by the environment? Explain. ______________________

   ____
3. Two identical twins were reunited. One twin had just recently developed glaucoma. Would you expect the other twin to develop glaucoma? Why? ______________________

   ____

Name ____________________ Date ____________________

Drug Abuse During Pregnancy

Almost all drugs taken by the mother will cross the placenta to the fetus. Many people believe that any drug taken by the mother that does not pose a major health threat to her also does not pose a health threat to the developing fetus. However, one only needs to look at the thalidomide tragedy to realize the error of this assumption. Thalidomide was introduced in Europe in the 1960s as a mild sedative and was prescribed to hundreds of pregnant women. A large number of malformed babies were born to women who had taken thalidomide. The babies lacked long bones in their arms and legs and had flippers for hands and feet.

Almost all commonly abused drugs have adverse effects on the fetus. Some of these drugs are discussed below.

Narcotics and Mind-Altering Drugs. The greatest impact of narcotics on the fetus is that the fetus can become addicted to such drugs *in utero,* or before birth. Narcotics include heroin, methadone, phencyclidine (angel dust), and phenobarbital. Additionally, many of these drugs are sold illegally and are often mixed with other substances that can have detrimental effects on the mother and the fetus. Compounding the problem is that many women who use narcotics also suffer poor nutrition. Poor nutrition results in small babies that do not thrive.

The use of cocaine, especially during the second half of pregnancy, occasionally results in separation of the placenta from the uterus. The separation results in fetal distress and may cause premature labor. Death of the fetus in heavy cocaine users also has been reported.

A more recent problem among babies of drug addicts is AIDS, or Acquired Immune Deficiency Syndrome. AIDS is common among addicts who inject drugs. AIDS can cross the placenta and be passed on to the fetus. Newborns with AIDS experience frequent infections, slow growth, and a high death rate.

Smoking. Studies have shown that when a pregnant woman smokes, she is cutting down the oxygen supply to the fetus. Smoking is linked to babies with low birth weights. The toxic substances that are inhaled with cigarette smoke—carbon monoxide and cyanide—retard fetal growth. These toxic substances can be found in the blood of fetuses whose mothers do not smoke but have been exposed to smoking by the baby's father.

Marijuana can no longer be considered harmless. Studies with monkeys show that marijuana causes stillbirths, small babies, birth defects, and early infant deaths. It is also known that THC (the main chemical in marijuana) builds up in the cells of the ovaries and testes. The damage to a man may be temporary because he continuously produces new sperm. Women, however, are born with a certain number of eggs. If those eggs are adversely affected, there is no way to replace them.

Alcohol. The National Institute on Alcohol Abuse and Alcoholism warns that more than two drinks a day, or a total of two ounces of whiskey, may be harmful to the fetus. If a pregnant woman has more than two drinks a day, there is a 10 percent chance that the baby will have fetal alcohol syndrome. Fetal alcohol syndrome is chracteristic in babies of pregnant women who drink excessive amounts of alcohol. Pregnant women who consume more than six alcoholic drinks a day for all or part of their pregnancies place their fetuses at great risk for fetal alcohol syndrome. Fetal alcohol syndrome may cause facial abnormalities, heart defects, abnormal limb development, and lower-than-average intelligence.

Questions:

1. If a pregnant woman uses narcotics and/or mind-altering drugs, what risks does she expose the developing fetus to? What would you recommend she do?
2. A woman smokes about a pack of cigarettes a day. Upon learning that she is pregnant, she quits smoking altogether. However, her husband also smokes. What responsibilities does the father have to the developing fetus? Explain.
3. A pregnant woman is attending a party. Everyone is drinking an alcoholic punch. The hostess hands a glass of the punch to the woman. Should she feel obligated to drink it? Explain.
4. A pregnant woman has developed a bad cold. She goes to the pharmacy to purchase various cold remedies. Should she take any of these over-the-counter medications without first consulting with her physician? Why?

Insect Metamorphosis

INCOMPLETE METAMORPHOSIS:
Grasshopper

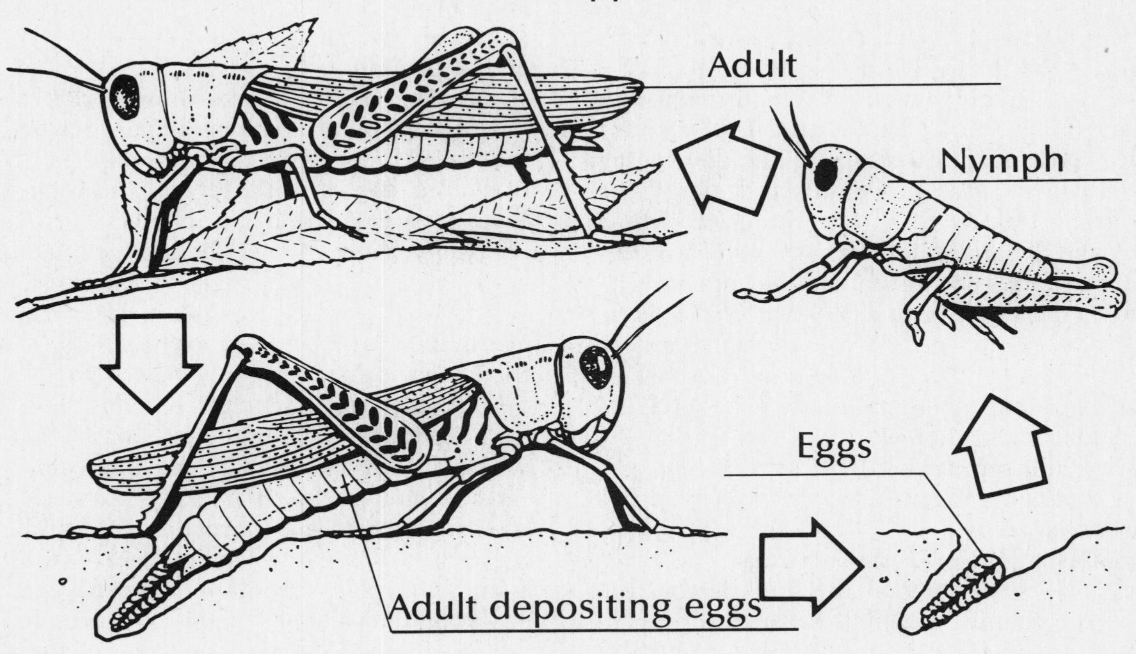

COMPLETE METAMORPHOSIS:
Butterfly

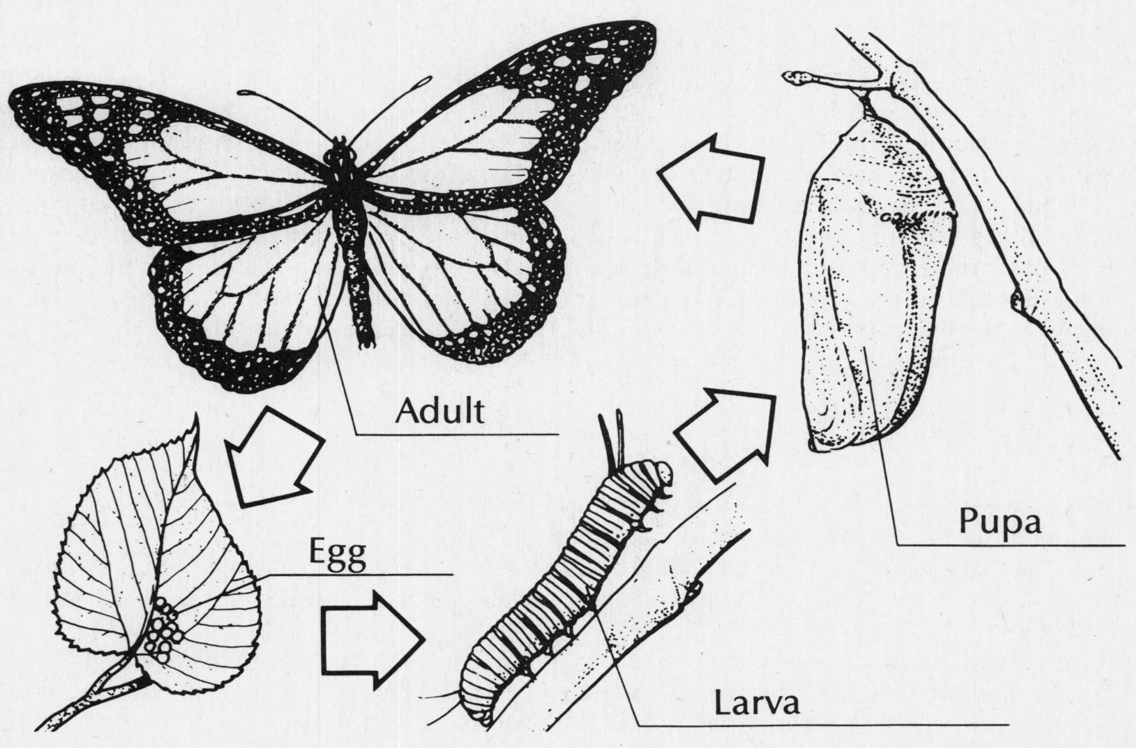

Frog Egg Development

CLEAVAGE

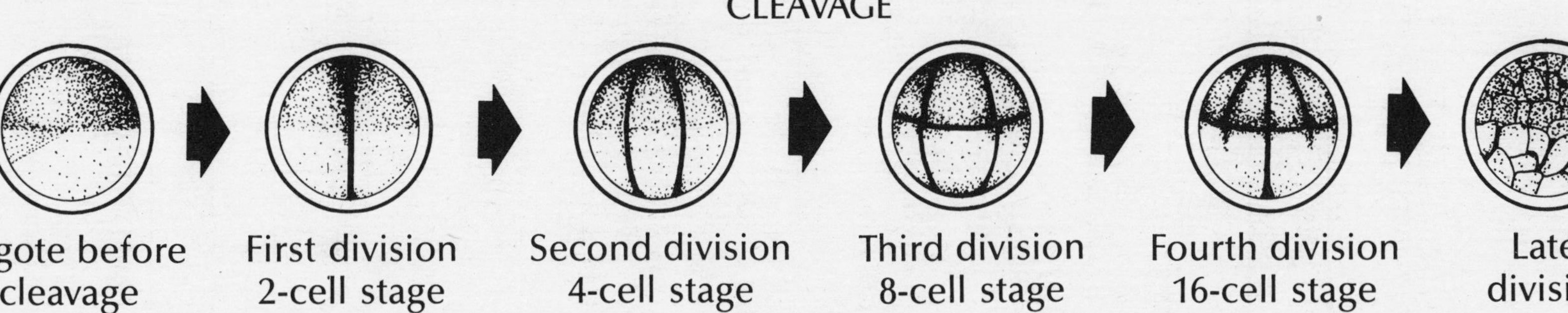

GASTRULATION

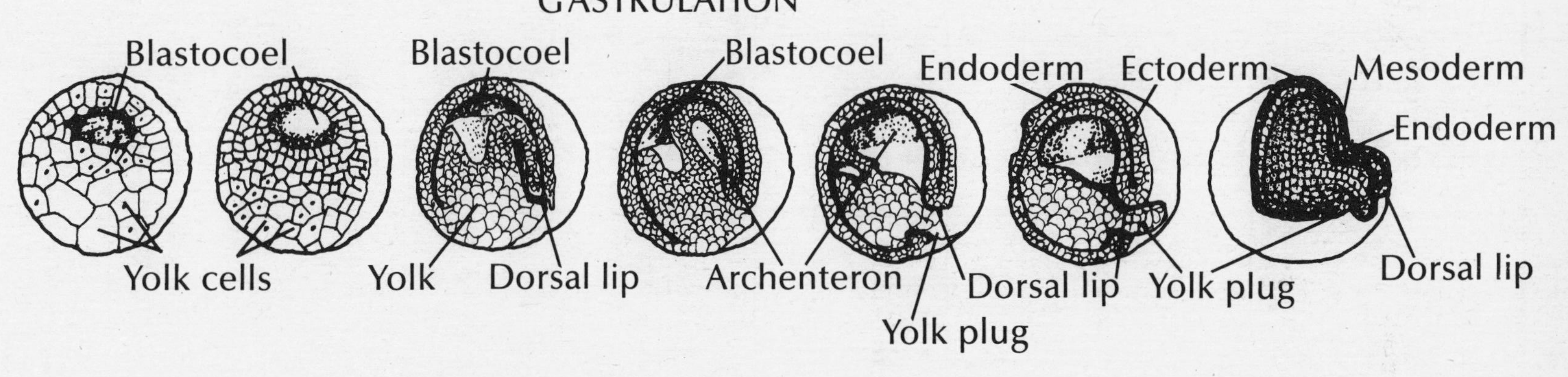

FORMATION OF NEURAL TUBE

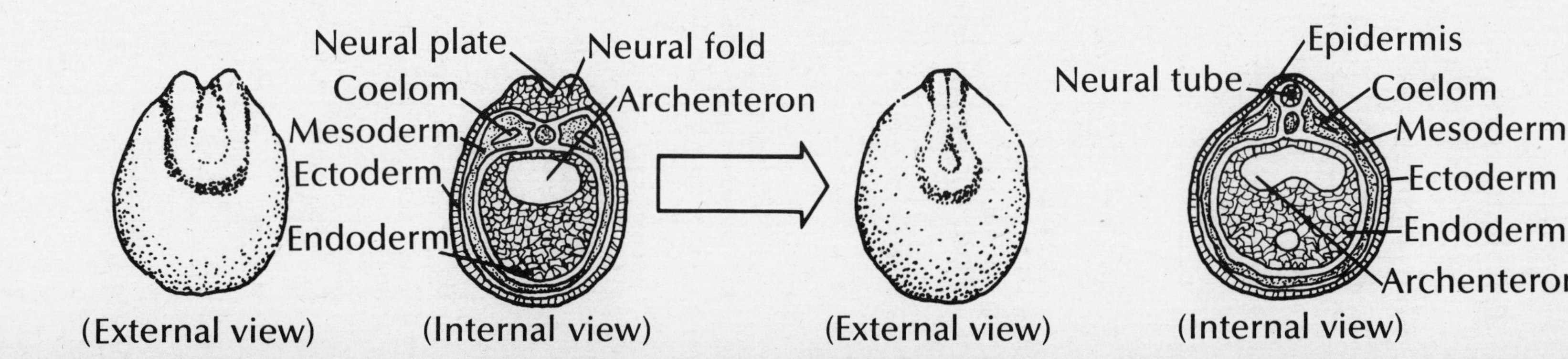

Name ____________________ Date ____________________

Problem: How does sea urchin egg development compare to human egg development?

(text page 510)

Data and Observations:

TABLE 24-2. DEVELOPMENTAL STAGES OF THE SEA URCHIN	
Stage a	Stage b
Stage c	Stage d
Stage e	Stage f
Stage g	

Questions and Conclusion:

1. Define: (a) development (b) external development (c) internal development. ____________________
2. Based on your definitions in question 1, explain how development of a sea urchin differs from that of a human. ____________________
3. Each time a cell divides by mitosis, two identical cells are formed. Describe the stage(s) that occur(s) between: (a) the 4-cell stage and the 16-cell stage (b) the 16-cell stage and the 64-cell stage. ____________________
4. (a) Does cell size increase or decrease with increasing number of cells? (b) What evidence do you have from your observations in Part A to support your answer to 4(a)? ____________________
5. (a) In humans, how long does it take for a fertilized egg to reach the uterus? (b) Through what structure must the fertilized egg pass? (c) Describe the changes that take place in the fertilized egg between the ovary and the uterus. ____________________
6. (a) In humans, what happens to the blastula after day 4 of development? (b) How does this differ from what happens in the sea urchin at the same time? ____________________
7. Why can diagrams for early sea urchin development be used to represent early stages of human development? ____________________

Conclusion: How does sea urchin egg development compare to human egg development? ____________________

PLANNING GUIDE	
TEXT	**UNIT 7 Animals** **Chapter 25 Food Getting and Digestion** **Investigation 25 How is the milk sugar lactose digested? p. 528**
TEACHER RESOURCE PACKAGE:	
READING AND STUDY GUIDE	Student Edition, p. 147 Teacher Edition, p. 39
RESOURCE MASTER BOOK	Student Master 25–1. Digestion and Absorption of Nutrients, p. 25–2 Student Master 25–2. Dietary Fat and Cancer, p. 25–3 Teaching Master 25–1. Digestion of Carbohydrates, p. 25–4 Investigation Worksheet, p. 25–5
EVALUATION PROGRAM	Test Masters, p. 97 Alternate Test Masters, p. 191
LABORATORY BIOLOGY: INVESTIGATING LIVING SYSTEMS	60 Protein Digestion, p. 233 61 A Nutrition Study, p. 235 62 Digestive System of Frog and Human, p. 237
PROBING LEVELS OF LIFE: A LABORATORY MANUAL	59 Ingestion and Digestion in Hydra and Planaria, p. 151 60 Digestion of Starches, Proteins, and Fats in Humans, p. 153

Name ______________________ Date ______________

Digestion and Absorption of Nutrients

The main dietary carbohydrates are polysaccharides, disaccharides, and monosaccharides. Starches and their derivatives are the only polysaccharides that are digested by the human digestive system. The major disaccharides that are digested are lactose (milk sugar) and sucrose (table sugar). Fructose and glucose are two monosaccharides that are digested. All carbohydrates are eventually broken down into three monosaccharides—glucose, galactose, and fructose—which are rapidly absorbed across the wall of the small intestine.

Protein digestion begins in the stomach, where large polypeptides are broken down into smaller polypeptides. In the small intestine, the polypeptides are digested by enzymes that are secreted by the pancreas and small intestine. The two major kinds of amino acids, neutral and basic, are the result. Absorption of the amino acids is rapid in the duodenum and jejunum, but slow in the ileum.

Fat digestion begins in the duodenum, with the assistance of an enzyme from the pancreas. The end products of fat digestion are fatty acids, glycerol, and glycerides. Fat absorption is greatest in the upper parts of the small intestine, but a small amount is also absorbed in the lower small intestine.

Vitamins and minerals are not broken down or digested. They are absorbed directly through the small intestine. Water-soluble vitamins are absorbed rapidly. Absorption of fat-soluble vitamins, such as A, D, E, and K, is slowed if the pancreatic and bile enzymes necessary for fat absorption are in short supply. Vitamin B_{12}, however, is absorbed in the ileum. Vitamin B_{12} binds to a protein secreted by the stomach and the resultant complex is absorbed in the ileum.

Many minerals, including calcium and iron, are mostly absorbed in the upper small intestine. Calcium absorption is facilitated by lactose and protein. Most of the dietary iron is in the ferric (Fe^{+3}) state. The ferrous (Fe^{+2}) state of iron is the form of iron that is most readily absorbed. Ascorbic acid, or vitamin C, facilitates the conversion of ferric iron to ferrous iron.

Table 25–1 summarizes the absorption sites of the digested products of carbohydrates, proteins, fats, and selected vitamins and minerals.

TABLE 25-1. ABSORPTION SITES OF SELECTED SUBSTANCES

Substance	Site in Small Intestine		
	Upper (duodenum and first half of jejunum)	Middle (second half of jejunum)	Lower (ileum)
Sugars (glucose, etc.)	2	3	2
Neutral amino acids	2	3	2
Basic amino acids	2	2	2
Fatty acids	3	2	1
Water-soluble vitamins	3	2	0
Vitamin B_{12}	0	1	3
Calcium	3	2	1
Iron (Fe^{+2})	3	2	1

NOTE: Relative absorption is graded from 0 to 3. No absorption = 0; greatest absorption = 3.

Questions:

1. What substance(s) is (are) absorbed the most in the upper part of the small intestine? The lower part? ______________________
2. What substance(s) is (are) not absorbed much or at all in the lower part of the small intestine? ______________________
3. In what two parts of the small intestine are most nutrients absorbed? ______________________

Name ______________________ Date ______________

Dietary Fat and Cancer

In most clinical trials that attempt to discover the cause of a particular disease or ailment, two randomly selected groups of people are chosen: the experimental group and the control group. The experimental group is exposed to a factor that may be suspected of causing a disease, while the control group is not. All other environmental factors concerning the two groups are kept the same. In this way the true effects of a particular factor can be deduced. This is an extremely useful, standard scientific method, but it is often difficult or impossible to apply when investigating the causes of certain diseases in humans. After all, is it ethical to use this method to test the hypothesis that low levels of diagnostic radiation, such as diagnostic X rays, cause cancer? Other hypotheses are hard to test because it can be difficult to get human subjects to follow a strict regimen that might be required by a scientific study. These hypotheses often involve a dietary regimen for the prevention of disease.

One popular diet-based hypothesis has been challenged recently. It has been proposed that eating too much fat promotes cancer, particularly cancers of the breast, prostate, and colon. Although this question has been studied extensively, it has never been tested fully in a clinical trial. To test the hypothesis, scientists have looked at various studies to see if the evidence gathered supports a cause-and-effect relationship between a high-fat diet and cancer.

There are certain requirements that must be met if a cause-and-effect relationship is to be established. One of the most important is consistency. Is the hypothesis consistently supported from study to study? This question must be asked about all studies concerning a high-fat diet and cancer. Another requirement is the finding of a *strong* relationship between a high-fat diet and cancer. A third requirement is showing that the presumed cause of a disease actually precedes the disease. Studies that deal with the cause of a disease over time are called temporal studies. With cancer, a disease that develops slowly, it is difficult to establish that a high-fat diet eaten throughout an individual's lifetime is the cause of the cancer or if there are other factors that could cause the disease.

A consistent link between high-fat diet and cancer has not been shown in a number of studies. For example, a study of vegetarians showed that they are as likely to develop cancers of the breast, prostate, or colon as those people who eat meat, a high-fat food. A study from Hawaii showed that fat is associated with breast and prostate cancers but not colon cancer. Still another study from Japan showed that a high-meat diet was associated with a *high* rate of breast cancer and a *low* rate of colon cancer.

Other temporal studies have failed to show that a high-fat diet promotes cancer. The amount of fat eaten by people in the United States has risen by 14 percent per person since 1940. The death rates due to breast, prostate, and colon cancer, however, have not changed significantly during the same period.

Although the relationship between dietary fat and cancer is still unclear, there are many, large-scale studies of the relationship currently underway. The National Cancer Institute is conducting a trial to determine if a low-fat diet can prevent breast cancer. One scientist, Ernst Wynder, hypothesizes that fat promotes the production of bile acids, which may enhance cancer tumors. Wynder also suggests that breast and other cancers of the female reproductive system may be related to an imbalance of hormones caused by excessive fat. Robert E. Olson, of the State University of New York at Stony Brook, is investigating a possible link between either high-fat or excessive calories and various forms of cancer. An excess of fat or calories has been shown to promote cancer in laboratory animals, and Olson has noted that people who eat large amounts of fat also tend to take in large amounts of protein and calories.

Questions:

1. Why might some people conclude that a high-fat diet promotes cancer?
2. What are some problems that might be encountered during a study to determine if a high-fat diet promotes cancer?
3. A high-fat, high-calorie diet seems to promote cancer in laboratory animals. Can one automatically assume that a high-calorie diet promotes cancer in humans? Why?
4. Do you support the hypothesis that a high-fat diet promotes cancer? If so, why? If not, what would convince you that there was such a relationship?

Digestion of Carbohydrates

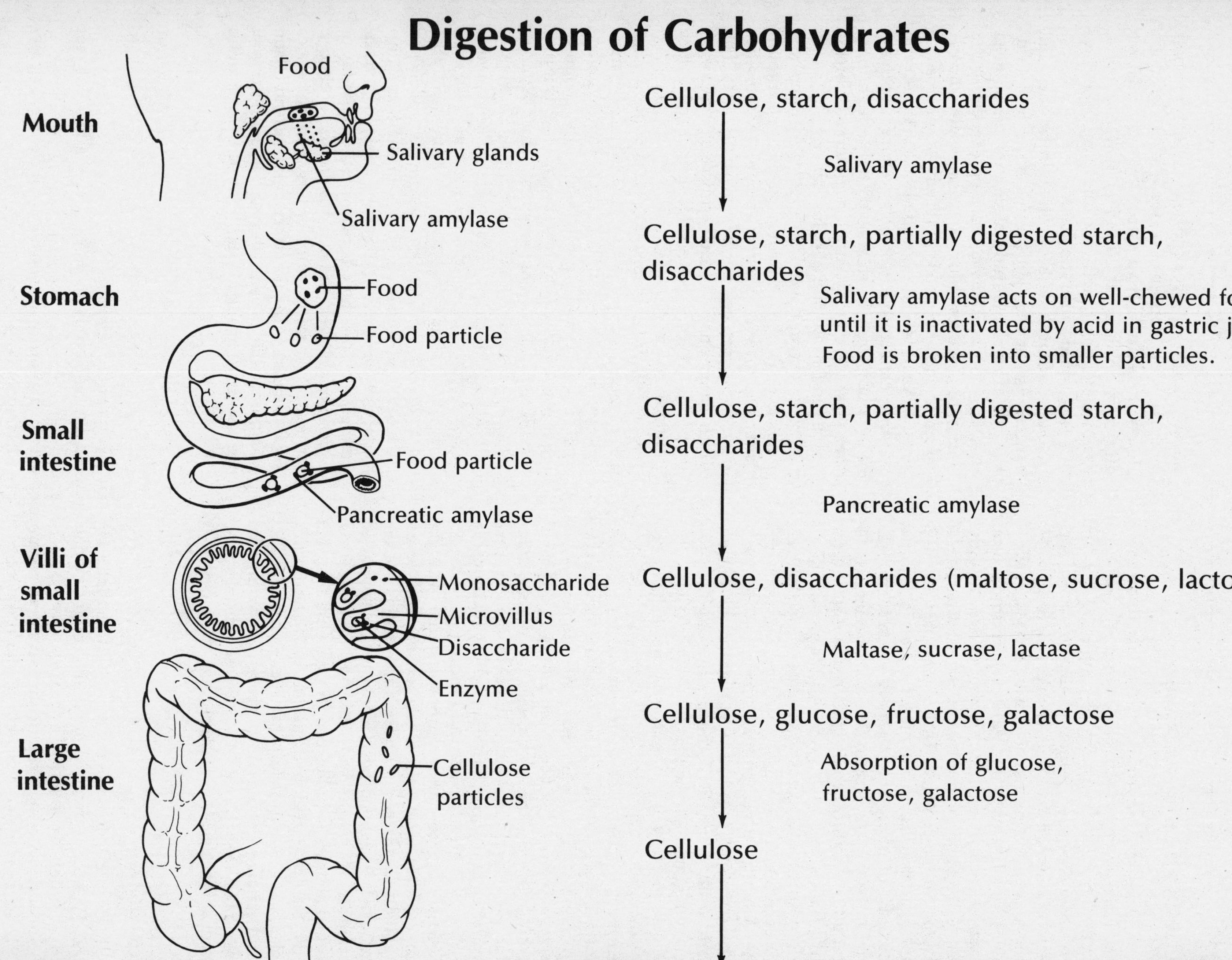

Name ______________________ Date ______________

Problem: How is the milk sugar lactose digested? (text page 528)

Data and Observations:

TABLE 25-4. LACTOSE DIGESTION			
Lactose and lactase model joined together		Lactose model after digestion by lactase	
Circle	Contents	Resulting color of TesTape	Glucose present?
1			
2			
3			
4			

Questions and Conclusion:

1. Define: (a) enzyme (b) substrate (c) digestion (d) lactose (e) lactase. ______________________

Name ______________________ Date ______________

2. Use your models from Part A to answer these questions. (a) What carbohydrate molecule is present in milk before it is digested? (b) What two smaller molecules form a molecule of lactose? (c) Does the glucose in the lactose molecule exist as a separate entity before the digestion of milk?

(d) What organ of the digestive system produces lactase? ______________________

3. Use your experimental results from Part B to answer these questions. (a) Was glucose present in milk? (b) Was glucose present in lactase? (c) Was glucose present in milk after the enzyme lactase was added? Explain. ______________________

4. Explain why it was helpful to test glucose with TesTape. ______________________

5. Explain the role of the enzyme lactase in the digestion of milk. ______________________

6. Some people cannot drink milk because their digestive systems do not produce lactase. If milk is drunk, it is not digested. This results in cramps, bloating, gas, and diarrhea. Suggest a treatment that would allow such a person to drink milk. ______________________

Conclusion: How is the milk sugar lactose digested? ______________________

PLANNING GUIDE	
TEXT	**UNIT 7 Animals** **Chapter 26 Transport** **Investigation 26 How does one analyze pulse and heartbeat? p. 546**
TEACHER RESOURCE PACKAGE:	
READING AND STUDY GUIDE	Student Edition, p. 153 Teacher Edition, p. 41
RESOURCE MASTER BOOK	Student Master 26–1. Cyclosporine and Transplants, p. 26–2 Student Master 26–2. Laser Canalization, p. 26–3 Teaching Master 26–1. Comparing Circulatory Systems, p. 26–4 Teaching Master 26–2. Circulation of the Blood, p. 26–5 Investigation Worksheet, p. 26–6, p. 12
EVALUATION PROGRAM	Test Masters, p. 101 Alternate Test Masters, p. 193
LABORATORY BIOLOGY: INVESTIGATING LIVING SYSTEMS	63 The Human Heart, p. 243 64 Blood, p. 249
PROBING LEVELS OF LIFE: A LABORATORY MANUAL	61 Capillary Circulation, p. 157 62 Effects of Exercise on the Heartbeat Rate, p. 159

Name ______________________ Date ______________

Cyclosporine and Transplants

In 1970, microbiologists at a Swiss pharmaceutical firm, Sandoz, Ltd., were looking for microbes that might produce chemicals with antibiotic properties. They brought a fungus from southern Norway to the laboratory. The fungus produced a substance with some unusual chemical properties. Further research showed that the substance was not effective as an antibiotic. But Jean Borel, an immunologist at Sandoz, saw that this substance—cyclosporine—suppressed the immune response in an unprecedented way.

Most medications that suppress the immune response curb the activity of all types of immune cells. As a result, these medications leave the body susceptible to all sorts of infections. Cyclosporine functions differently. It selectively suppresses the activities of helper T cells.

Helper T cells are called into action when foreign substances, or antigens, are detected in the body. These antigens may be in the form of surface proteins on foreign tissue or invading microorganisms. When helper T cells detect antigens, they send out substances called lymphokines. Lymphokines signal other cells of the immune system to mount an attack. Cyclosporine inhibits helper T cells but leaves enough of the immune response intact to fight infections.

Borel's findings caught the attention of Cambridge scientist David White. White and transplant surgeon Roy Calne tried cyclosporine on animals that received organ transplants. They were impressed with the results of cyclosporine treatment. The transplanted organs were not rejected, and the animals' immune systems were not suppressed to the point of being unable to fight off ordinary infections.

Calne's first attempts at using cyclosporine for human organ transplants were highly successful. The transplanted organs were not rejected. Also, patients treated with cyclosporine were able to fight infections better than patients treated with traditional immunosuppressant medications.

As use of cyclosporine increased, two effects were noted. First, transplant patients receiving cyclosporine experienced fewer complications and recovered from surgery more rapidly than patients taking traditional immunosuppressants. Second, one-year survival rates for transplant patients improved. Use of cyclosporine increased the one-year survival rate for heart transplant patients from 63 percent to 83 percent. Perhaps the most dramatic improvement in survival rates can be observed in liver transplant patients. Treatment with cyclosporine has doubled the one-year survival rate for those patients to more than 70 percent. As a result, liver transplants are now considered therapeutic rather than experimental.

The beneficial effects of cyclosporine have not been limited to transplant patients. Cyclosporine also has been used to treat patients with juvenile-onset diabetes. When treated with cyclosporine, half of a group of patients who had just been diagnosed as diabetic were able to stop using insulin temporarily.

In 1984, the U.S. Food and Drug Administration approved cyclosporine for controlled trials in juvenile-onset diabetes patients. Clinical trials to test the effectiveness of cyclosporine on autoimmune diseases such as multiple sclerosis also are planned.

Although cyclosporine can be considered a breakthrough in the medical field, it does have a few drawbacks. Cyclosporine must be taken for an entire lifetime. No one knows what the long-term effects might be. Also, cyclosporine is not inexpensive. Annual costs for ongoing treatment range from $3000 to $5000.

Questions:

1. How does cyclosporine work? ______________________
2. How is cyclosporine different from traditional immunosuppressants?

____

____

3. What are some benefits of cyclosporine? ______________________

____

Name ______________________ Date ______________

Laser Canalization

A human heart has two thin-walled atria that receive circulating deoxygenated blood and two ventricles that pump blood. The atria and ventricles are completely separate. The heart of a reptile also has two thin-walled atria that receive circulating blood. However, the heart of a reptile has one ventricle that pumps blood. The ventricle is divided by a thin wall of tissue—the septum. The division of the ventricle is not complete (except in crocodiles) and allows some mixing of oxygenated and deoxygenated blood.

Of great interest to cardiovascular surgeons is the fact that the reptilian heart does not have well-developed coronary arteries. Coronary arteries supply the hearts of many other animals, including humans, with blood. These arteries are so important that when the flow of blood becomes partly blocked, heart damage can result. If blockage of the arteries is severe enough, the result may be a sudden, fatal heart attack.

For cardiovascular surgeons, the absence of coronary arteries in the hearts of reptiles raises an important question: How is the reptilian heart nourished without being fed by an elaborate arterial system? The answer to this question is that blood from the ventricle of a reptile seeps into the sinusoids, or tiny spaces in the myocardium. The myocardium is the wall of muscle that encases the heart. The blood that seeps into the sinusoids nourishes the heart. Human hearts have sinusoids, too. This fact provides the basis for a new method in cardiovascular surgery called laser canalization. The left ventricle is chosen for this procedure because it is the more powerful pumping chamber.

Laser canalization is an open-heart operation, but it is far less complicated than the bypass surgery that is employed currently. In bypass surgery, blood is shunted around coronary artery obstructions by attaching one end of a vein—usually taken from the leg or chest—to the aorta; the other end of the vein is attached to the blocked artery just beyond the obstruction. Bypass surgery often takes hours to perform. Laser canalization takes only minutes and involves tapping ventricular blood by boring 8 to 14 holes through the wall of the left ventricle with a hand-held, high-powered, carbon dioxide laser. Blood seeps through the tiny holes and into the sinusoids, thus nourishing the damaged area of the heart. Bleeding from the laser holes outside of the ventricle wall is minimal because the laser-bored holes seal at the surface by means of the natural clotting process.

Laser canalization is done in the United States, Japan, and the Soviet Union. Dr. Mahmood Mirhoseini of St. Luke's Hospital in Milwaukee, Wisconsin, has performed laser canalization on a number of patients. Because laser canalization is still a new procedure, eligible patients include those who have had at least one standard bypass operation and have areas of the heart that are too damaged for conventional grafts. All of Dr Mirhoseini's patients that underwent laser canalization are still alive and well. X rays of their hearts and blood vessels show that the operations were successful. In one patient, the areas of the heart that received laser canalization are receiving more blood than the sections that underwent traditional bypasses.

Questions:

1. What are some similarities and differences between reptilian and human hearts? ______________

2. On what principle is laser canalization based? ______________

3. What are some advantages and disadvantages of bypass surgery? ______________

Comparing Circulatory Systems

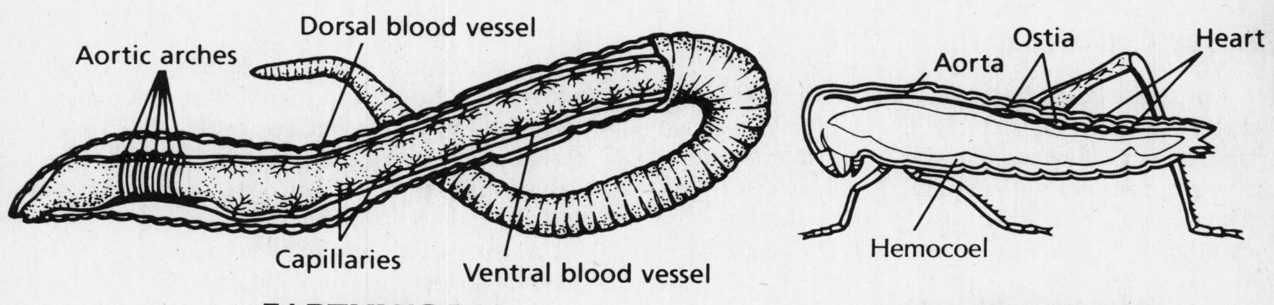

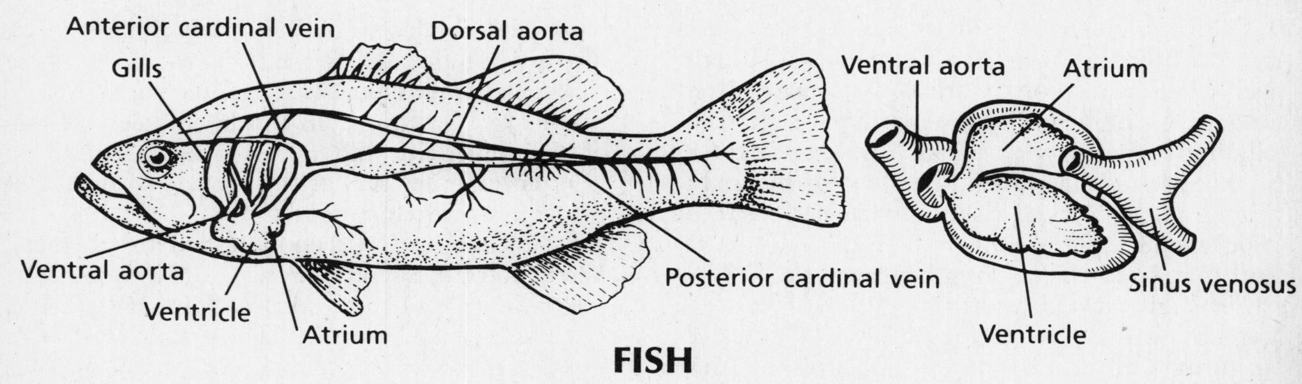

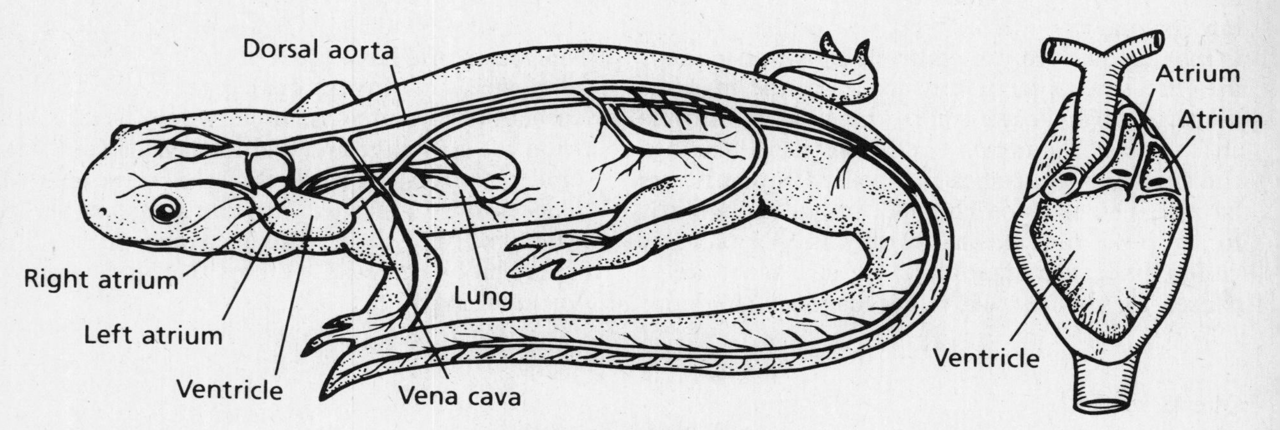

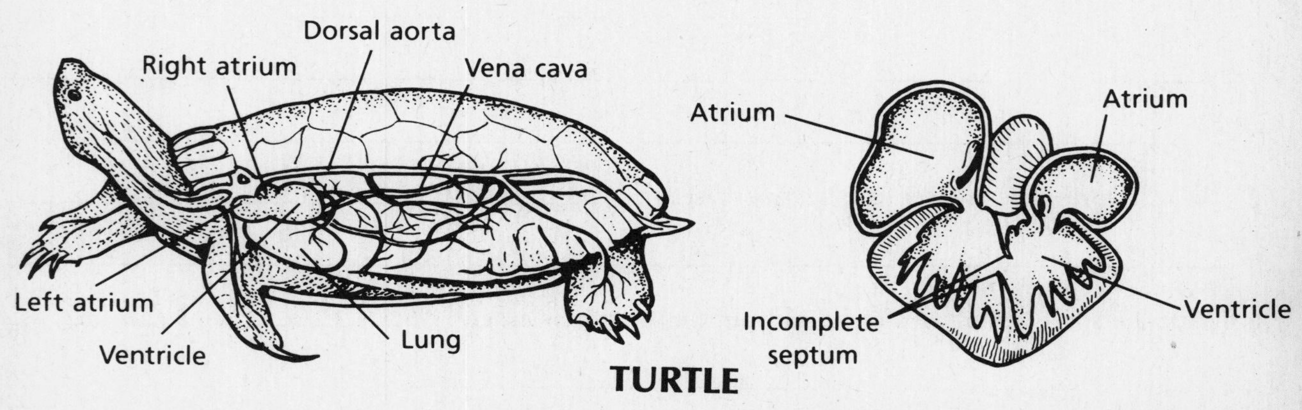

Circulation of the Blood

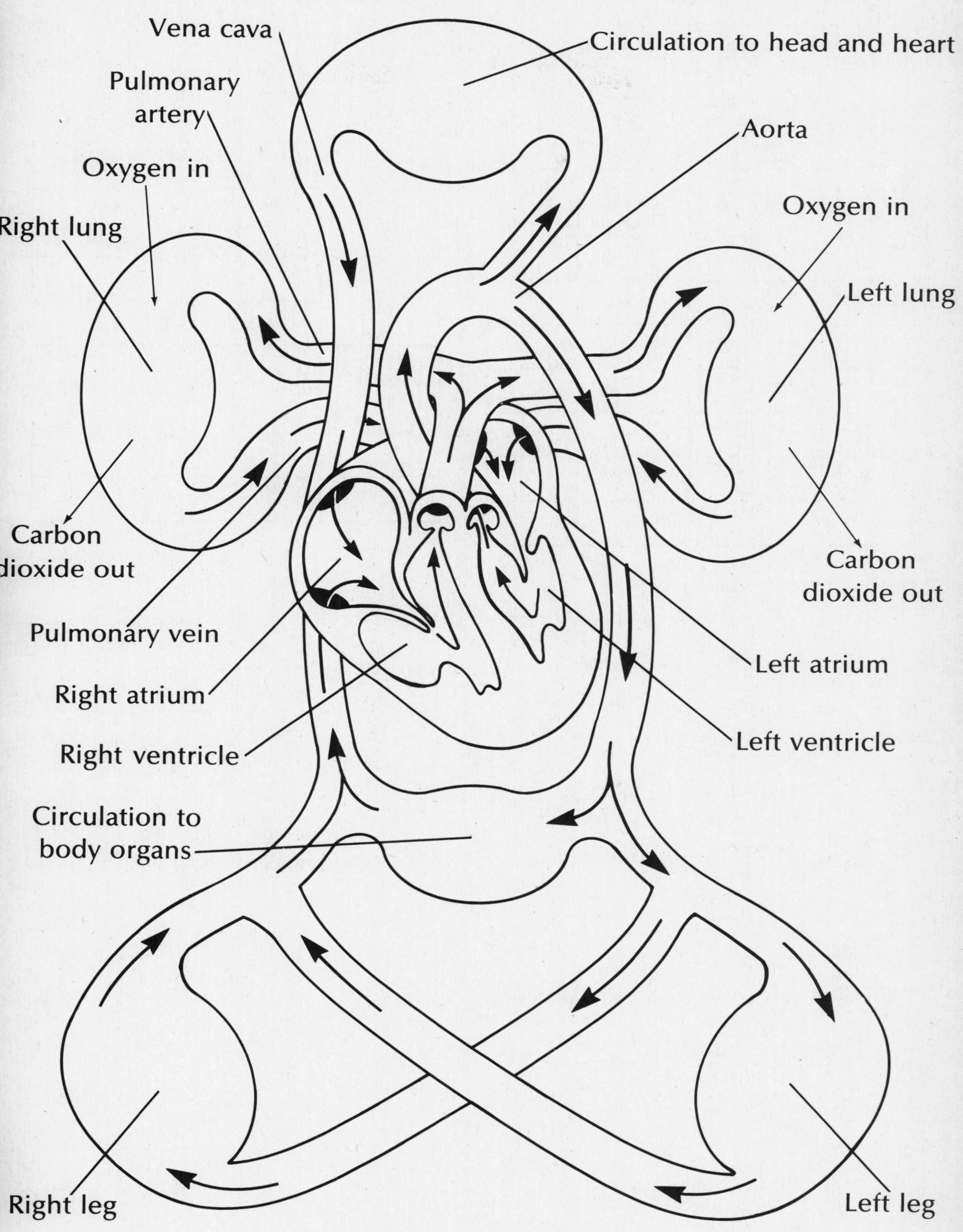

Name ______________________ *Date* ______________

Problem: How does one analyze pulse and heartbeat? (text page 546)

Data and Observations:

TABLE 26-1. PULSE RATES

Trial	Wrist	Neck	Running pulse for 15 seconds	Running pulse for 1 minute
1				
2				
3				
4				
5				
Total				
Average				

TABLE 26-2. TIME SEQUENCE DURING NORMAL HEARTBEATS

	Shown on ECG by which letter segments	Time needed to complete event(s)
Atria relaxed		
Ventricles relaxed		
Atria contracted		
Ventricles contracted		

Questions and Conclusion:

1. What is your pulse and what does it exactly agree with? ______________________
2. Explain why you can feel a pulse in your wrist and neck. ______________________
3. Define: (a) systole (b) diastole. ______________________
4. Using the ECG in Figure 26A, determine what line segment corresponds to each of the following normal heartbeat events: (a) atrium systole (b) ventricle systole (c) atrium diastole (d) ventricle diastole. NOTE: Keep in mind that when one set of chambers is contracting, the other is relaxing. ______________________

Conclusion: How does one analyze pulse and heartbeat? ______________________

PLANNING GUIDE	
TEXT	**UNIT 7 Animals** **Chapter 27 Respiration and Excretion** **Investigation 27 How is urine used to help diagnose diseases? p. 580**
TEACHER RESOURCE PACKAGE:	
READING AND STUDY GUIDE	Student Edition, p. 159 Teacher Edition, p. 42
RESOURCE MASTER BOOK	Student Master 27–1. Choking and First Aid, p. 27–2 Student Master 27–2. Air Pollution and Its Effects, p. 27–3 Teaching Master 27–1. Human Respiratory System, p. 27–4 Teaching Master 27–2. Excretory Organs, p. 27–5 Investigation Worksheet, p. 27–6
EVALUATION PROGRAM	Test Masters, p. 105 Alternate Test Masters, p. 195
LABORATORY BIOLOGY: INVESTIGATING LIVING SYSTEMS	65 Lung Capacity, p. 251 66 Urinalysis, p. 255
PROBING LEVELS OF LIFE: A LABORATORY MANUAL	63 Effect of Temperature Changes on Breathing of Fish, p. 163 64 Effect of Exercise on Carbon Dioxide Release in the Human Body, p. 165

Name ______________________ Date ______________

Choking and First Aid

The larynx is a highly specialized organ. Although it acts as a valve for preventing swallowed food and foreign objects from entering the lower respiratory passages, it is specifically designed for voice production. Movement of the cartilages in the larynx causes the size of the opening between the vocal folds, or vocal cords, to change, thereby producing sound.

The mucous membranes of the upper part of the larynx are very sensitive. If a piece of food or any other foreign body comes into contact with this part of the larynx, explosive coughing immediately follows. Although the person may appear to be in danger, the coughing itself is a reflex and indicates that he or she is not choking. If the person grabs the throat and is unable to speak, he or she may indeed be choking. Choking results when an object enters the larynx and muscles of the larynx go into spasms. These spasms cause the vocal cords to become tense. As a result, air cannot enter the trachea, bronchi, or lungs.

A first aid technique that has been proven successful in helping people who are choking is the Heimlich maneuver, developed by Dr. Henry J. Heimlich. This technique is effective if the choking person is still conscious and able to sit or stand. If a person suspected of choking cannot speak and nods "yes" when asked if he or she is choking, then life-saving measures, such as the Heimlich maneuver, are imperative.

First, the individual administering the Heimlich maneuver stands behind the choking person and wraps his or her arms around the person's waist. Next, a fist is made with one hand. The thumb knuckle of the fisted hand is placed next to the victim's abdomen, slightly above the navel and below the rib cage. Grabbing the fisted hand with the free hand, the person administering aid presses into the choking person's abdomen with a quick upward thrust. The thrust must be repeated several times, if necessary. The abdominal thrusts usually drive air from the lungs with enough force to dislodge the foreign object. Improper techniques include squeezing the chest or slapping the back. Squeezing the chest may result in broken ribs, and slapping the back may cause the foreign object to become lodged more tightly.

Questions:

1. A member of your family just took a swallow of milk. He or she begins coughing violently. Should you administer any first aid procedure? Why? ______________________

____

2. You are eating at a restaurant. A man at the next table quickly stands up and with a panicked expression begins to grab his throat. What should you do? ______________________

____

3. Do you think it is important for everyone to know how to perform the Heimlich maneuver? Why? ______________________

FIGURE 27–1. Heimlich maneuver

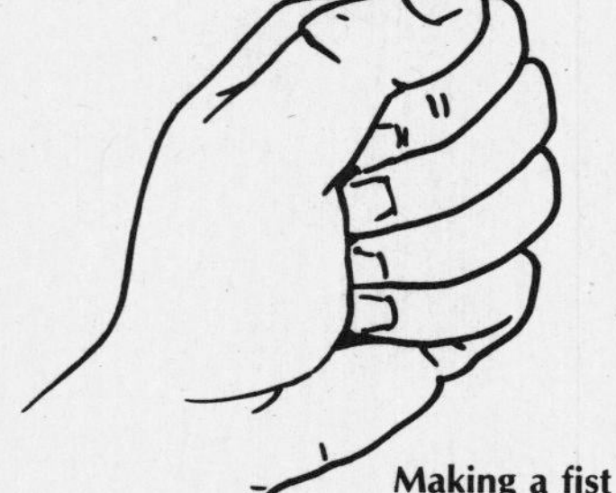

Making a fist

a

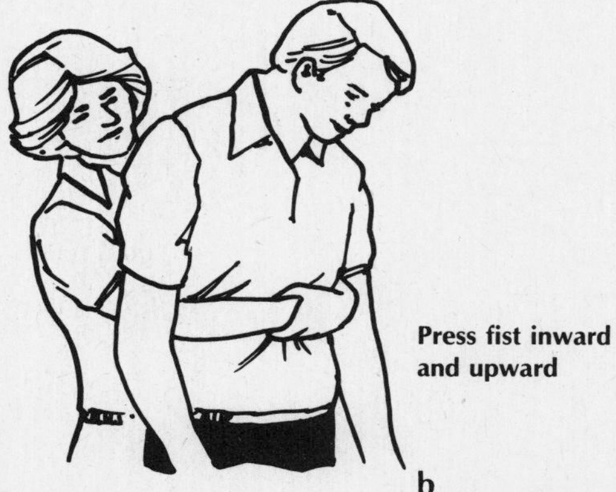

b

Name ______________________ Date ______________

Air Pollution and Its Effects

People who live in large cities are highly aware of air pollution. The blue or brown haze that hangs in the air and is referred to as smog irritates the mucous membranes and respiratory system. The term smog was coined by combining two words, "smoke" and "fog." Smog is a byproduct of combustible substances. The substances involved in smog formation include fossil fuels, such as coal, oil, natural gas, and gasoline.

There are two basic types of smog—reducing smog and photochemical smog. Reducing smog is formed when fossil fuels with high sulfur content are burned. The principal pollutant given off by the burning of fossil fuels is sulfur dioxide (SO_2). In the presence of oxygen, SO_2 is converted to SO_3. Thus, SO_2 has a reducing effect. When SO_3 combines with water droplets in the air, sulfuric acid (H_2SO_4) is produced. Sulfuric acid is a chief ingredient in acid rain. Acid rain not only damages buildings and plant life, but it is also harmful to lung tissues. Other pollutants resulting from the burning of fossil fuels include soot and ash.

Photochemical smog differs from reducing smog in that photochemical smog does not contain large amounts of sulfur. Photochemical smog requires sunlight to catalyze its formation.

Photochemical smog is very common in cities where there are numerous automobiles. When automobiles burn gasoline, atmospheric nitric oxide (NO) increases. NO is then oxidized in the presence of oxygen, forming nitrogen dioxide (NO_2), a brown gas that absorbs ultraviolet (UV) radiation. Absorption of UV radiation causes NO_2 to split into NO and atomic oxygen ($O^{\cdot}$). Atomic oxygen combines with oxygen (O_2) to form ozone (O_3). Incompletely burned hydrocarbons (HC) from automobile exhaust react with ozone to form aldehydes and peroxyacylnitrates, or PAN.

The various components of photochemical smog, PAN, and ozone are toxic to plants. Plants that are exposed to these substances form yellow spots, or mottling, on their leaves. Mottling damages many leafy crops, including spinach and grapes. Mottling also causes trees to drop their leaves. In addition, ozone attacks the chloroplasts and thereby destroys the photosynthetic capabilities of the plant.

Smog seriously affects humans and animals. Although aldehydes, PAN, and other components of photochemical smog irritate the respiratory system, ozone is perhaps the real villain. It is 10 times more toxic than both PAN and nitrogen oxides. Ozone's main target is the lungs. The main effects that ozone has on the lungs can be both acute and chronic. Acute, or immediate, effects result from breathing high levels of ozone for a short period of time. Chronic, or long-term, effects result from breathing low levels of ozone for a prolonged period.

With acute effects, the lungs become inflamed and the alveoli, air spaces within the lungs, partially fill with water. Water in the alveoli decreases the efficiency of the lungs by interfering with the exchange of gases. The other acute effect of ozone is inhibition of the normal breathing reflex. Breathing becomes shallow and the volume of oxygen taken in is reduced.

The most significant change in the lungs due to chronic exposure is an irreversible decrease in respiratory capacity, known as emphysema. In emphysema, the respiratory tubes, or bronchioles, become fibrous and resist the movement of air into and out of the lungs. The walls of the alveoli begin to break down, which reduces the efficiency of gas exchange. Other long-term effects of breathing ozone are stiffening of the joints and decreased visual acuity. Both of these symptoms are characteristic of the aging process. Thus, the effect of chronic exposure to ozone is the acceleration of physical changes associated with aging.

Questions:

1. In what ways do reducing smog and photochemical smog differ?
2. Is one kind of smog more hazardous to a person's health than the other kind of smog?
3. Many people complain that antipollution devices on cars decrease gas mileage. Do you think this is a valid reason to remove such devices? Why?
4. You and your friends live in a large city. There has been no wind for the last two days. You notice that there is a haze in the air. One of your friends has asthma and asks you to join him in a game of tennis after school. What would you do? Why?

Human Respiratory System

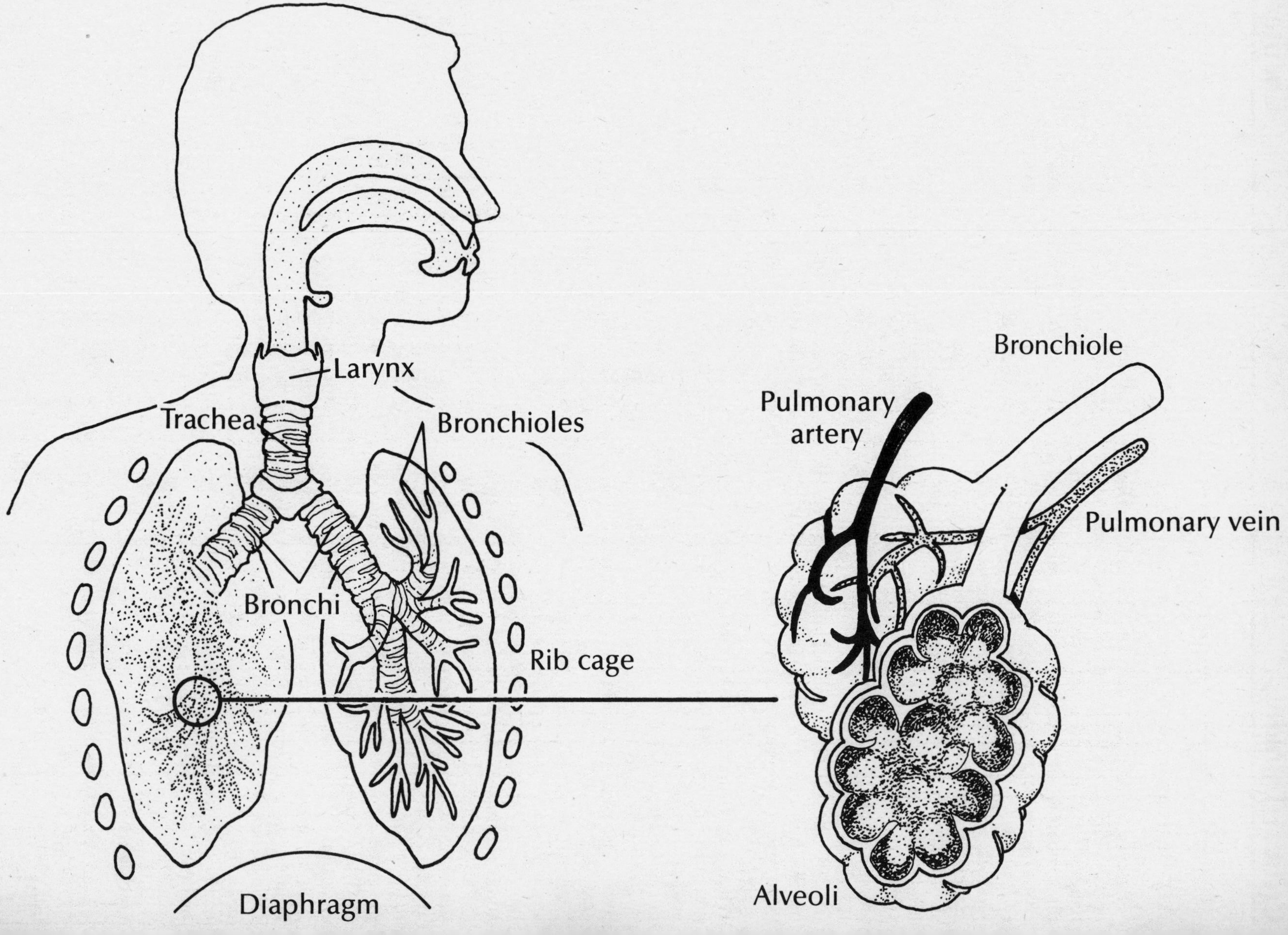

Larynx
Trachea
Bronchioles
Bronchi
Rib cage
Diaphragm
Bronchiole
Pulmonary artery
Pulmonary vein
Alveoli

Excretory Organs

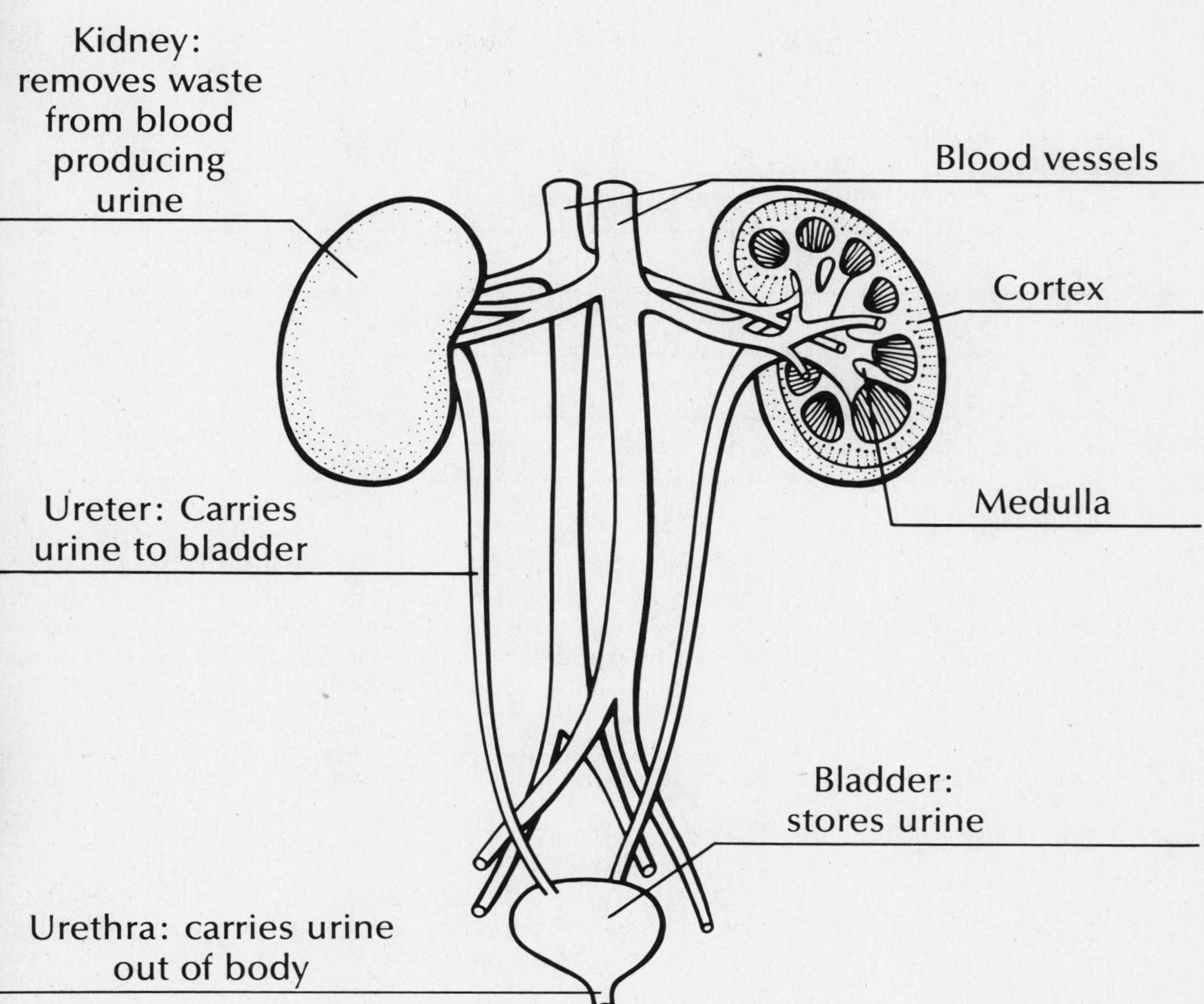

Comparison of Excretory Organs			
The Three Organs of Excretion	**Kidneys**	**Lungs**	**Skin**
excretes water	√	√	√
excretes carbon dioxide		√	
excretes urea	√		
excretes salt	√		√
aids maintenance of body temperature		√	√
produces urine	√		
brings oxygen to blood		√	

Name ______________________ Date ______________

Problem: How is urine used to help diagnose diseases? (text page 580)

Data and Observations:

TABLE 27-2. RESULTS OF URINE SAMPLE TESTS				
Sample	Specific gravity	pH	Acid, base, or neutral	Glucose
Distilled water				
Urine A				
Urine B				
Urine C				

Questions and Conclusion:

1. Normal urine has a specific gravity of 1.010–1.025. A high specific gravity (over 1.025) means that many dissolved chemicals such as salt, glucose, and protein are present in the urine. A low specific gravity (below 1.010) indicates few dissolved chemicals. (a) What was the specific gravity of distilled water? (b) Offer an explanation for why it was so low. (c) Which urine samples were normal for specific gravity? (d) Which urine samples were abnormal for specific gravity?

2. Normal urine has a pH of about 6. (a) What was the pH of distilled water? (b) Which urine samples were normal for pH? (c) Which samples were abnormal for pH? ______________

3. Normal urine has no glucose present. (a) Was glucose present in the distilled water? (b) Which urine samples had glucose? (c) Which urine samples had no glucose?

4. These problems may show in the urine: diabetes mellitus is indicated by glucose and high specific gravity. Diabetes insipidus is indicated by a very low specific gravity. Basic urine indicates possible kidney infection, anemia, or kidney stones. Acid urine indicates fever or high protein diet. List the urine sample(s) that might be associated with each of these diseases or conditions: (a) diabetes insipidus (b) diabetes mellitus (c) fever (d) anemia (e) kidney infection. ______________

Conclusion: How is urine used to help diagnose diseases? ______________

PLANNING GUIDE	
TEXT	**UNIT 7 Animals** **Chapter 28 Chemical Control** **Investigation 28 How does the body control calcium balance? p. 598**
TEACHER RESOURCE PACKAGE:	
READING AND STUDY GUIDE	Student Edition, p. 165 Teacher Edition, p. 44
RESOURCE MASTER BOOK	Student Master 28–1. The Pineal Gland, p. 28–2 Student Master 28–2. Brain Grafts, p. 28–3 Teaching Master 28–1. The Endocrine System, p. 28–4 Investigation Worksheet, p. 28–6, p. 13
EVALUATION PROGRAM	Test Masters, p. 109 Alternate Test Masters, p. 197
LABORATORY BIOLOGY: INVESTIGATING LIVING SYSTEMS	67 Thyroid Gland, p. 259 68 Insect Metamorphosis, p. 263
PROBING LEVELS OF LIFE: A LABORATORY MANUAL	65 Effects of Iodine Compounds on Tadpole Metamorphosis, p. 167

Name ______________________ Date ______________

The Pineal Gland

The pineal gland is a ductless gland located near the center of the brain. It is smaller than an aspirin, and there has been considerable debate over its function.

Much of what researchers know about the pineal gland comes from animal studies. In these studies, the gland was removed from various animals. Removal of the gland caused these animals to lose their seasonal instincts and habits. Birds lost the urge to migrate, and deer grew antlers at the wrong time.

Richard Wurtman, an endocrinologist, believes that the pineal gland acts as a neuroendocrine transducer, a system that converts a nerve-type signal into an endocrine signal. In this system, the hormone melatonin, which is produced in the pineal gland, is affected by the length of daylight.

In nonmammalian animals, such as the frog, the pineal gland senses light and dark. However, in mammals, the presence of light is first detected by the eyes. This information travels from the optic nerve to the spinal cord and from the spinal cord to the pineal gland.

In daylight, the pineal gland converts the amino acid tryptophan into serotonin. Serotonin is stored in the pineal gland. At night, nerve cells that are connected to the pineal gland release neurotransmitters, NAT (N-acetyltransferase) and HIOMT (hydroxyindole-O-methyltransferase). These enzymes increase in concentration and turn serotonin into melatonin, which then flows into the bloodstream. The level of melatonin in the bloodstream is converted into a time signal that gives an animal its sense of the seasons. The animal's ability to recognize seasonal changes helps its survival. Survival may depend on the seasonal habits of migration and reproduction, addition of winter fur, deposition of body fat, or winter hibernation.

In humans, the pineal gland may affect the sleep cycle. Studies show that melatonin makes people drowsy. Some researchers feel that it may influence the onset of puberty. The pineal gland also may be responsible for Seasonal Affective Disorder, or SAD. This disorder is characterized by the winter blues that many people experience from November until spring.

Norman Rosenthal, a psychiatrist at the National Institute of Mental Health, put several SAD sufferers in front of very bright lights twice a day for several hours. These people no longer experienced the winter doldrums, but what caused this change is unknown.

Questions:

1. To what system does the pineal gland belong? Explain. ______________________

____

2. In what way is the pineal gland closely associated with the nervous system? ______________________

____

3. What outside force seems to have a direct effect on pineal gland functions? ______________________

____

4. What does the pineal gland help regulate in animals? ______________________

____

5. What effect might the pineal gland have on humans? ______________________

____

Name ______________________ Date ______________

Brain Grafts

Transplanting brain tissue is not a new idea. Elizabeth Dunn, a researcher at the University of Chicago, successfully grafted tissue into rat brains as early as 1903. Then in the late 1960s, Geoffrey Raisman of Cambridge University identified a phenomenon known as collateral sprouting. By utilizing electron microscopy, he demonstrated that a damaged area of the brain was able to regain some of its functions when nearby neurons sprouted fibers that grew into the damaged area. Fernando Nottebohm at Rockefeller University showed that the cerebral cortices of birds grew and changed each year as they learned new songs. Also, Marian Diamond at the University of California, Berkeley, reported that adult rats living in a stimulating environment showed enlarged, branched nerve cells with new connections.

In 1966, Lars Olson and Åke Seiger of Sweden began transplanting brain tissue from rat fetuses into the irises of adult rats. The iris was a logical choice, since eyes of rats are protrusions of the brain and new tissue growth would not compromise the animal's sight. As the brain tissue began to grow and new fibers extended outward, Olson and Seiger became convinced that transplanted neurons could function like replacement neurons.

The reports of Olson and Seiger brought them together with scientists from the United States. An international collaboration was formed to study the effects of brain grafts on Parkinson's disease. Parkinson's disease is a progressively disabling disorder marked by increased rigidity of the arms and legs, loss of facial expression, and a shaking, shuffling gait. Severely affected patients have difficulty speaking and swallowing. This disease results from a deficiency of dopamine, a chemical that is produced by the brain and enables electrical impulses to cross the gaps between neurons. When specific brain cells are damaged, dopamine production is impaired.

People with Parkinson's disease are somewhat able to control their symptoms by taking L-dopa, a medication that increases dopamine levels in the body. Unfortunately, the medication gradually loses its effectiveness and larger doses are required.

The international team of scientists reproduced symptoms of Parkinson's disease by injecting rats with 6-hydroxydopamine. Later, brain grafts were performed with dopamine-secreting neurons from fetal rats. In all but one of the animals, the grafts succeeded; new fibers sprouted, and dopamine was produced. Most of the symptoms of the disease abated. However, the scientists felt that application of these experiments to humans would be unlikely because the ethics of using human fetal brain tissue to perform the grafts were questionable.

The scientists looked for another source of transplant material—adrenal glands. These tiny glands, located on top of each kidney, produce dopamine. Scientists removed the adrenal glands from one of the rats and then injected the tissue into dopamine-producing regions of the brain. The adrenal tissue elongated, began to resemble nerve fibers, and produced dopamine. However, some of the rats showed little or no improvement.

In 1982, similar adrenal tissue grafts were performed in Sweden on patients with Parkinson's disease. These patients no longer responded to medication and their conditions were deteriorating. After the grafts were performed, improvement was seen. However, the effects did not last very long.

In April, 1987, an article appeared in the *New England Journal of Medicine.* Ignacio Navarro Madrazo, a Mexican neurosurgeon, was performing brain graft surgery with tissue from the adrenal glands. He was more successful due to a slight change in the graft procedure. He implanted adrenal tissue into the ventricle, a brain cavity in which the tissue is bathed in nutritive cerebrospinal fluid. Dopamine from the implant flowed into the fluid-filled ventricle and was transported throughout the brain more efficiently. The value of this new procedure will become clearer after years of studying the patients.

Questions:

1. How did the surgical procedures of Olson and Seiger differ from the procedures of Madrazo?
2. At present, should brain graft surgery be available for all Parkinson's disease patients? Explain.
3. Suppose improvements experienced by Madrazo's patients last for only one year. Is this time long enough to justify the grafts? Why?

The Endocrine System

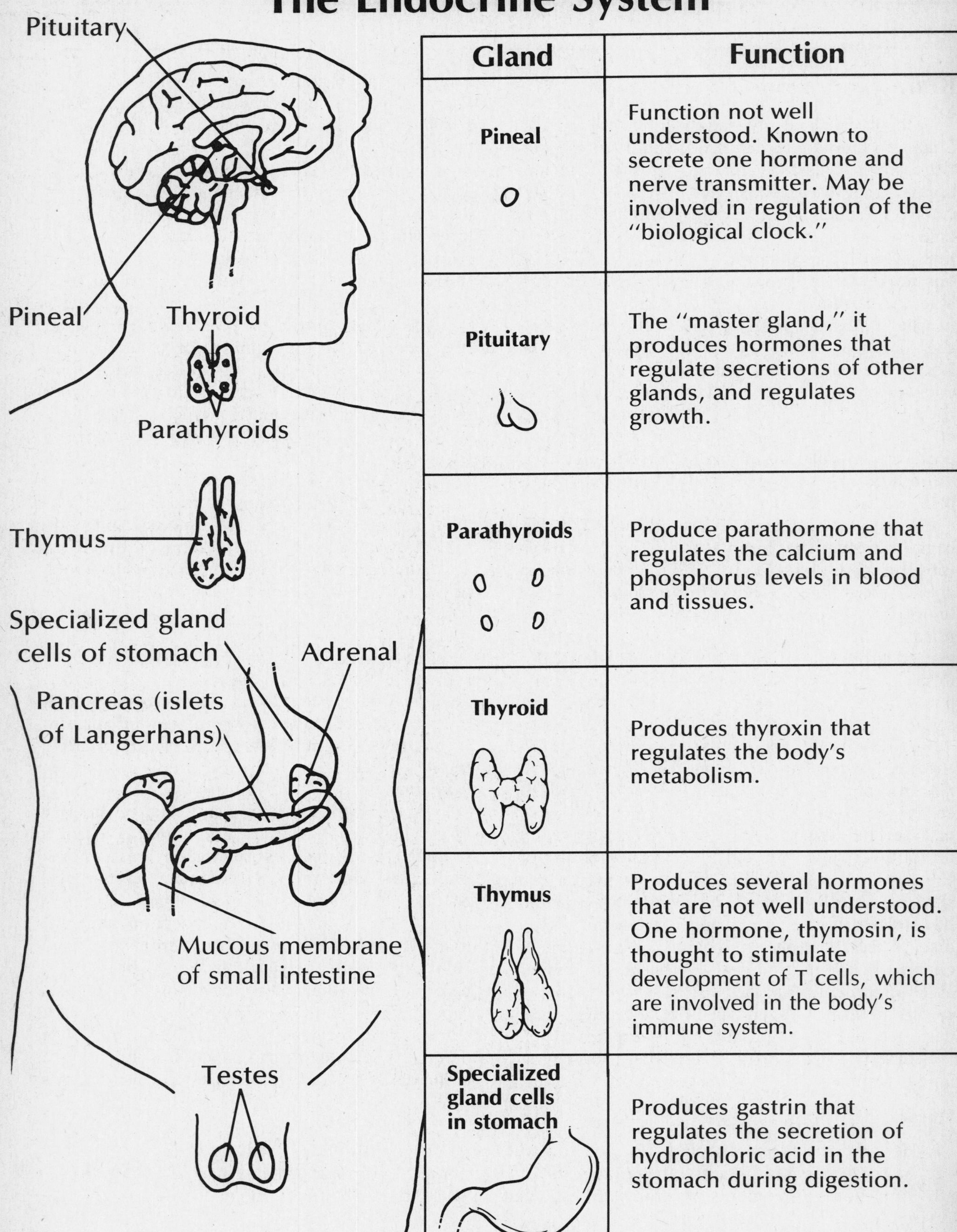

Gland	Function
Pineal	Function not well understood. Known to secrete one hormone and nerve transmitter. May be involved in regulation of the "biological clock."
Pituitary	The "master gland," it produces hormones that regulate secretions of other glands, and regulates growth.
Parathyroids	Produce parathormone that regulates the calcium and phosphorus levels in blood and tissues.
Thyroid	Produces thyroxin that regulates the body's metabolism.
Thymus	Produces several hormones that are not well understood. One hormone, thymosin, is thought to stimulate development of T cells, which are involved in the body's immune system.
Specialized gland cells in stomach	Produces gastrin that regulates the secretion of hydrochloric acid in the stomach during digestion.

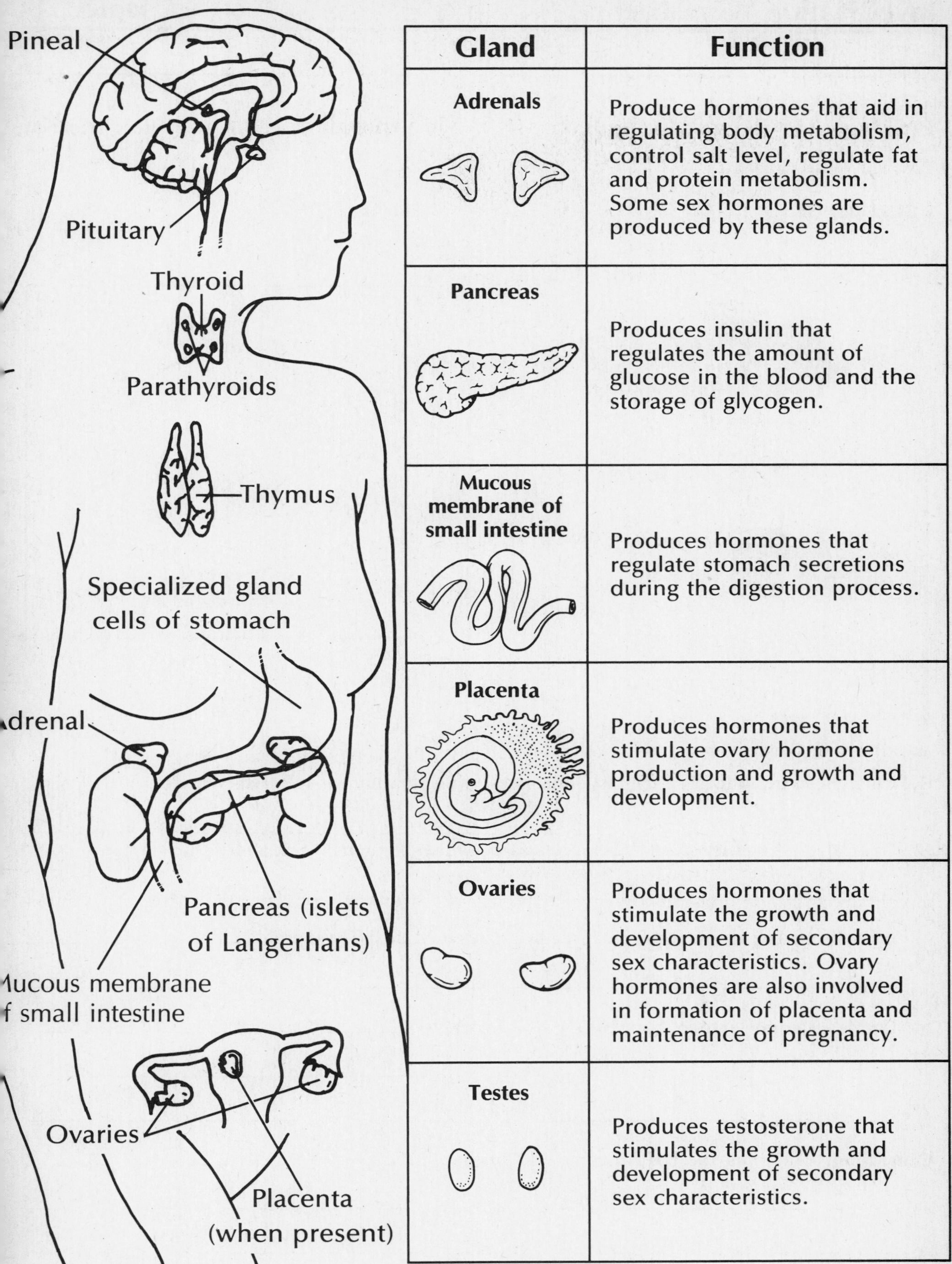

Gland	Function
Adrenals	Produce hormones that aid in regulating body metabolism, control salt level, regulate fat and protein metabolism. Some sex hormones are produced by these glands.
Pancreas	Produces insulin that regulates the amount of glucose in the blood and the storage of glycogen.
Mucous membrane of small intestine	Produces hormones that regulate stomach secretions during the digestion process.
Placenta	Produces hormones that stimulate ovary hormone production and growth and development.
Ovaries	Produces hormones that stimulate the growth and development of secondary sex characteristics. Ovary hormones are also involved in formation of placenta and maintenance of pregnancy.
Testes	Produces testosterone that stimulates the growth and development of secondary sex characteristics.

Name ______________________ *Date* ______________

Problem: How does the body control calcium balance? (text page 598)

Data and Observations:

FIGURE 28–15.

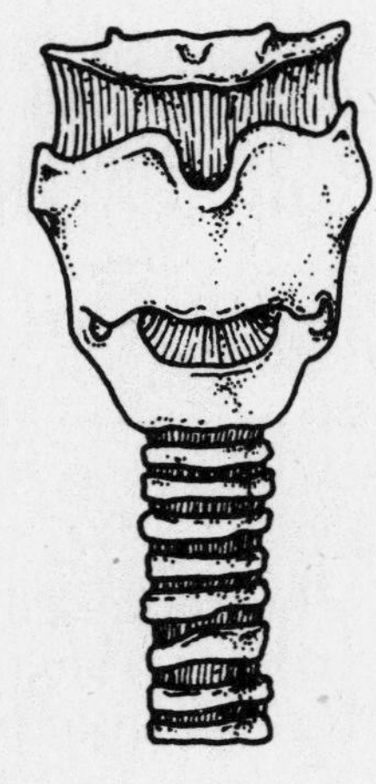

FIGURE 28–16.

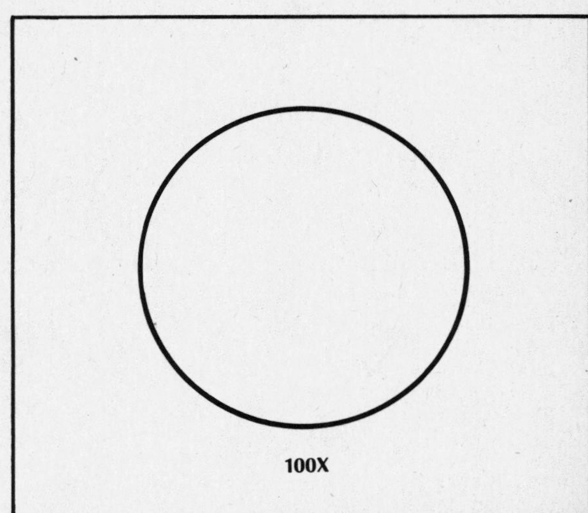

Questions and Conclusion:

1. When the calcium level in the blood increases, which hormone is released? Which is not?

____

2. When the calcium level in the blood decreases, which hormone is released? Which is not?

____

3. Is calcitonin or parathormone produced by the parathyroids? The thyroid? ______________

____

4. Define endocrine system, hormone, and homeostasis. ______________

____

____

Conclusion: How does the body control calcium balance? ______________

____

____

____

PLANNING GUIDE	
TEXT	**UNIT 7 Animals** **Chapter 29 Nervous Control** **Investigation 29 What is the function of certain brain parts? p. 622**
TEACHER RESOURCE PACKAGE:	
READING AND STUDY GUIDE	Student Edition, p. 171 Teacher Edition, p. 45
RESOURCE MASTER BOOK	Student Master 29–1. Comparison of Vertebrate Brains, p. 29–2 Student Master 29–2. Mapping Brain Activity, p. 29–3 Teaching Master 29–1. The Nervous System, p. 29–4 Investigation Worksheet, p. 29–5, pp. 14, 15
EVALUATION PROGRAM	Test Masters, p. 113 Alternate Test Masters, p. 199
LABORATORY BIOLOGY: INVESTIGATING LIVING SYSTEMS	69 The Eye, p. 267 70 Reflex Arc, p. 271
PROBING LEVELS OF LIFE: A LABORATORY MANUAL	66 Effects of Adrenaline on *Daphnia* Heartbeat, p. 169 67 Taste Perception in Humans, p. 171 68 Earthworm Anatomy, p. 173

Name ______________________ Date ______________

Comparison of Vertebrate Brains

The central nervous system is a complex arrangement of communication cells. It is made up of the brain and spinal cord. In all vertebrates, the brain forms from an enlarged bulb of nervous tissue. The spinal cord develops posteriorly to the bulb and continues down the trunk of the animal.

Parts of the brain are developed to various degrees in vertebrates. This development is related to function. In Figure 29–1, one can see how brain development and function are related.

In fish, amphibians, reptiles, and birds, the optic lobes (the vision center), are large. This is because eyesight is important in these types of animals. Although vision is important in mammals, the optic lobes are not as large and are located just below the cerebrum.

The medulla oblongata, located at the base of the brain, is well developed in fish and amphibians. The lateral lobes of this brain section allow aquatic vertebrates to determine water pressure and current changes. The medulla oblongata contains neurons that act as regulatory centers for tail movements that are used for locomotion in the water.

When comparing vertebrate brains, one notices that olfactory lobes become less prominent in mammals and birds as compared to fish, amphibians, or reptiles. In contrast, one also notices that the cerebrum and cerebellum become noticeably larger and more complex in birds and mammals when compared to the same brain structures in fish, amphibians, or reptiles.

The cerebellum, which is responsible for motor coordination, is highly developed in birds and mammals. In both of these groups this brain area becomes folded. This folding allows more brain tissue to be accommodated in a small space.

The cerebral hemisphere (responsible for conscious and mental processes) makes up the largest parts of the avian and mammalian brains. In mammals the development of this section is more complex. This is illustrated by the convolutions, which are not present in the avian brain.

Questions:

Answer the following questions by examining Figure 29–1.

1. In which vertebrate would smell play a more important role, amphibian or mammal? Explain.

 ____

2. How does the cerebellum in a bird differ from the cerebellum in a fish?

 ____

3. How does the cerebrum of a mammal differ from that of a reptile?

 ____

4. Which vertebrate would have a higher ability for association and consciousness? Explain.

 ____

FIGURE 29–1.

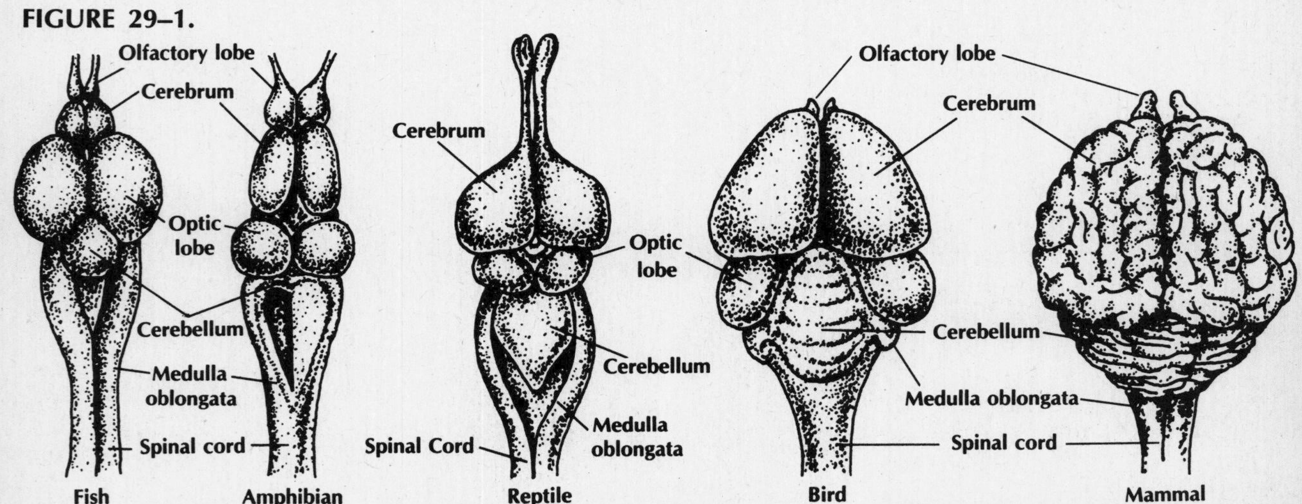

Name ______________________ Date ______________

Mapping Brain Activity

Physicians have various imaging techniques available to them to observe the physical structures of the brain. These techniques include X rays, computerized tomography (CT), magnetic resonance imaging (MRI), and positron emission tomography (PET). Compared to these imaging techniques, a new technique, known as magnetoencephalography (MEG), has the unique ability to indicate which parts of the brain are active, not just the structures of the brain. The difference between the older imaging techniques and MEG is like that between a detailed map of a city and a display that shows which telephones in the city are active at any given time.

Magnetoencephalography was made possible with the invention of a Superconducting Quantum Interference Device, or SQUID. SQUID is the most sensitive magnetometer known. It can detect magnetic fields less than one-billionth as strong as those of Earth. That is the strength of the magnetic fields generated within the brain by the electrical activity of the neurons.

The principles on which SQUID works were discovered by Brian Josephson in 1962. He was studying the current flow through a superconductor. A superconductor is a material that loses all electrical resistance when cooled below a critical temperature. Normally, electrical currents require a voltage, or a "push," in order to flow. But a supercurrent in a superconductor can flow without voltage.

Josephson wondered what would happen if he cut a superconductor in half and then joined the two pieces with a thin layer of electrical insulation. Would the electric current, or electrons, stop at the insulation? Josephson found that although the electrons were capable of passing through the insulation, their flow produced a weak magnetic field. The magnetic field, in turn, increased the insulating properties of the barrier between the two pieces of superconductor. Thus, whenever current was interrupted, Josephson knew that magnetic fields were being produced. From this idea came the SQUID.

Several SQUIDs are grouped together to map the magnetic field of the brain. Remember that weak magnetic fields are produced by the normal functioning of a neuron. During a nervous impulse, ions—electrically charged sodium or potassium atoms—flow along the nerve pathway. Such a flow simulates an electric current and generates a magnetic field. The group of SQUIDs can detect this magnetic field and thus map brain activity.

Until MEG, the only way to measure the brain's electrical activity was to attach electrodes to the skull or directly to the brain. This technique is known as electroencephalography, or EEG. However, the skull distorts the pattern of electrical activity, thus limiting EEG's usefulness. Cutting holes in a patient's skull to install electrodes directly on the brain is painful, risky, and costs $20 000 or more. MEG makes mapping the brain easier because the brain's magnetic fields pass through the skull without distortion, and surgery is not necessary.

Magnetic imaging of the brain with MEG is still considered an experimental technique. MEG is available at a few medical centers for research use only. Researchers have been focusing on treatment of epilepsy with this new technique. Epilepsy is characterized by seizures—uncontrolled movements of the arms and legs, abrupt memory loss, and/or loss of consciousness. For some people, medication is not effective in controlling seizures. Surgery is the only remedy. MEG now offers a way for neurosurgeons to precisely locate damaged neurons. Apart from its value in medical diagnosis, researchers are hopeful that MEG may offer insights into the working of the normal brain, such as how the brain responds to stimuli.

Questions:

1. What is magnetoencephalography, or MEG, based on? ______________________

____

2. What has made MEG possible? ______________________

____

3. What advantages does MEG have over EEG? ______________________

____

The Nervous System

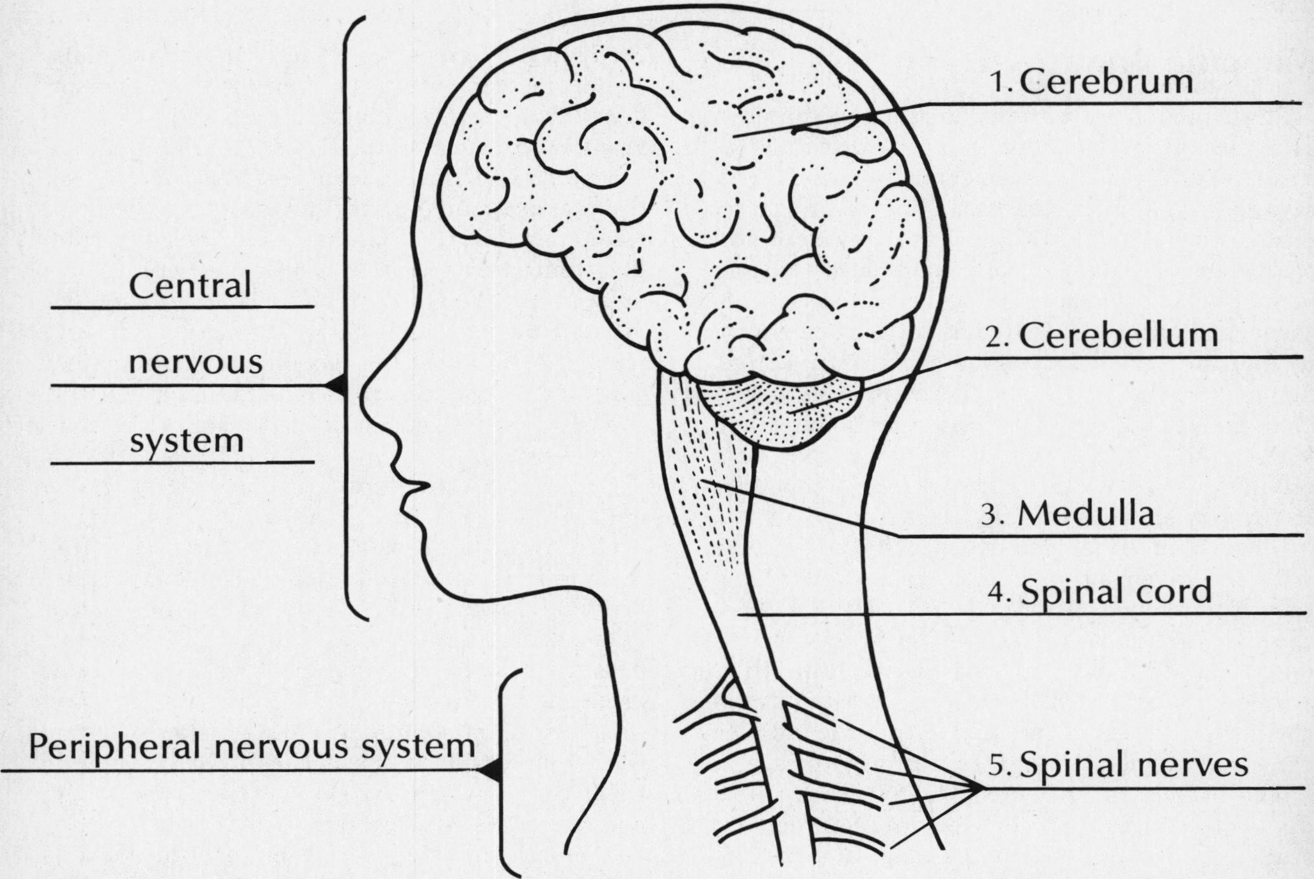

Major Functions
1. **Cerebrum:** largest part of brain; center of intelligence and awareness; controls thought, memory, learning, seeing, hearing, taste, smell, touch, and voluntary movement
2. **Cerebellum:** controls balance and muscular behavior
3. **Medulla:** controls breathing, heartbeat, digestive tract muscles, some gland secretions, coughing, sneezing, swallowing, vomiting
4. **Spinal cord:** receives impulses from sensory neurons and sends impulses to motor neurons; carries impulses to and from the brain
5. **Spinal nerves:** carry impulses between spinal cord and body parts

Name ______________________ *Date* ______________

Problem: What is the function of certain brain parts? (text page 622)

Data and Observations:

TABLE 29-2. BRAIN ANATOMY	
Area	Name
1	
2	
3	
4	
5	
6	
7	
8	
9	
10	
11	
12	

Name ______________________ *Date* ______________

Questions and Conclusion:

1. In relation to the central fissure as well as the left and right cerebrum sides, describe the location of the brain tissue that controls each of the following functions: (a) muscle movement on right side of body (b) muscle movement on left side of body (c) sensations on right side of body (d) sensations on left side of body. ______________________

2. Cite evidence that: (a) most functions are evenly distributed on both sides of the brain (b) certain functions are controlled by only one brain side. ______________________

3. Damage to each of the following areas would probably interfere with what normal functions? (a) right cerebrum side: L-4, 5 (b) right cerebrum side: V-12, 13, 14 (c) left cerebrum side: L-7,8 (d) left cerebrum side: H-8,9 ______________________

Conclusion: What is the function of certain brain parts? ______________________

PLANNING GUIDE	
TEXT	**UNIT 7 Animals** **Chapter 30 Support and Locomotion** **Investigation 30 How does muscle shorten when it contracts? p. 642**
TEACHER RESOURCE PACKAGE:	
READING AND STUDY GUIDE	Student Edition, p. 177 Teacher Edition, p. 47
RESOURCE MASTER BOOK	Student Master 30–1. Bone Development, p. 30–2 Student Master 30–2. Osteoporosis, p. 30–3 Teaching Master 30–1. Bone and Joint Structure, p. 30–4 Investigation Worksheet, p. 30–5, p. 11
EVALUATION PROGRAM	Test Masters, p. 117 Alternate Test Masters, p. 201
LABORATORY BIOLOGY: INVESTIGATING LIVING SYSTEMS	71 Skeletal Muscles, p. 275 72 Measuring Differences in Muscular Activity, p. 281
PROBING LEVELS OF LIFE: A LABORATORY MANUAL	69 Muscle and Bone Tissue, p. 176 70 Locomotion in Earthworms, p. 178 71 Frog Anatomy, p. 180

Name ____________________ Date ____________________

Bone Development

Bones develop from embryonic connective tissue. This tissue is apparent when a fetus is about 5 weeks of age. In a fetus, some of the embryonic connective tissue will ossify, or develop into bone tissue directly. Direct ossification takes place in bones that are needed for protection, such as the flat bones of the skull. In other parts of the fetus, which include most of the skeleton, the embryonic connective tissue is first replaced by cartilage. This process is almost complete when the fetus is about 6 weeks of age. The cartilage later undergoes ossification to be replaced by bone tissue.

Ossification in the cartilage of a long bone starts near the center of what will be the shaft. This area where ossification begins is called the diaphyseal, or primary center of ossification. Bone that originates at a primary center of ossification is called the diaphysis. Bones that form directly from embryonic connective tissue also have a primary center of ossification. Primary centers appear at different times in different bones. However, most primary centers appear when the fetus is 7 to 12 weeks old. Figure 30–1 shows the primary centers of ossification in an 11-week-old fetus. Almost all primary centers are present by birth. At this time, ossification has progressed almost to the ends of the long bones.

At birth or shortly after, another center of ossification may appear at the ends of the long bone. This secondary center of ossification is called the epiphyseal. The bone that originates at a secondary center is called the epiphysis.

Between the diaphysis and the epiphysis is a plate of cartilage known as the growth plate, or the epiphyseal cartilage plate. Continued lengthening of bone tissue takes place at the epiphyseal cartilage plate. This process takes place between puberty and the twenty-fifth year.

The endocrine system exerts an important control over bone growth. The growth hormone from the anterior lobe of the pituitary gland stimulates bone growth at the epiphyseal cartilage plates. Hormones from the gonads (testes and ovaries), on the other hand, bring about cessation of growth by causing the epiphyseal cartilage plate to ossify.

Questions:

1. The illustration below shows a femur of a young child. Identify the diaphysis, the two epiphyses, and the two epiphyseal cartilage plates.
2. Identify the primary tissue that makes up the long bone in a fetus that is 5 weeks, 6 weeks, and 12 weeks old. ____________________

   ____
3. Why is an injury at the epiphyseal cartilage plate serious in a young child? ____________________

   ____

   ____

FIGURE 30–1.

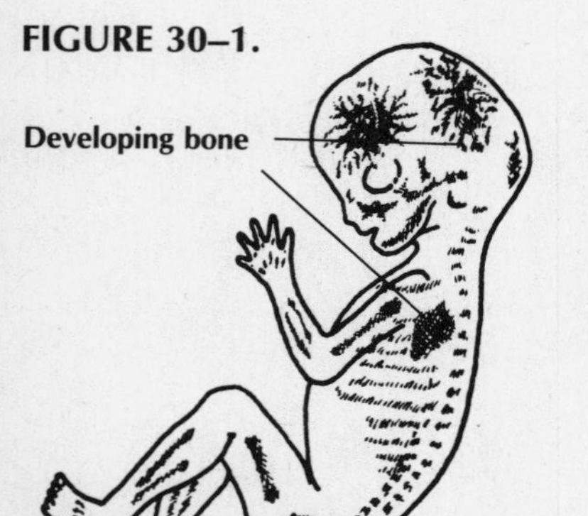

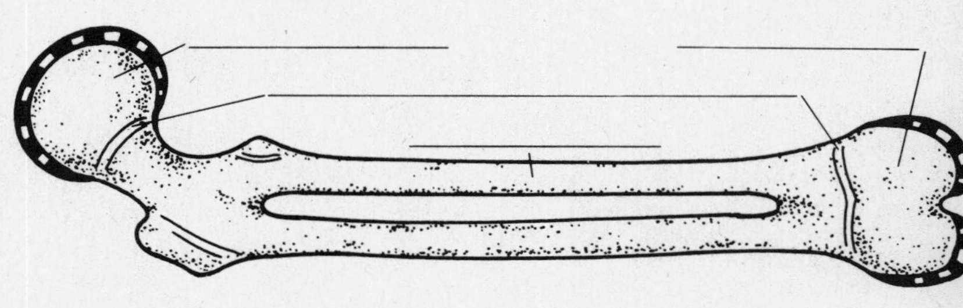

Name ____________________ Date ____________________

Osteoporosis

Osteoporosis is also known as bone thinning. Although bone thinning—caused by a loss of calcium—is a part of the aging process, it is a particular problem in women. Women typically lose 30 percent of their bone mass between the ages of 30 and 70. Men, who reach adulthood with 40 percent more bone mass than women, lose bone mass at a much slower rate. Osteoporosis has been linked to low levels of calcium intake and hormonal changes. (Low levels of estrogen after menopause increase the loss of calcium from bone.) Osteoporosis leaves a person susceptible to compression of the spine, which causes a loss of height, development of a severely bent back, and bone fractures.

Most American women consume less than 600 milligrams of calcium a day. The daily Recommended Dietary Allowance (RDA) for calcium is 800 milligrams a day for men and 1000 milligrams for women. However, a National Institutes of Health consensus panel on osteoporosis recommends that postmenopausal women increase their calcium intake to 1200 to 1500 milligrams of calcium a day. As a result, millions of women are now taking calcium supplements.

There are, however, some concerns about taking calcium supplements. Calcium comes in many forms, such as calcium carbonate, calcium lactate, calcium phosphate, calcium gluconate, and bone meal. Bone meal and other natural forms of calcium (oyster shell and dolomite) should be avoided. All of these forms of calcium may contain lead from their surrounding environments. The Food and Drug Administration (FDA) encourages manufacturers to keep levels of lead below 5 micrograms per gram of supplement. It is also important that pregnant women or women who are breastfeeding not take natural calcium supplements. Lead can easily cross the placenta or be passed to the baby in breast milk.

The amount of elemental calcium is different in the various forms of calcium compounds. For example, calcium carbonate has the highest amount of elemental calcium—40 percent. About 13 percent of calcium lactate is elemental calcium. Only 9 percent of calcium gluconate is elemental calcium.

Taking calcium tablets is not recommended for people who are susceptible to kidney stones. Additional calcium intake may cause kidney stones to form. Therefore, people who have had a history of kidney problems should take calcium supplements only upon the advice of their physicians.

There is also concern about how other substances in food affect calcium absorption. For instance, fiber can bind with calcium, making it less available to the body. On the other hand, not only are milk and dairy products good sources of calcium, but the lactose and vitamin D in these sources enhance calcium absorption. Milk and dairy products also contain manganese. Recent research indicates that manganese may be as essential as calcium for building strong bones. No one knows why, but the calcium in milk—unlike the calcium in supplements—does not interfere with manganese absorption.

In addition to calcium and manganese, regular exercise may help prevent osteoporosis. Studies have shown that regular exercise increases bone mass in early years and retards loss of bone mass in later years. Exercise that puts stress on bones is best. Athletes have denser bones than inactive people, and bones that receive the most stress are the most dense. Joggers, for example, have higher bone density in their legs than in the bones of their upper bodies. On the other hand, astronauts, even though they exercise while on space flights, lose significant amounts of calcium and bone mass. The reason for this loss is that the gravity-free environment of space does not put stress on the bones.

Questions:

1. What steps can be taken to help reduce the chance of developing osteoporosis?
2. What is the best source of calcium? Why?
3. You are looking for a way to increase your calcium intake. You notice that there are many new calcium-fortified foods on the market. One such food that captures your attention is a calcium-fortified, high-fiber cereal. Would you choose this food? Why?
4. Your grandmother takes a calcium supplement (made of calcium carbonate) to help her meet the recommended 1500 milligrams of calcium. She takes the supplement with a meal and a glass of milk. Why is this a sound practice?

Bone and Joint Structure

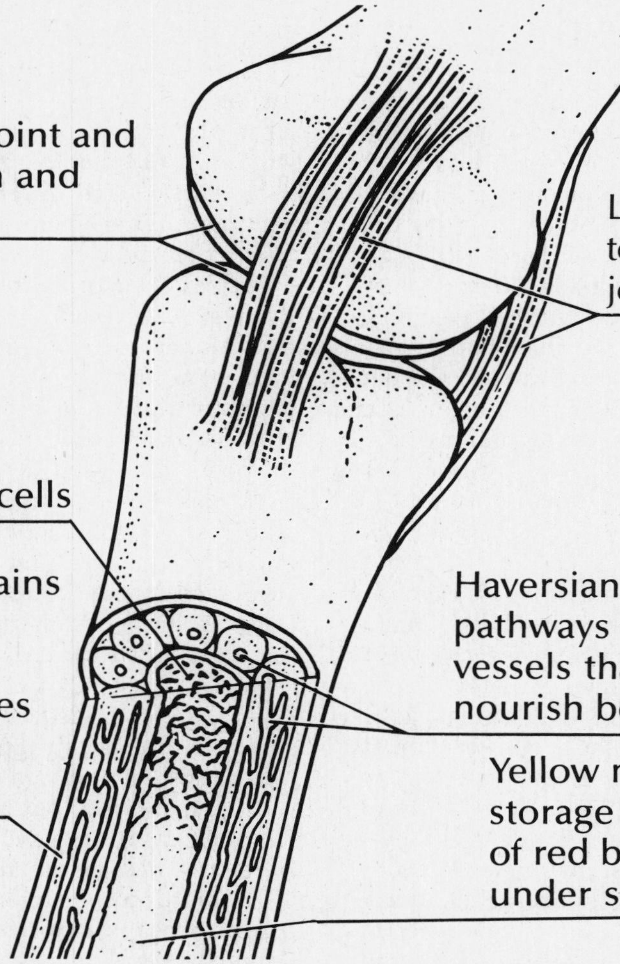

Cartilage: lines joint and provides cushion and lubrication

Ligaments: hold bones together at moveable joints

Red marrow: produces blood cells

Bony layer: contains minerals such as calcium and phosphorus; gives bone its strength and hardness

Haversian canals: pathways for blood vessels that nourish bone cells

Yellow marrow: fat storage and production of red blood cells under some conditions

Common types of joints	Name	Movement	Example
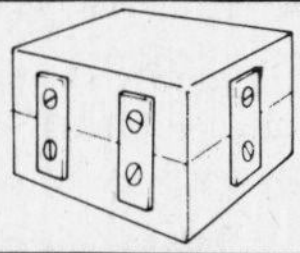	fixed	none	skull
	ball and socket	in all directions	shoulder
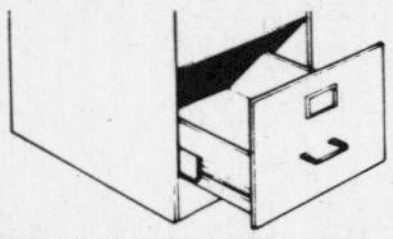	gliding	back and forth side to side	ankle/arch
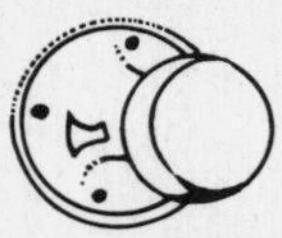	pivot	rotation	neck
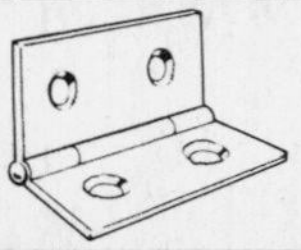	hinge	back and forth only	knee

Name ____________________ Date ____________

Problem: How does muscle shorten when it contracts?

(text page 642)

Data and Observations:

TABLE 30-1. PARTS AND AREAS ON FIGURE 30-20, PART A		
1		
2		
3		
4		
SARCOMERE MEASUREMENTS, PART B		
Length of	Relaxed	Contracted
one thin filament		
one thick filament		
A band		
I band (both together)		
H zone		
one sarcomere		

Name ______________________ Date ______________

Questions and Conclusion:

1. Define the following terms: (a) skeletal muscle (b) muscle fibril (c) sarcomere (d) relaxed muscle (e) contracted muscle. ______________________

2. Describe briefly what provides skeletal muscle with its characteristic striated or banded appearance. ______________________

3. As muscle contracts, how does each of the following change? (a) thick filament length (b) thin filament length (c) sarcomere length (d) A band length (e) I band length (f) H zone length ______________________

4. When a muscle contracts, it shortens in length. (a) Which filaments are responsible for sliding when contraction occurs? (b) Over what do these filaments slide? ______________________

5. Explain how it is possible for a muscle to shorten during contraction when there is no actual change in the length of the thick and thin filaments. (This is called the sliding filament hypothesis.) ______________________

6. Explain how the thin filaments actually slide over the thick filaments. ______________________

Conclusion: How does muscle shorten when it contracts? ______________________

PLANNING GUIDE	
TEXT	**UNIT 8 Environment** **Chapter 31 Behavior** **Investigation 31 How can you study the behavior of an animal? p. 656**
TEACHER RESOURCE PACKAGE:	
READING AND STUDY GUIDE	Student Edition, p. 183 Teacher Edition, p. 48
RESOURCE MASTER BOOK	Student Master 31–1. Memory, p. 31–2 Student Master 31–2. Psychiatric Medicines, p. 31–3 Teaching Master 31–1. Honeybee Communication, p. 31–4 Teaching Master 31–2. Routes of Long-Distance Migrants, p. 31–5 Investigation Worksheet, p. 31–6
EVALUATION PROGRAM	Test Masters, p. 121 Alternate Test Masters, p. 203
LABORATORY BIOLOGY: INVESTIGATING LIVING SYSTEMS	73 Reliability of Your Visual Sense, p. 285 74 Earthworm Behavior, p. 289
PROBING LEVELS OF LIFE: A LABORATORY MANUAL	72 Plant Behaviors, p. 185 73 Response of Multicellular Animals to Light, p. 187

Name ______________________ Date ______________

Memory

Memory is considered to be a major factor in learning and depends on storage of information.

There appear to be two types of information storage—short-term memory storage and long-term memory storage. In short-term memory storage, memory lasts from a few minutes to a few hours. An example of short-term memory is memorizing a telephone number long enough to dial it correctly. Long-term memory storage often requires constant repetition of the learning experience or rehearsal. Therefore, to remember a particular telephone number permanently, you must look it up and dial it many times, or repeat it over and over to yourself. It is thought that once information becomes a part of long-term memory storage, the information, or memory trace, lasts a lifetime.

Just how information becomes a memory is still largely unknown. One of the biggest breakthroughs in this area occurred by accident in the early 1950s. A man known as H. M. had a particularly severe form of epilepsy. H. M.'s doctors decided on a drastic treatment. They removed a small section of his brain, which included most of the hippocampus, the amygdala, and some surrounding cortex. The surgery had the expected result—less severe epileptic seizures. However, H. M. could no longer learn new facts.

H. M.'s form of amnesia demonstrated that there are different types of memory connected with different parts of the brain. Declarative memory involves remembering facts such as names, dates, and places. For example, if you were to remember something and declare, "I know where the keys are," you would be using declarative memory.

The other type of memory is procedural memory. This type of memory is acquired by repetition or conditioning. It includes skills such as riding a bicycle. Procedural memory is not affected by damage to the hippocampus and amygdala as is declarative memory.

Mortimer Mishkin is chief of neuropsychology at the National Institute of Mental Health. He has been conducting elaborate experiments that are providing glimpses of how the brain processes information into declarative memory. What Dr. Mishkin has discovered is that the most important parts of the visual memory system are located in the hippocampus and amygdala. He also found that each structure performs a unique function. Removing the hippocampus destroys an animal's ability to remember how two objects are related spatially.

The amygdala serves to store information with emotional overtones. Removing the amygdala does not alter an animal's performance on spatial relationships.

Mishkin believes that emotions help determine what is stored in long-term memory. He believes that every memory cannot become a part of long-term memory storage; therefore, the brain must be able to discriminate between what must be stored and what does not need to be stored. Many people say that their strongest and clearest memories are connected with very emotional events.

Studies also have been done by Richard F. Thompson at Stanford University to determine the site of procedural memory. Working with rabbits, he has determined that procedural memory is stored in a different part of the brain than declarative memory. His studies show that procedural memory is stored in the cerebellum.

Questions:

1. How do short-term memory and long-term memory storage differ? ______________________________

____

____

2. All memories can be stored as short-term or long-term. However, there are two major kinds of memory associated with different parts of the brain. What are these two kinds of memory?

____

3. A person can remember which houses were on his or her block but cannot remember which houses are next to one another. Which part of this person's brain is associated with the inability to remember the houses' locations? ______________________________

Name ______________________ Date ______________________

Psychiatric Medicines

Over the past 30 years, medications have become common in treating psychological disorders. Problems such as schizophrenia or manic-depression can be long-term and severe. Problems also can be short-term and relatively common, such as mild depression or anxiety.

Most therapists agree that for severe disorders, medication is the only effective treatment. Psychological counseling is also recommended for patients with severe disorders to help them understand the need for the medication. People with manic-depression, a condition marked by drastic mood swings from severe depression to extreme mania, are often reluctant to take their medications. These people often miss the feeling they had while manic, and stopping the medication allows that feeling to return.

Over the last several years, it has become increasingly common to treat mild disorders with medications. The most widely prescribed medicines used in treating psychological disorders are tranquilizers belonging to a family of compounds called benzodiazepines.

Benzodiazepines are effective in treating generalized anxiety disorders and mild depression. However, people who take them often develop a psychological dependence on them. Also, the long-term effects of benzodiazepines are not known. Because of the psychological dependence produced by benzodiazepines, some therapists refuse to use this medication when treating anxiety disorders. These therapists prefer to have their clients talk about what is causing their anxiety and then work on ways to reduce that anxiety. Other therapists prefer to prescribe benzodiazepines for a short period and claim that the benzodiazepines reduce the anxiety level sufficiently so that psychotherapy becomes effective more quickly.

Depression is the most common psychological complaint in the United States. It is estimated that up to 20 percent of the population faces at least one episode of depression. Depression not only occurs in adults, but also appears in adolescents and children.

Antidepressant medications, which alter the action and distribution of brain chemicals in an unknown way, are given to many people who experience depression. Improvement is reported in about 70 percent of those recipients.

There are few studies comparing the effectiveness of psycho- and medicinal therapies. The National Institute of Mental Health is conducting a five-year study contrasting the two forms of therapy for depression. Therapists who do not prescribe antidepressants for mild depression feel that the adverse side effects of the drugs outweigh the benefits. These therapists claim that suicide, sometimes a result of depression, has increased at a shocking rate in recent years in spite of the medications prescribed. These therapists are concerned that drugs only alter moods, perceptions, and the resulting behavior and do not offer a solution to the person's underlying reasons for depression. Other therapists feel that when used with discretion, antidepressants and other medications can be a valuable addition to the various forms of psychotherapy.

Questions:

1. Should severe psychological disorders be treated with medications? Explain.
2. Should mild and common psychological disorders be treated with medications? Explain.
3. A friend of yours has been feeling very depressed. He talked with his family physician. The physician wrote a prescription for an antidepressant. Your friend is not sure that he wants to take the medication. What advice would you give your friend? Why?
4. You sometimes feel stress from trying to keep up with school sports, work, and studies. You would like some help in learning about different ways to relax. Your parents agree that a therapist can help you. At your first visit, the therapist prescribes a form of benzodiazepine. He tells you to take the medication as directed until your next appointment, which is three weeks away. What will you do? Why?

Honeybee Communication

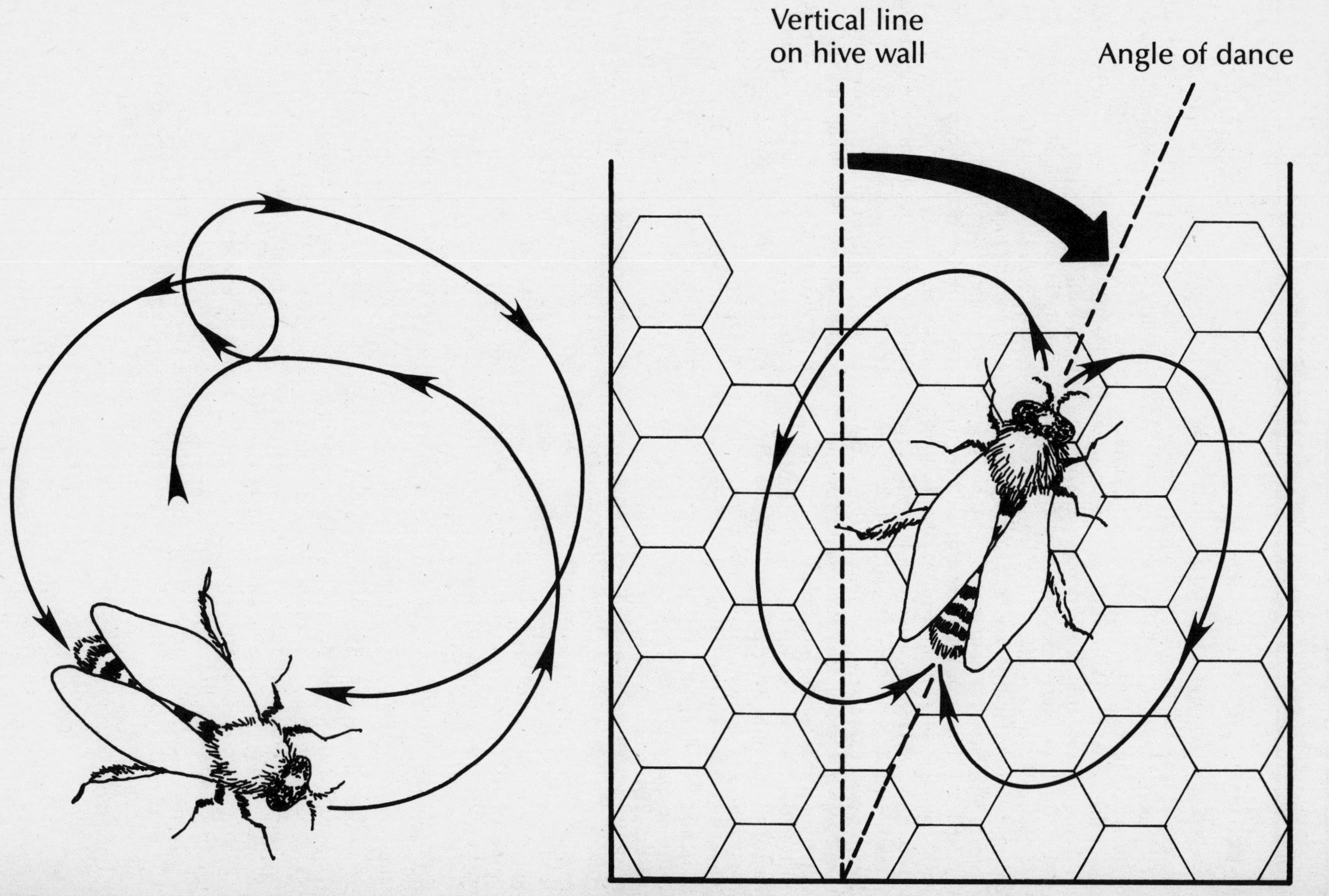

Routes of Long-Distance Migrants

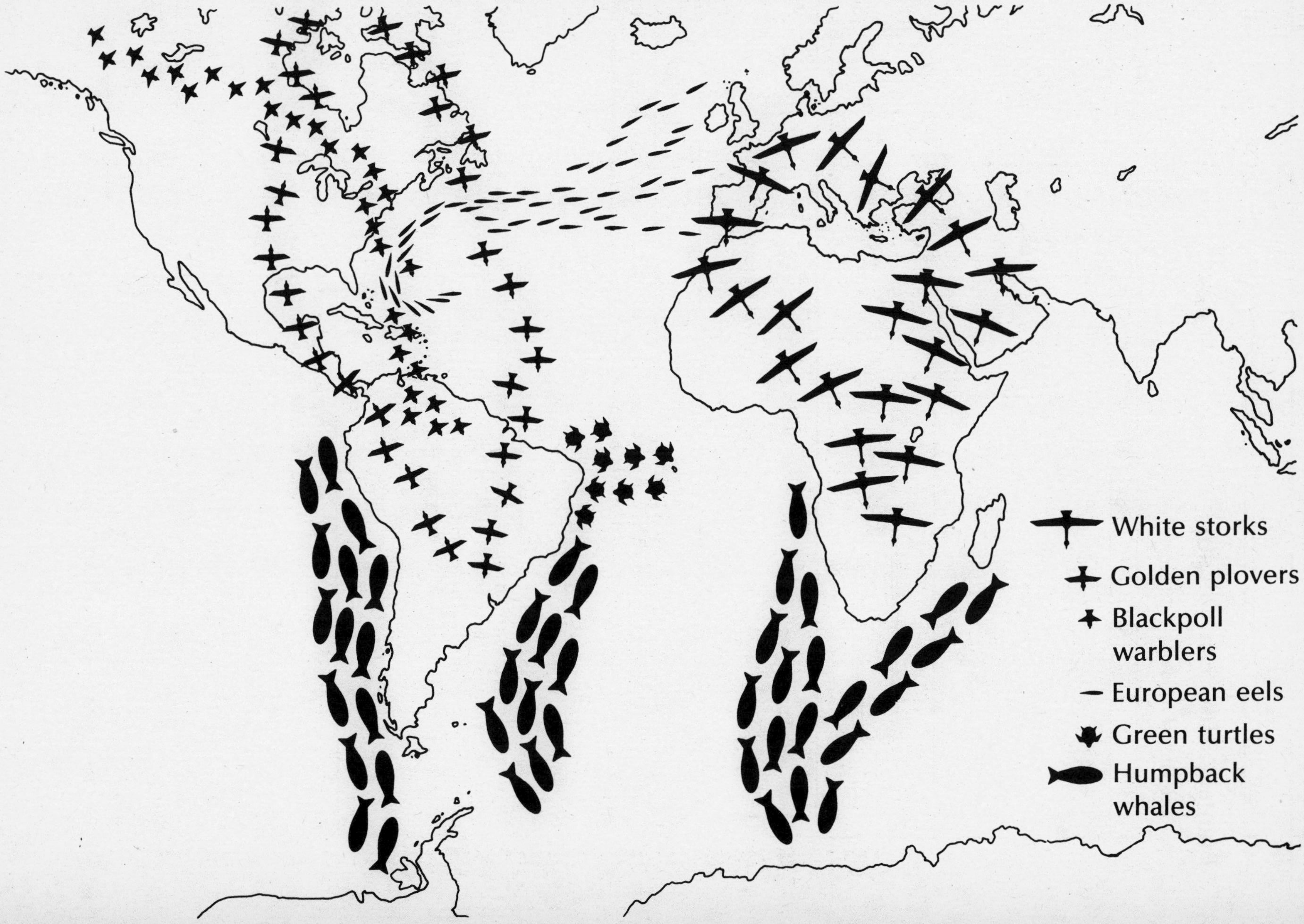

White storks
Golden plovers
Blackpoll warblers
European eels
Green turtles
Humpback whales

Name ______________________ *Date* ______________

Problem: How can you study the behavior of an animal? (text page 656)

Data and Observations:

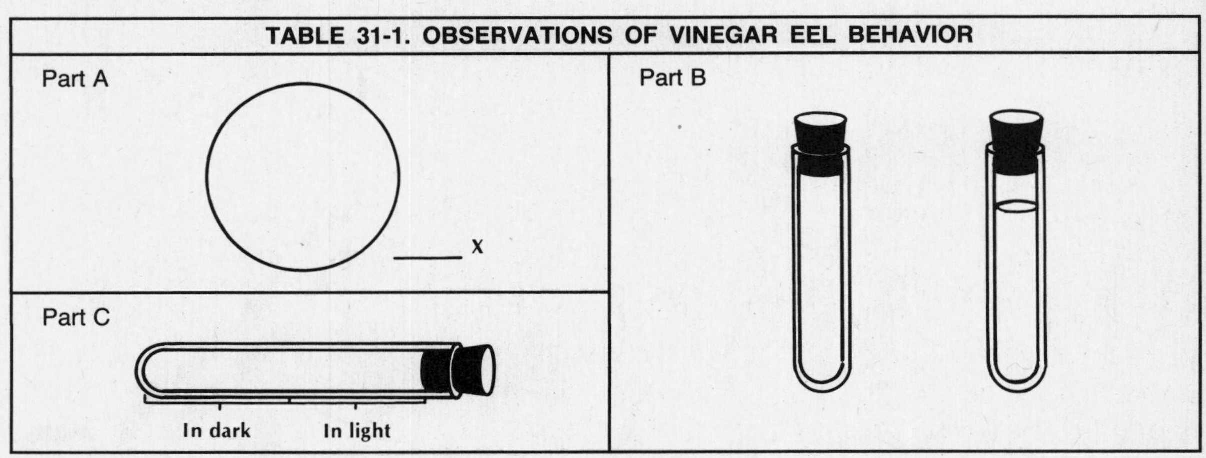

Questions and Conclusion:

1. Define: (a) behavior (b) positively geotropic (c) negatively geotropic (d) positively phototropic (e) negatively phototropic. ______________________

2. Vinegar eels are roundworms. They are members of the phylum Nematoda. (a) List several characteristics of animals in this phylum. (b) Name those characteristics that you observed in vinegar eels. ______________________

3. Answer these questions based on your observations in Part B. (a) Are vinegar eels positively geotropic or negatively geotropic? (b) What evidence supports your answer to 3(a)? (c) What experimental evidence do you have that the animals are responding to gravity as opposed to the air at the top of the tube? (d) How do your observations and conclusions compare to those of your classmates? ______________________

4. Answer these questions based on your observations in Part C. (a) Are vinegar eels positively phototropic, negatively phototropic, or neutral with respect to light? (b) What evidence supports your answer to 4(a)? (c) How do your observations and conclusions compare to those of your classmates? ______________________

5. Based on your answers to questions 3(d) and 4(c), are the experimental results obtained from studies of behavior easily interpreted? Explain. ______________________

Conclusion: How can you study the behavior of an animal?

____

PLANNING GUIDE	
TEXT	**UNIT 8 Environment** **Chapter 32 Population Biology** **Investigation 32 How do population changes alter population pyramids? p. 688**
TEACHER RESOURCE PACKAGE:	
READING AND STUDY GUIDE	Student Edition, p. 189 Teacher Edition, p. 50
RESOURCE MASTER BOOK	Student Master 32–1. Prairie Dogs, p. 32–2 Student Master 32–2. Wolves in Yellowstone National Park, p. 32–3 Teaching Master 32–1. Population Growth, p. 32–4 Investigation Worksheet, p. 32–5, pp. 16, 17
EVALUATION PROGRAM	Test Masters, p. 125 Alternate Test Masters, p. 205
LABORATORY BIOLOGY: INVESTIGATING LIVING SYSTEMS	75 A Yeast Population Study, p. 293 76 Changes in the Survival Rate of U.S. Population, p. 297
PROBING LEVELS OF LIFE: A LABORATORY MANUAL	74 Dandelion and Plantain Populations, p. 191 75 Predation—A Limiting Factor in Population Growth, p. 194 76 Microarthropod Populations in Leaf Litter, p. 197

Name ______________________ Date ______________

Prairie Dogs

Prairie dogs are social animals that live in large groups known as prairie dog towns. The prairie dog towns range in size from about 0.5 hectare (1 hectare = 10 000 m^2) to over 100 hectares. The larger towns are subdivided by topography or vegetation into wards. A ward may be compared to a neighborhood and is usually less than 0.5 hectare.

Within each ward, the prairie dogs are united in a cohesive, cooperative unit called a coterie. The members of a coterie defend their ward against all trespassers. Breeding coteries usually contain only 1 adult male, 3 or 4 adult females, and their young up to one year of age. The breeding season is mid-March to mid-April and the gestation period is from 28 to 36 days. The size of a litter varies from 2 to 8 young, which are nursed by the mother for about 6 weeks. During May and the early part of June, the pups begin to emerge from their burrows for the first time.

Nonbreeding coteries may contain 2 to 30 members. The members may be all males, more males than females, or an equal number of both sexes. No social hierarchy exists, although one male, usually the most aggressive and the strongest defender of the ward, may dominate the rest.

Members of the coterie coöperate with one another. Competition for food and shelter is uncommon in a coterie. Social relations within a coterie are friendly and intimate. These relationships include grooming, play activities, and an identification kiss—a recognition display in which each individual turns its head and opens its mouth to permit contact with the other.

Vocal communication emphasizes the unity of the coterie. Vocal sounds include warning barks, territorial calls, defense barks, fighting snarls, tooth chattering, and fear screams. The sounds mean the same thing to each member of the coterie, and the members react the same to each sound. For example, the warning bark is given at the first sign of intrusion. If the intruder is a predator, all the prairie dogs react to the signal by repeating the bark and running toward their burrow. Many of the burrows are interconnected, so escape routes remain open even if a predator chases a prairie dog down a burrow. In addition to predator defense, prairie dogs within a coterie defend against intrusions by other prairie dogs.

Overpopulation in a coterie may force territorial expansion. In this case, the dominant, or defending, male of the adjacent coterie is driven out. The prairie dogs from the overpopulated coterie may then take over abandoned burrows in the adjacent coterie. Overpopulation may also result in social unrest and the eventual emigration of the yearlings. Adults may leave to escape the demands of the new pups or to seek more abundant food. When prairie dogs relocate, they may dig new burrows at the edge of the town. Or, they may go a few kilometers away to start up new towns.

Black-tailed prairie dogs are found in a 644-kilometer-wide zone that lies east of the Rocky Mountains and extends from southern Saskatchewan to southern Texas. Regarded as a nuisance by some people, the numbers of prairie dogs have been reduced drastically through attempts to eradicate them. Not only have the eradication measures affected the numbers of prairie dogs, they also have indirectly affected the black-footed ferret. The ferret's diet consists mainly of prairie dogs. The prairie dog's burrow provides shelter for the ferret during extreme temperatures and inclement weather. The decline of the prairie dog is partly responsible for endangering the black-footed ferret.

Questions:

1. Why are prairie dogs considered social animals? ______________________
2. What is the relationship between prairie dog towns and wards? ______________________
3. What makes up a ward? ______________________
4. What are some behaviors that express social relationships in a coterie? ______________________

Name ____________________ Date ____________________

Wolves in Yellowstone National Park

For 15 million years wolves roamed the territory that includes Yellowstone National Park. For the last 2 million years *Canis lupus,* the gray wolf, has been there. But in 1915, Yellowstone Park management decided that the wolves were a menace to herds of elk, deer, bighorn sheep, and pronghorn antelope. A formal extermination plan began. Between 1915 and 1926 at least 136 wolves were killed.

Elsewhere, wolves were killed to protect livestock. Today about 1200 wolves survive in Minnesota, and 50 wolves survive in Michigan and Wisconsin. If a disease were to hit these populations, it could be the end of the species.

When a species is on the brink of extinction, the Endangered Species Act says that stabilization of the population is not enough. The federal government must take steps to increase the numbers of the endangered animal or plant. The federal government may soon embark on a plan for returning the wolf to Yellowstone National Park. This project was first introduced in 1983 by the U.S. Fish and Wildlife Service and is now called the Northern Rocky Mountain Wolf Recovery Plan.

Yellowstone, as of 1985, was missing three major elements in its ecosystem—the peregrine falcon, the whooping crane, and the gray wolf. The peregrine falcon recovery program is underway, and the outlook for the whooping crane is promising. All that is needed is the gray wolf.

Reintroducing the wolf could help control the elk population in Yellowstone. Since the 1960s, the elk population has swelled to 25 000. This number of elks is more than the land can support, and every winter hundreds of elks die of starvation and disease. As a natural predator of elks, the wolf would help stabilize the elk population.

Many tourists of Yellowstone National Park also approve of the wolves. A poll conducted by David McNaught of the University of Montana shows that 74 percent of the people who visited Yellowstone in the summer of 1985 agreed that "having wolves in the park would improve the Yellowstone experience." Sixty percent agreed that "if wolves can't return to Yellowstone on their own, then we should put them back ourselves."

Ranchers in areas surrounding Yellowstone are not convinced that reintroducing the wolf is a good idea. They are concerned that the wolves may venture out of Yellowstone and kill cattle and sheep. Ranchers are not reassured by studies of L. David Mech, which show that wolves prey on less than one-fifth of 1 percent of available livestock in any given year. Hunters also are concerned about the reintroduction of the wolf. They feel that they may end up paying for the cost of the recovery program through higher license fees to state game departments. Commodity producers—from oil and gas drillers to logging companies—fear the wolf may force them to curtail activities in key habitat areas.

Compromises are possible. The recovery plan would create three zones. Zone One would be the wolves' primary habitat and would include Yellowstone and four adjacent wilderness areas. Here, the wolf would have priority. In Zone Two, wolves and activities such as grazing and logging, would have equal status. Management decisions could go either way. In Zone Three, ranching and other activities would take priority over wolves. In addition to zones, all wolves released would be fitted with radio collars. The radio collars not only would help biologists study the wolves, but could also help locate those wolves that might continually cause problems for ranchers.

Questions:

1. What are some advantages and disadvantages of reintroducing wolves into Yellowstone National Park?
2. What new information could biologists learn from reintroducing wolves into Yellowstone National Park?
3. Wolves are endangered animals. Do you feel the zone system should be done away with and that wolves should have full protection wherever they may be found? Explain.
4. Yellowstone is a national park and therefore falls under the jurisdiction of the federal government. As a citizen of the United States, you have the right to voice your opinion concerning the reintroduction of wolves into Yellowstone. What is your opinion? To whom might you write asking for support of your viewpoint?

Population Growth

YEAR	POPULATION OF THE UNITED STATES
1790	3 929 214
1800	5 308 483
1810	7 239 881
1820	9 638 453
1830	12 866 020
1840	17 069 453
1850	23 191 876
1860	31 443 321
1870	39 818 449
1880	50 155 783
1890	62 947 714
1900	75 994 575
1910	91 972 266
1920	105 710 620
1930	122 775 046
1940	131 669 275
1950	151 325 798
1960	179 323 175
1970	203 211 926
1980	223 889 000

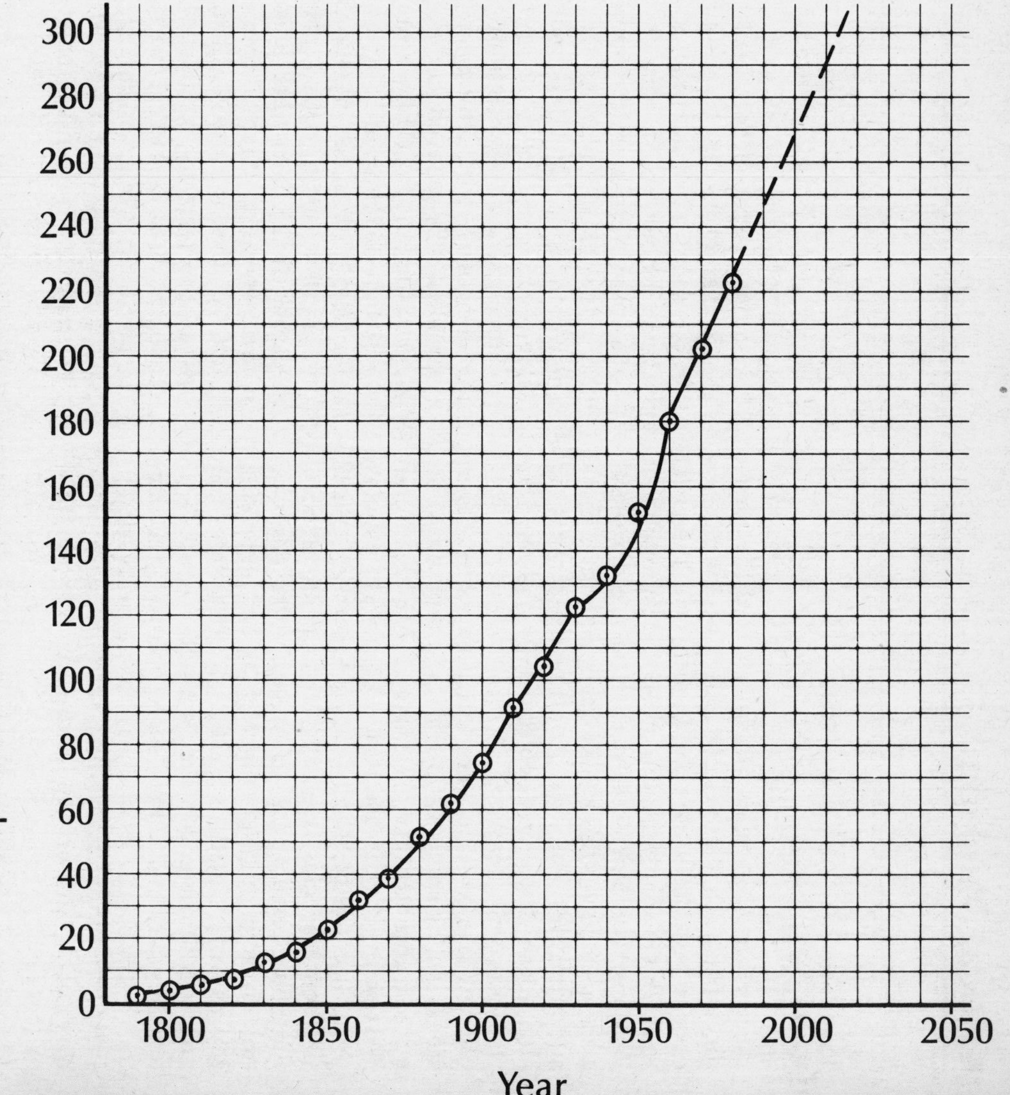

Name ______________________ Date ______________________

Problem: How do population changes alter population pyramids? (text page 688)

Data and Observations:

TABLE 32-4. STATIONARY POPULATIONS	
Question	Answer
(a)	
(b)	
(c)	
(d)	
(e)	
(f)	
(g)	

Questions and Conclusion:

1. Define: (a) population (b) prereproductive group (c) reproductive group (d) postreproductive group (e) stationary population (f) growing population. ______________________

2. The graphs that you have constructed are called population pyramid graphs. Describe and compare the general pyramid shapes for the two population graphs. ______________________

3. Compare the following categories for a stationary population to those of a growing population. (a) percent of prereproductive groups (b) percent of reproductive groups (c) percent of postreproductive groups ______________________

Name ______________________ Date ______________

4. Based on your percentages in question 3 and the general pyramid shapes of question 2, explain what problems or trends may be seen in the future in terms of food supply, housing, waste disposal, and impact on the environment: (a) for a stationary population (b) for a growing population (c) explain your answers to (a) and (b). ______________________

5. The following pyramid graph was prepared for a population. (a) Could it be considered as a stationary, growing, or declining population? (b) How does this population appear to differ from the others studied in regard to the percent of prereproductive groups? ______________________

Conclusion: How do population changes alter population pyramids? ______________________

PLANNING GUIDE	
TEXT	**UNIT 8 Environment** **Chapter 33 The Ecosystem** **Investigation 33 How does one measure soil humus? p. 710**
TEACHER RESOURCE PACKAGE:	
READING AND STUDY GUIDE	Student Edition, p. 195 Teacher Edition, p. 51
RESOURCE MASTER BOOK	Student Master 33–1. Living Together—Amensalism, p. 33–2 Student Master 33–2. The Plight of the Asian Elephant, p. 33–3 Teaching Master 33–1. Food Chains, p. 33–4 Investigation Worksheet, p. 33–5
EVALUATION PROGRAM	Test Masters, p. 129 Alternate Test Masters, p. 207
LABORATORY BIOLOGY: INVESTIGATING LIVING SYSTEMS	77 Testing Water Quality, p. 301 78 Soil Chemistry, p. 305
PROBING LEVELS OF LIFE: A LABORATORY MANUAL	77 Interspecific Relationships between Populations, p. 200 78 Physical Factors of Soil, p. 205 79 Field Studies of a Freshwater Ecosystem, p. 207

Name ____________________ Date ____________________

Living Together—Amensalism

Every plant or animal lives in a community and associates with many species. In certain cases, neither species is affected by the presence of the other. This kind of relationship is called neutralism.

Most people are familiar with the relationship characterized by two species benefiting from each other (mutualism). It is a positive, or helpful, interaction. Lichens, an alga and a fungus, are an example of mutualism. The alga provides food for the lichen, and the fungus provides the moisture.

In some relationships, one species suffers and the other species benefits. This type of interaction can be parasitism or predation. In parasitism, the parasite takes nourishment from its host, and leaves the host in a weakened state. In predation, the predator kills and eats its prey.

Another harmful interaction that many people are not aware of is amensalism. In this interaction, one species produces a chemical that inhibits the other and prevents it from sharing the same resources. The species that produces the substance is not affected by it. Amensalism is more common among plants and probably evolved long ago because the chemical compounds involved seem to be normal metabolic wastes. These chemicals are known as antimetabolites or antibiotics.

The resins in conifers and the latex in milkweeds are two examples of antibiotic compounds. These compounds are effective against most animals that may try to eat the plant. The giant coastal redwoods produce an antibiotic that is found in their bark. The compound inhibits the growth of lichens, mosses, and other plants that could otherwise live on the surface of the bark. This compound may be responsible for the ability of redwood lumber to resist rotting and termite destruction.

The walnut tree shows amensalism, but in an indirect way. The tree produces a nontoxic substance called juglone. It is present in the leaves, fruit, and tissues of the tree. The fruit and leaves fall to the ground and release juglone into the soil. In the soil, the juglone is oxidized to a substance that inhibits the growth of certain plants, such as heaths and broadleaf herbs.

Molds, fungi, and bacteria also produce antibiotics. In particular, soil fungi secrete antibiotics so powerful that only a small amount is needed to inhibit the growth of competing organisms. The products of amensalism also have medicinal purposes; they are used frequently to fight bacterial infections.

Questions:

1. What is amensalism? ____________________

   ____

2. Why is amensalism considered a negative interaction? ____________________

   ____

3. In the desert shrub community, it is not unusual to see soft chaparral growing in the middle of a circular patch devoid of any other plant growth. At the edge of the circle, extending outward, plant life flourishes. How might you explain this phenomenon? What type of interaction does it represent? ____________________

   ____

Name ____________________ Date ____________________

The Plight of the Asian Elephant

Asian elephants are very large animals. They weigh up to 4.5 metric tons and stand as high as 3 meters. Unlike African elephants, in which both males and females have tusks, only male Asian elephants have tusks. The percentage of male elephants with tusks varies from region to region. About 7 percent of the male Asian elephants in Sri Lanka have tusks. However, in southern India about 90 percent of the males have tusks. Killing elephants for their tusks is known as ivory poaching. Although poaching presents a threat to the existence of the Asian elephant, it is not nearly as serious a threat as the rapid and widespread loss of suitable elephant habitat.

At one time, elephants played a major role in the economies of many Asian countries. Today, however, their use is limited to the logging industry in countries such as Burma and Sri Lanka. There, they are used to haul logs in terrain that is too rugged for motorized vehicles. But many tasks that were formerly accomplished by elephants are now handled by machines. Therefore, the demand for the elephant's services is declining rapidly.

Even more of a problem to the elephants is their direct competition with people for land and food. In the past, the elephants had vast areas of forest and grassland. Now, the Asian elephant is making its last stand in many areas.

In Sri Lanka, the human population has doubled to about 16 million in the last 20 years. As a result, many of the forests have been turned into farmland. Many herds of elephants are losing their natural habitat and are forced into the small pockets of jungle that remain. Because there is not enough food in these areas to sustain the elephants, they emerge at night to feed on the surrounding crops of rice and legumes. In southern India as much as 90 percent of a given crop can be eaten and trampled by food-seeking elephants. Threatened with losing their crops and homes, the people frantically defend their villages. In an attempt to frighten away the elephants, bonfires are lit and cans are banged together. Shouts and explosions ring through the air in the attempt to drive back the elephants. As many as 300 people lose their lives each year while defending against the elephants.

Elsewhere in the elephant's range the story is similar. The Indonesian government chose Sumatra as a resettlement area for millions of people from Java, Madura, and Bali. To make room for these people, many forests were cleared. Indonesia has an elephant population of 2800 to 4000. More than one-third of those elephants remain in the area that has been designated for resettlement. As a result, food for the elephants is scarce and they have turned to the crops as a food source.

In the Malaysian state of Sabah the elephant population is 500 to 2000. It is estimated that 200 to 300 of these elephants are bound to lose their habitat to palm-oil plantations and logging, both of which are already in operation.

In Nepal, only a tiny herd of 35 elephants remains. In a desperate search for food, these elephants also raid crops. Just as desperate, the people have enlisted the help of the army to fight off the elephants.

Sanctuaries have been established for the elephants in some Asian countries, but questions remain: how long will it be before the elephant sanctuaries give way to human population growth and development programs? Some sanctuaries now hold more elephants than they can support. Will the elephants in these overcrowded sanctuaries suffer from starvation, become weak, and succumb to disease? Can Asian elephants coexist with the growing human population? The answers to the questions are complex and remain to be seen.

Questions:

1. Who has a greater right to the land, people or elephants? Explain.
2. What, if anything, should be done to lessen the conflict between people and Asian elephants?
3. Should poaching for ivory be curtailed in any way? Why?
4. If no steps are taken to solve the problems between people and elephants, what do you think will happen to the Asian elephant 10 years from now?

Food Chains

FOOD CHAIN RELATIONSHIPS

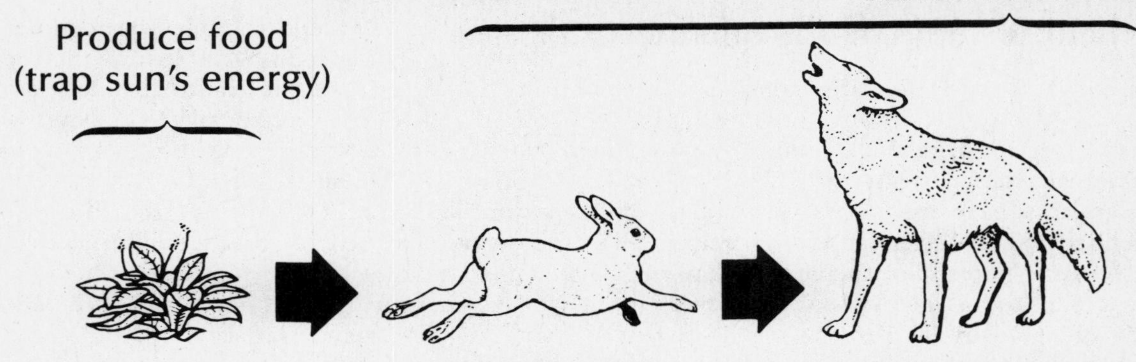

Consume food (ingest food containing stored sun's energy)
Produce food (trap sun's energy)
Plant: producer
Animal (herbivore): primary consumer
Animal (predator): secondary consumer

CONSTRUCTING A FOOD CHAIN AND ENERGY PYRAMID

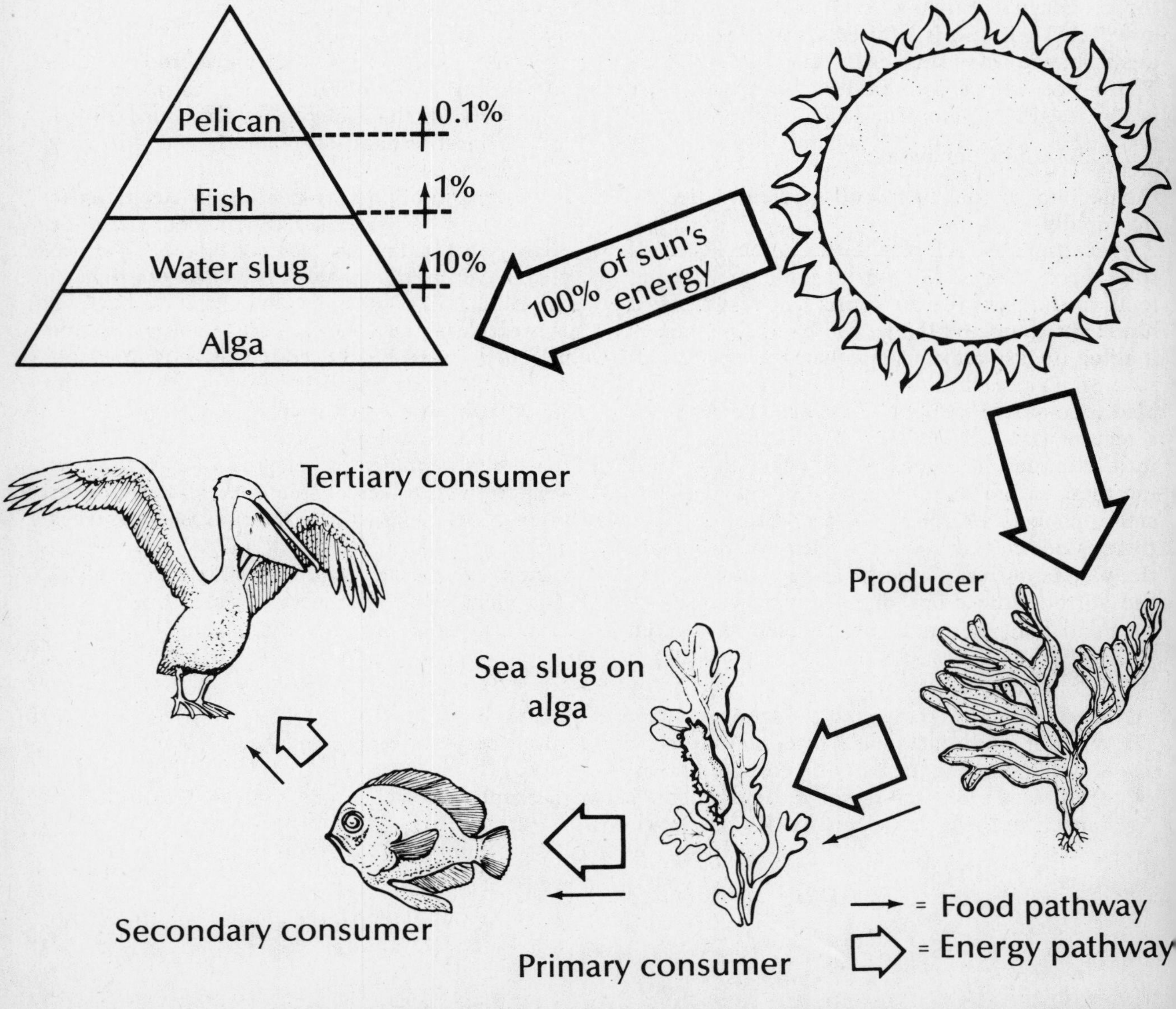

Pelican
Fish
Water slug
Alga
0.1%
1%
10%
100% of sun's energy
Tertiary consumer
Producer
Sea slug on alga
Secondary consumer
Primary consumer
= Food pathway
= Energy pathway

Name ______________________ Date ______________

Problem: How does one measure soil humus? (text page 710)

Data and Observations:

TABLE 33-2. MEASUREMENT OF GAS PRODUCTION		
Soil sample	Type/location of soil sample	Volume of gas formed by humus
A		
B		
C		
D		
E		

Questions and Conclusion:

1. Define: (a) soil (b) topsoil (c) humus. ______________________

2. Hydrogen peroxide (H_2O_2) reacts chemically with humus (mainly carbon) to form oxygen gas. In this investigation: (a) What gas was formed during the reaction? (b) What chemical was the source of this gas? (c) Where was the gas observed or collected? ______________________

3. The amount of gas produced by a soil sample is directly related to the amount of humus contained in it. (a) Which sample produced the most gas? (b) Which sample contained the most humus? (c) Which sample produced the least gas? (d) Which sample contained the least humus? ______________________

Name ______________________ Date ______________

4. (a) Describe the source of humus in soil. (b) Considering your answer to 4(a), explain why samples A and B, even though they were both taken from the same place, had different amounts of humus present. ______________________

5. Water retention and mineral availability to plants is improved by the amount of humus present in soil. (a) Which soil sample would possibly be best for growing plants? (b) Explain. (c) Which soil sample would possibly be worst for growing plants? Explain. ______________________

Conclusion: How does one measure soil humus? ______________________

PLANNING GUIDE	
TEXT	**UNIT 8 Environment** **Chapter 34 Origin and Distribution of Communities** **Investigation 34 How do biomes of North America differ? p. 734**
TEACHER RESOURCE PACKAGE:	
READING AND STUDY GUIDE	Student Edition, p. 201 Teacher Edition, p. 53
RESOURCE MASTER BOOK	Student Master 34–1. Factors Influencing Succession, p. 34–2 Student Master 34–2. The Succession of Mount St. Helens, p. 34–3 Teaching Master 34–1. Mean Annual Precipitation, p. 34–4 Investigation Worksheet, p. 34–5, p. 17
EVALUATION PROGRAM	Test Masters, p. 133 Alternate Test Masters, p. 209
LABORATORY BIOLOGY: INVESTIGATING LIVING SYSTEMS	79 A Soil Community, p. 309 80 Microcommunities, p. 313
PROBING LEVELS OF LIFE: A LABORATORY MANUAL	80 Effect of Temperature on Seed Germination, p. 213 81 Field Study of a Terrestrial Community, p. 215 82 Ecological Succession in a Microenvironment, p. 224

Name ____________________ Date ____________________

Factors Influencing Succession

Succession is characterized by progressive changes in species, structure, and energy flow. It involves a gradual and continuous replacement of species until the community is completely replaced.

Succession in areas that are not inhabited already is called primary succession. Rocks and bare cliffs are common sites of primary succession. Succession that continues from a state in which organisms are already present is called secondary succession. Secondary succession occurs in areas disturbed by humans, animals, or natural forces.

Fire. No matter what stage of succession a community is in, fire always retards succession. However, sometimes fire is vital to maintain a particular biome. For example, prairie fires often inhibit succession in grasslands by destroying any young hardwood trees. The fires burn the exposed parts of the grasses, but the roots survive. Shrubs and very young hardwood trees cannot survive the hot prairie fires. Thus, only the grasses grow and maintain the prairie biome.

Lumbering. Removal of a forest by methods such as clear-cutting returns the land to an earlier stage of succession. Because sunlight and nutrients are now available for the smaller plants, the cut area fills in with herbs, shrubs, and seedlings of trees. The shrub stage passes into the "even-aged pole forest," characterized by trees 10 to 20 centimeters in diameter. Eventually, the area becomes a mature forest again.

Grazing. Grazing by wild or domestic animals can stop succession or even reverse it. The first grasses in a prairie are short. Later, tall-grass species move into the area. American bison stop succession as they graze on the taller grass. Thus, the grazing bison permit the short grass to remain the dominant vegetative life form. Overgrazing by domestic animals also can change a grassland into a desert.

Cultivation. Cultivation turns back succession. If plots of grassland and young forests are turned into farmland but are not carefully managed, erosion by both wind and water can render the land useless. The water and wind can remove the nutrient-rich topsoil and expose the hard clay subsoil. Crops cannot grow in the subsoil, so the land is abandoned. Often, the vegetation natural to the area cannot grow in the subsoil. As a result, new forms of vegetation colonize the area and change the entire flora of the ecosystem.

Succession of a barren area almost always begins with grasses. Next, the low shrubs move into the area, followed by high shrubs. Eventually there is a shrub-tree mixture. The young trees grow and shut out the sunlight from the forest floor. Many of the shrubs are not able to survive and soon disappear from the community. The low-tree community matures into a high-tree forest.

Questions:

1. In terms of succession, why are fires important to certain biomes? ____________________

____

2. How could the succession of a forest be affected by lumbering practices? ____________________

____

3. How can overgrazing reverse the succession of a grassland ecosystem? ____________________

____

Name ______________________ Date ______________

The Succession of Mount St. Helens

On May 18, 1980, Mount St. Helens exploded. The powerful jolt caused an extremely large portion of the mountain's north face to slide away. Hot gases, steam, and gritty ash rocketed out. Trees toppled or were torn from their trunks, leaving ragged stumps. The top layer of soil was stripped away. The hot gases burned everything they contacted.

Millions of flying insects died from the heat and fell from the sky. The blast also killed an estimated 11 million fish, one million birds, 5000 deer, 200 black bears, and 1500 Roosevelt elk. Millions of metric tons of ash smothered the scorched terrain.

Ever since 1980, life has been creeping back into the landscape. In 1983, Congress created the Mount St. Helens National Volcanic Monument. The monument will remain unplanted and will serve as a location where succession can be studied.

Some of the life at Mount St. Helens was not destroyed by the volcanic eruption. Many organisms living in the soil at the time of the blast escaped the hot ash that covered the slopes. Plants that were buried in the snow also survived. Those plants whose roots survived the explosion were some of the first to spring up. The shoots of fireweed and bracken ferns were observed poking through the ash only 10 days after the blast.

Insects were the first animals to come into the area. Daily, insects were carried to Mount St. Helens on wind currents. Spiders spun parachute webs that they used to sail into the very center of the devastated area. The quick return of the insects surprised some ecologists because many thought that plants would have to become well-established first. But, some insects seem to do well without plants. For example, the ground beetle survived high up on the barren mountain, feeding strictly on airborne insects.

In addition to the insects, wind currents also carried new seeds and spores into the area. Rain and its runoff attacked the ash covering, digging gullies where new seeds and spores could sprout. Pocket gophers and earthworms tilled the soil from beneath the ash, giving still more places for the seeds and spores to sprout.

Spirit Lake and many other freshwater lakes were devastated by the blast. Meta Lake was more fortunate. It was covered by a thick layer of ice and snow at the time of the eruption. As a result, most of the aquatic organisms living in the lake survived. Trout and crayfish are two types of animals that have been observed inhabiting the lake.

It did not take long for mammals and birds to migrate to Mount St. Helens. Elk and deer now graze there. Birds feed on insects, seeds of flowers, and grasses. Squirrels and mice forage for food. Tracks of black bears, beavers, and bobcats have been found along a few clear-running streams in which salmon have been observed spawning.

Eight years after the blast, Mount St. Helens is teaming with life. Virtually every species that lived in the region before the eruption has returned. Some of the young evergreens that were wrapped in protective snow on the day of the blast are now over 3 meters tall. Succession is well underway. Mount St. Helens is healing. However, ecologists estimate that it may be several centuries before the area returns to its original state.

Questions:

1. What were the first animals to reappear at Mount St. Helens? ______________
2. Pocket gophers are usually considered more of an enemy to plants than an ally because they eat plants and damage them when burrowing. In the succession of Mount St. Helens, how are the gophers considered helpful?

____

3. What forms of life would you expect to find in Meta Lake besides trout and crayfish?

____

4. It is not unusual for snowfall to last on Mount St. Helens until May. If the volcano had erupted in July instead of May, how might the succession be different than that now observed?

____

Mean Annual Precipitation

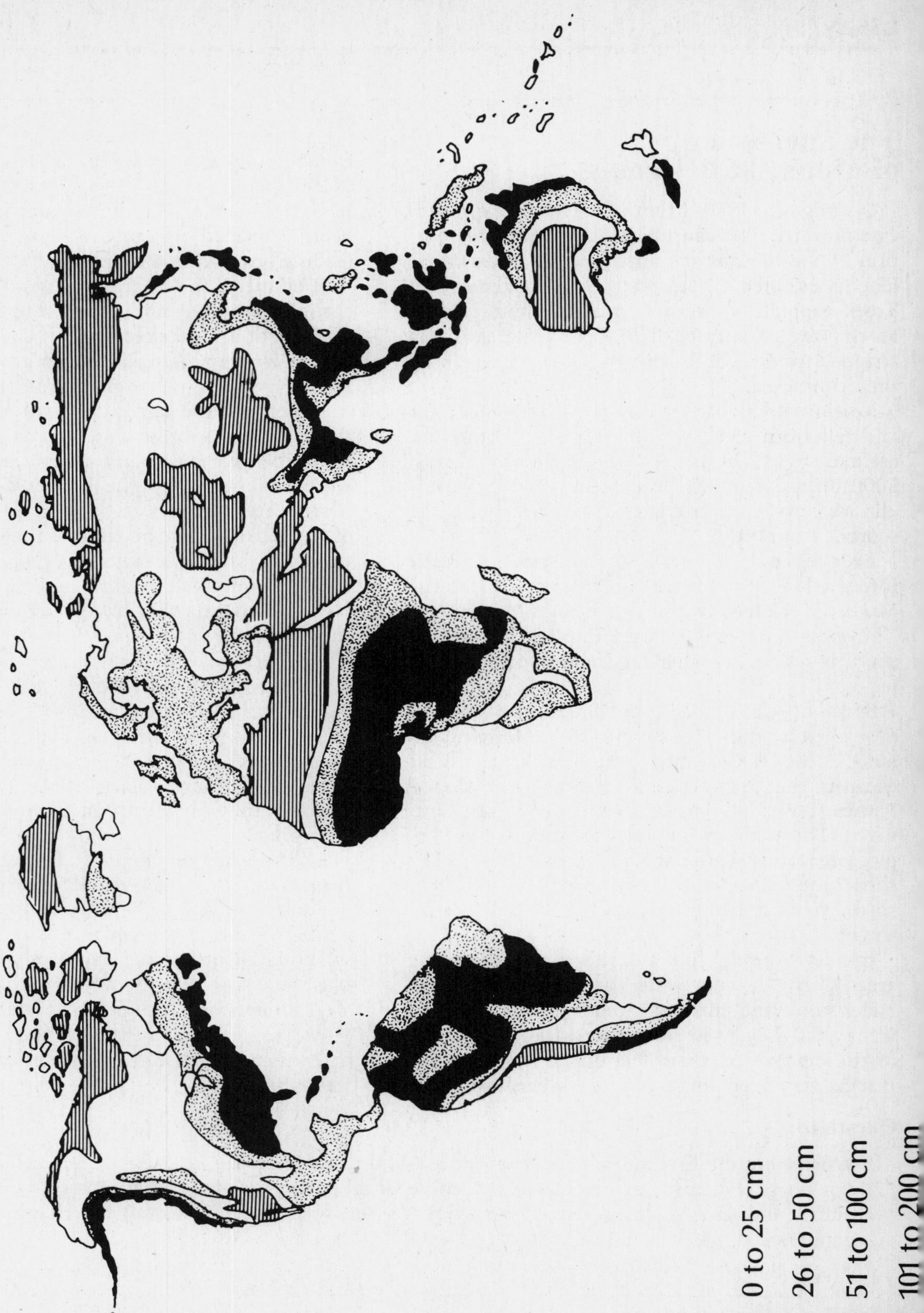

0 to 25 cm
26 to 50 cm
51 to 100 cm
101 to 200 cm

Name ______________________ Date ______________

Problem: How do biomes of North America differ?

(text page 734)

Data and Observations:

TABLE 34-1. KEY TO NORTH AMERICAN BIOMES					
Biome	Color	Average Temperature	Average Precipitation	Major Plant Forms	Major Animal Forms
Tundra					
Taiga					
Temperate forest					
Grassland					
Chaparral					
Desert					
Tropical forest					

Questions and Conclusion:

1. Define: (a) biome (b) climatogram (c) precipitation. ______________________

2. Using your climatograms, describe how the pattern of precipitation differs during the seasons in a (a) chaparral versus a desert (b) grassland versus a chaparral. ______________________

3. Make an estimate as to the length of the growing season for plants in (a) tundra (b) taiga (c) chaparral (d) tropical forest (e) grassland. ______________________

Name ______________________ Date ______________

4. Which biome appears to have the: (a) highest annual average precipitation (b) lowest annual average precipitation (c) highest annual average temperature (d) lowest annual average temperature (e) largest area in North America (f) smallest area in North America? ______________________

5. The map of North America is marked off in degrees of latitude. In general, (a) how do the biomes change in regard to annual precipitation and temperature as one moves farther north in latitude (b) how do these changes affect the type of plant life present? ______________________

6. (a) What biome do you live in? (b) Based on your climatograms and your completed map of North America, describe the average annual precipitation, high and low months of precipitation, average annual temperature, high and low months of temperature, and expected type of vegetation present in the biome where you live. ______________________

Conclusion: How do biomes of North America differ? ______________________

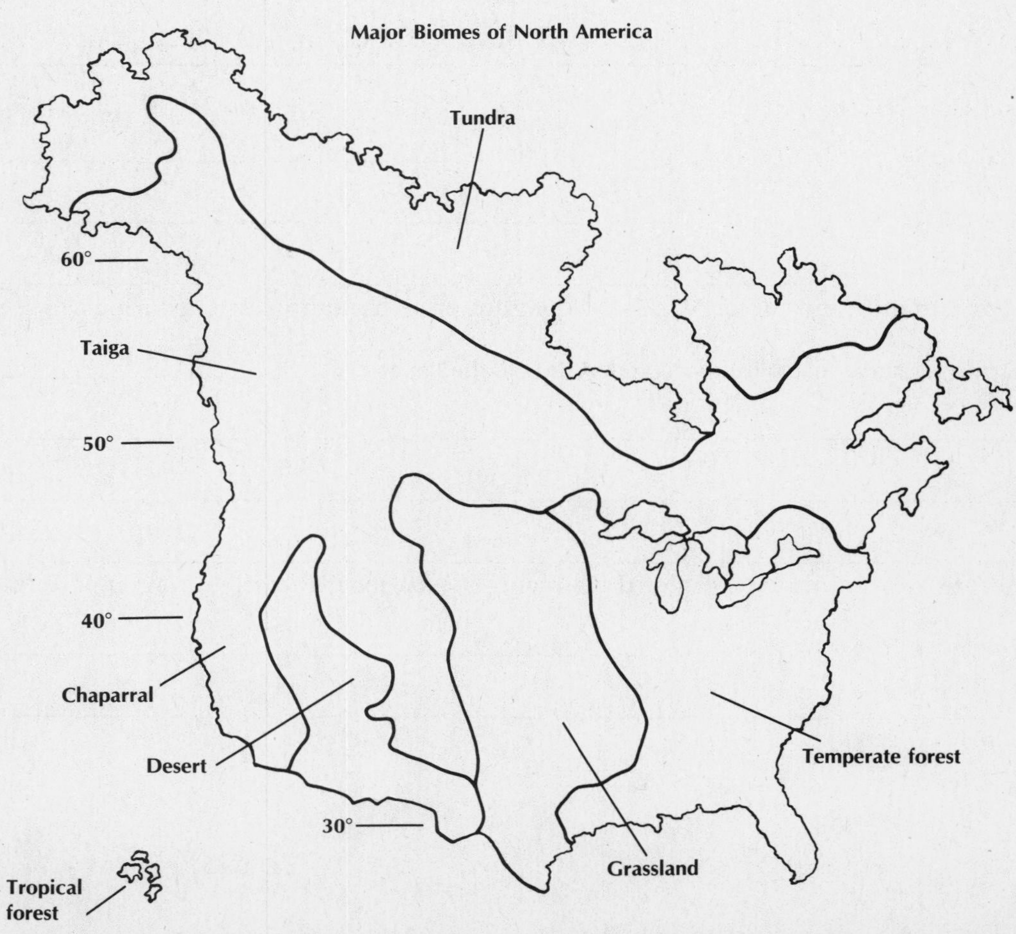

PLANNING GUIDE	
TEXT	**UNIT 8 Environment** **Chapter 35 Humans and the Environment** **Investigation 35 What evidence is there that the greenhouse effect is occurring? p. 750**
TEACHER RESOURCE PACKAGE:	
READING AND STUDY GUIDE	Student Edition, p. 207 Teacher Edition, p. 54
RESOURCE MASTER BOOK	Student Master 35–1. The Effects of DDT, p. 35–2 Student Master 35–2. Should Marine Mammals Be Free? p. 35–3 Teaching Master 35–1. Acid Rain, p. 35–4 Teaching Master 35–2. Major Energy Resources, p. 35–5 Investigation Worksheet, p. 35–6, p. 18
EVALUATION PROGRAM	Test Masters, p. 137 Alternate Test Masters, p. 211
LABORATORY BIOLOGY: INVESTIGATING LIVING SYSTEMS	81 Thermal Pollution, p. 317 82 Acid Rain, p. 321
PROBING LEVELS OF LIFE: A LABORATORY MANUAL	83 Effects of a Pollutant on Protozoan Populations, p. 227 84 Growth of the Human Population in the United States, p. 229

Name ______________________ Date ______________________

The Effects of DDT

Dichloro-diphenyl-trichloroethane, or DDT, was synthesized in 1874 by a German chemist. Its importance, however, was not recognized until 1939. That year Paul Müller, a research chemist in Switzerland, tested various chemicals for their insecticidal properties. He discovered the effectiveness of DDT. In 1941, the Swiss used DDT to successfully combat the Colorado potato beetle, and in 1943, the United States also confirmed DDT's effectiveness. In 1948 Müller received the Nobel Prize for his discovery.

DDT is highly toxic to insects and low in toxicity to mammals, especially humans. During World War II, DDT was used to control mosquitoes. It was sprayed on the walls of tropical houses to control insects and insect-borne diseases such as malaria and yellow fever. It was used to control the cotton boll weevil and to improve agricultural and forestry yields.

The miracle of DDT was short-lived. When exposed to pesticides, such as DDT, insect populations build up an immunity. Because DDT lowered the population of the pests, it also indirectly lowered the populations of insect predators. Immunity and lack of predators allowed the pest population to make a rapid comeback. DDT is a broad-spectrum pesticide that persists in the general environment. Its broad toxicity assured that it would affect many organisms other than insects, such as crabs and fish. Its persistence assured that repeated use would enable DDT to accumulate in the environment. In 1945, these dangers were cited by biologists Clarence Cottam and Elmer Higgins of the U.S. Fish and Wildlife Service. Despite this warning, DDT was still used.

By the 1960s, studies showed that DDT was accumulating in the soils of forests in Maine and New Brunswick. Mountain lakes were contaminated with DDT. Penguins and seals in Antarctica had DDT residues in their bodies. Virtually every organism on Earth contained measurable quantities of DDT.

Since living systems obtain energy, water, and nutrients from their environment, they also may accumulate persistent toxins, such as DDT. The accumulation of DDT within the food chain of a marsh was well documented. The water contained concentrations of DDT residues of less than 0.001 ppm, or parts per million. Plankton contained residues between 0.01 and 0.1 ppm; fish contained a few ppm. Birds, especially carnivorous and scavenging birds, contained 10–100 ppm of DDT residues.

Perhaps the most observable effects of DDT on carnivorous birds were seen in the peregrine falcon, the osprey, and the bald eagle. Ospreys feed on fish. DDT residues in the fish caused the birds to produce soft-shelled eggs that were easily broken in the nest. As a result, there were few or no offspring. Within a few years, the osprey population declined. The peregrine falcon and the bald eagle faced similar fates.

The problems associated with broad-spectrum toxins such as DDT were presented in a book written by Rachel Carson. The book, *Silent Spring,* was published in 1962 and focused attention on the effects of pesticides on the environment. A young lawyer, Victor Yannacone, obtained an injunction against the use of DDT. The case was heard in court and in 1974, the Environmental Protection Agency banned the use of DDT in the United States.

Questions:

1. Why was DDT used so widely at first? ______________________

____

2. What are some problems associated with DDT? ______________________

____

____

3. How did DDT help spur the environmental movement?

____

____

Name ______________________ Date ______________

Should Marine Mammals Be Free?

In films one sees bottlenose dolphins leaping, chasing fish, and riding the bow waves of boats. These dolphins are wild and free. In a number of oceanariums we see a different picture of dolphins. Dolphins jump through hoops and respond to questions in order to obtain a morsel of fish. The question may be raised: Should any marine mammal be kept in captivity?

Activist groups for animal rights say that marine mammals should not be kept in captivity. They believe that keeping marine mammals in a tank is cruel and equivalent to keeping an innocent person in jail. The activists pose three fundamental objections to keeping these creatures captive.

First, the activists charge that removing marine mammals from the wild is endangering local populations of the mammals. The activists claim that capture of marine mammals could put some species in jeopardy. As an example, they cite the killer whale. In the late 1960s and early 1970s, so many female killer whales were captured that the birth rates of the wild killer whale fell. However, the activists do agree that most cetacean species (dolphins, porpoises, whales) are not endangered. They also agree that most pinnipeds (seals, sea lions, walruses) in oceanariums today were born in captivity or were found sick or injured on beaches.

Second, the advocates of animal rights say that treatment of the captive animals is inadequate. They contend that animals kept in tanks die at a younger age. For example, of the 31 beluga whales captured since 1972, only 19 are still alive. Over a 15-year period, one oceanarium collected 31 spinner dolphins. Twenty-nine died in captivity. Two were released.

Third, the activists claim that even if an animal survives, it is made to exist within tanks or pens. They feel that captive marine mammals become lethargic, indifferent, and neurotic and that their health deteriorates. Also, they claim that dolphins become mute and that their brains shrink by as much as 30 percent.

Mammalogists, on the other hand, claim that dolphins do not become mute in captivity. Although dolphins emit sounds less frequently when in captivity, mammalogists think that vocal communication is replaced by visual communication. Dolphins in the wild must communicate vocally because they are often out of the visual range of one another. Also, there is no substantiated evidence that dolphins' brains shrink in captivity. A direct examination of the brain weights of captive and wild dolphins showed no significant difference.

Marine mammals are breeding in captivity. In 1983, one-third of all captive bottlenose dolphins were born in captivity. In 1985 one killer whale was born in captivity. Seals and sea lions breed so well in oceanariums, that caretakers do not know what to do with all the offspring. Mammalogists say that the reproductive rates of captive marine mammals demonstrate good quality care. Unhappy and unhealthy animals do not breed.

The data on mortality of captive marine mammals does not tell the whole story. Most deaths of marine mammals in oceanariums occurred during first attempts at caretaking. Those early losses sharply tip the mortality rates to the negative side. Oceanariums no longer try to keep difficult species, and survival rates are steadily rising for pinnipeds and some cetaceans.

The quality of life for captive marine mammals is debatable. Recent evidence indicates that cetaceans and pinnipeds are far more intelligent than people once suspected. It is disquieting to think that people may be causing marine mammals mental anguish by keeping them captive.

Questions:

1. Should marine mammals be kept for public display? Explain.
2. Should marine mammals be kept for scientific observation? Explain.
3. When should a captive marine mammal be released to its natural habitat? Explain.

Acid Rain

Major Energy Resources

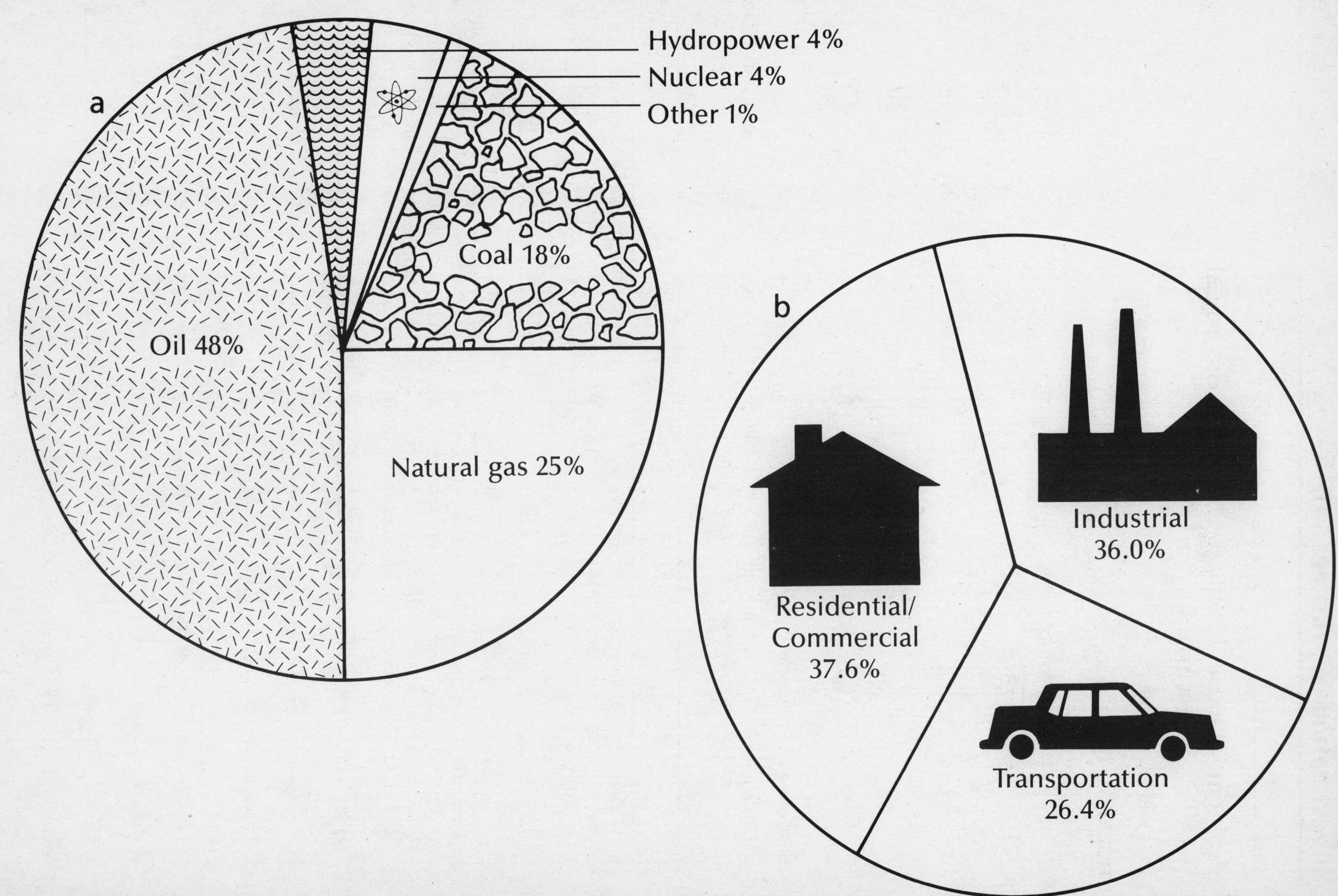

Name ______________________ *Date* ______________

Problem: What evidence is there that the greenhouse effect is occurring? (text page 750)

Data and Observations:

FIGURE 35–11.

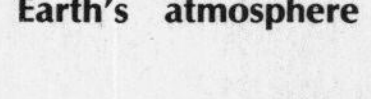

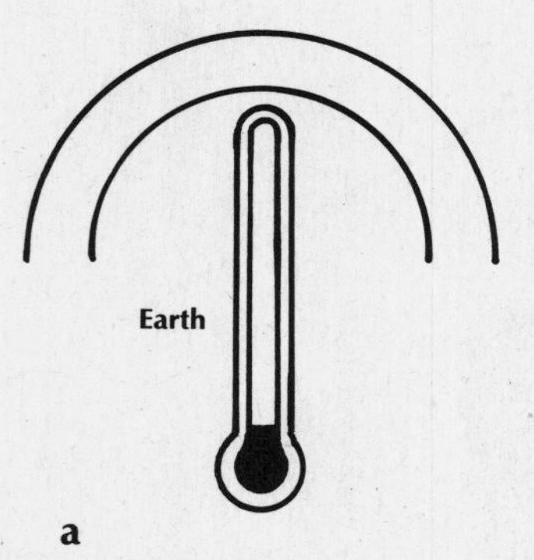

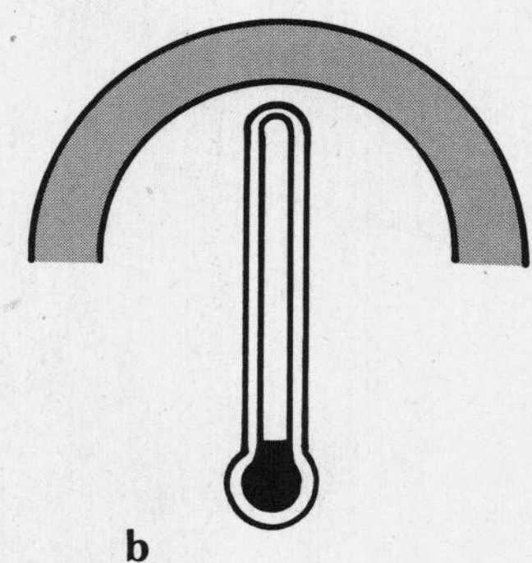

Questions and Conclusion:

1. Explain how: (a) Earth's temperature is affected by the amount of infrared radiation absorbed (b) Earth's temperature is affected by the amount of carbon dioxide present in the atmosphere.

2. (a) Explain how your graphs support your answer to question 1(b). (b) Does the trend seen in years past seem to continue into the year 2000? (c) What is the expected average temperature change by the year 2000? (d) What is the expected change of carbon dioxide in ppm by the year 2000?

3. There are several causes for increased carbon dioxide levels in our atmosphere. One is the burning of fossil fuels. A second cause is the continued destruction of forests for agricultural use. (a) What are fossil fuels? (b) List several ways in which the burning of fossil fuels may be lessened. (c) Explain how destruction of forests can increase the amount of carbon dioxide in the atmosphere. (d) List several ways to reduce the destruction of forests. ______________

4. Predict several outcomes if Earth's average temperature were to rise even a few degrees because of the greenhouse effect. ______________

Conclusion: What evidence is there that the greenhouse effect is occurring? ______________

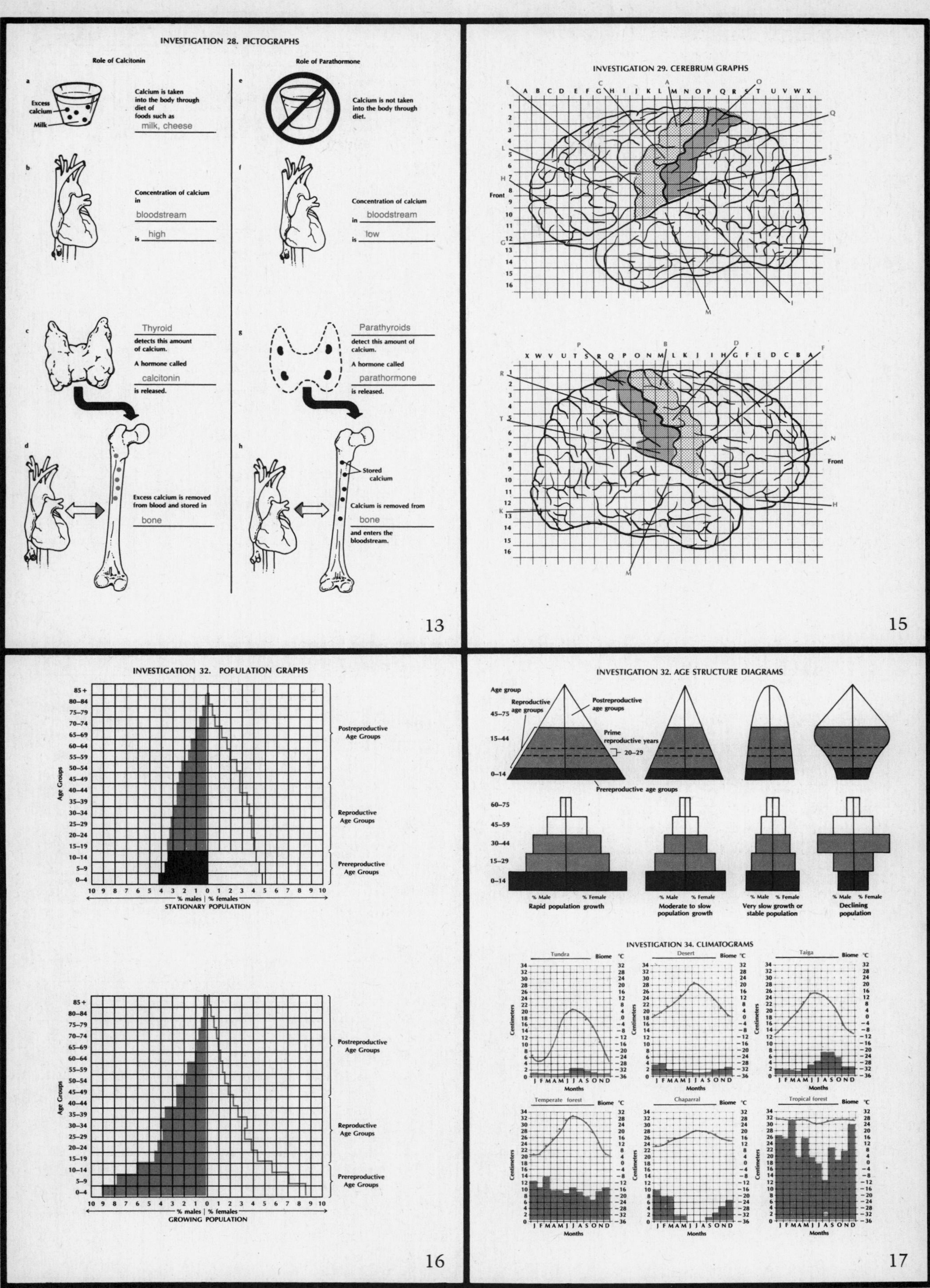
INVESTIGATION 28. PICTOGRAPHS
Role of Calcitonin
Role of Parathormone
Excess calcium
Milk
Calcium is taken into the body through diet of foods such as
milk, cheese
Calcium is not taken into the body through diet.
Concentration of calcium in
bloodstream
is high
Concentration of calcium
in bloodstream
is low
Thyroid
detects this amount of calcium.
A hormone called
calcitonin
is released.
Parathyroids
detect this amount of calcium.
A hormone called
parathormone
is released.
Excess calcium is removed from blood and stored in
bone
Stored calcium
Calcium is removed from
bone
and enters the bloodstream.
13
INVESTIGATION 29. CEREBRUM GRAPHS
Front
Front
15
INVESTIGATION 32. POPULATION GRAPHS
Age Groups
Postreproductive Age Groups
Reproductive Age Groups
Prereproductive Age Groups
% males | % females
STATIONARY POPULATION
GROWING POPULATION
16
INVESTIGATION 32. AGE STRUCTURE DIAGRAMS
Age group
Reproductive age groups
Postreproductive age groups
Prime reproductive years
20–29
Prereproductive age groups
Rapid population growth
Moderate to slow population growth
Very slow growth or stable population
Declining population
INVESTIGATION 34. CLIMATOGRAMS
Tundra
Desert
Taiga
Temperate forest
Chaparral
Tropical forest
Biome
Centimeters
Months
17

Change in Temperature

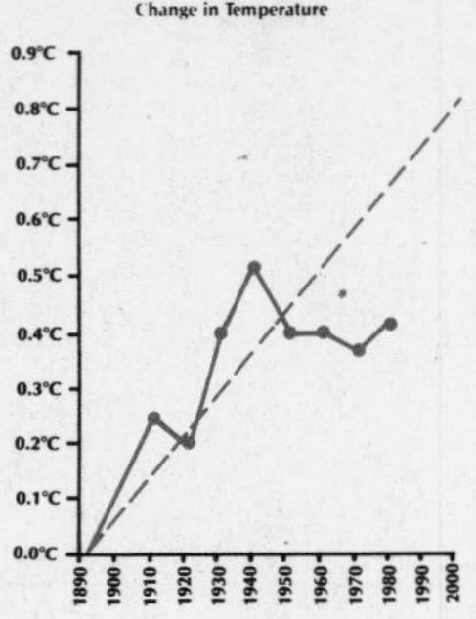

Change in Levels of Carbon Dioxide

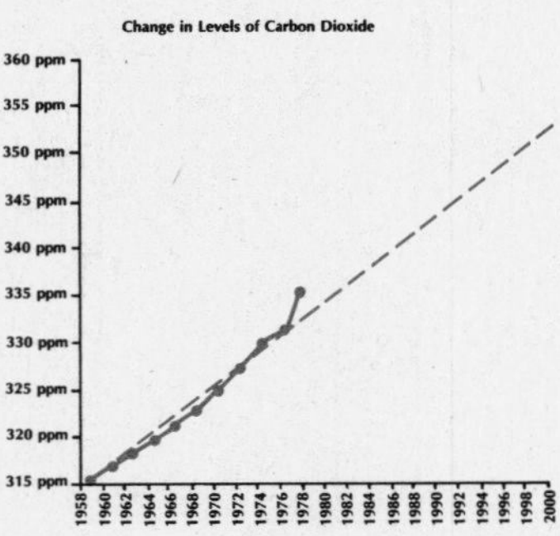

Name ______________________ Date ______________

A Study of Population Growth

Population growth can be studied easily by using small organisms such as bacteria and yeast. The following graph represents the growth curve of bacteria that were put into a test tube of nutrient broth. The test tube was then exposed to conditions ideal for optimal growth. However, no additional food was added to the test tube. Because bacteria multiply rapidly, the population of the bacteria was determined every hour. Study the graph below. Then answer the questions that follow the graph.

FIGURE 1–1.

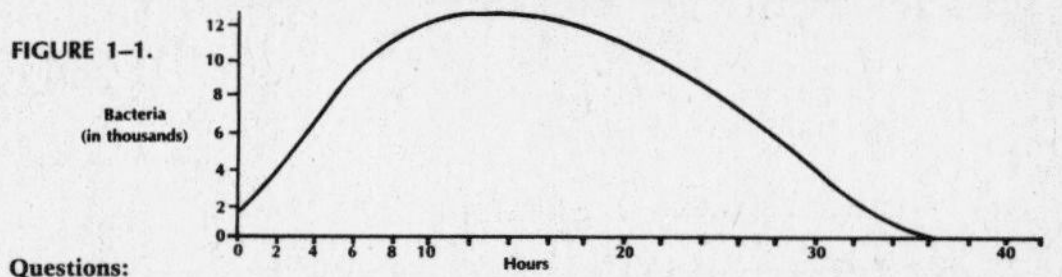

Questions:

1. Explain the results for the first 6 hours indicated by the curve on the graph. The bacteria multiplied rapidly and thus the population increased rapidly.
2. Explain the results that occurred from hour 10 to hour 16. The number of bacteria that died equaled the number of new cells formed so the population remained stable during these hours.
3. Explain the results that occurred from hour 18 to hour 37. What caused this result? The number of dead bacteria outnumbered the bacteria produced. Therefore, the population decreased. This decrease may be caused by lack of food or an increase in the amount of wastes in the broth. The increase in wastes could be caused by a buildup of metabolic wastes and by decaying bacteria.
4. The human population of the world is continuously increasing. Will Earth be able to support an unlimited human population? Explain your answer. Earth will not be able to support an unlimited human population. There is only so much living space available on Earth. Also, the land can only provide food for a certain number of people.
5. What do you suppose will happen if the world's population increases beyond its carrying capacity? Answers will vary. Some students may say that there will be less energy and water available for each person. Also, there will not be enough food to feed all of the people. Because of a lack of food and water, people will begin to starve. Then the population will begin to decrease as more people die than are born. Accept any reasonable answer.

Name ______________________ Date ______________

Problem: Do living systems release carbon dioxide? (text page 12)

Data and Observations:

TABLE 1-1. OBSERVATIONS OF BROMTHYMOL BLUE

	Part A Detecting CO_2	Part B Do Producers Release CO_2?	Part C Do Consumers Release CO_2?	Part D Do Decomposers Release CO_2?
Color of:	Tube B "before" blue	Tube C blue	Flask E "before" blue	Tube F blue
Color of:	Tube B "after" yellow	Tube D green	Flask E "after" green	Tube G green

Questions and Conclusion:

1. Define each of the following terms: (a) producer (b) consumer (c) decomposer. (a) makes its own food (b) cannot make its own food (c) causes decay
2. Put each organism in this activity into one of the following categories: (a) producer (b) consumer (c) decomposer. (a) *Elodea* or water plant (b) human (c) yeast
3. Explain how to experimentally detect the presence of carbon dioxide gas. Bubble a gas through bromothymol blue and look for a color change.
4. Do producers release carbon dioxide into their surroundings? What is your evidence? yes; Tube D containing a producer caused the bromothymol blue to change color.
5. Do consumers release carbon dioxide into their surroundings? What is your evidence? yes; Exhaled air from the consumer caused the bromothymol blue to change color.
6. Do decomposers release carbon dioxide into their surroundings? What is your evidence? yes; Tube G containing a decomposer caused the bromothymol blue to change color.
7. What life process is responsible for the release of carbon dioxide by organisms into their surroundings? cellular respiration
8. In part B, why did you place a tube with no *Elodea* plant in the dark? to verify that the producer caused the color change and not the dark itself
9. In part D, why did you place a tube that contained no yeast in the dark? to verify that it was the decomposer that caused the color change and not the dark itself
10. If you repeated parts B, C, and D of the experiment, but this time tested to see if water was given off, what results might you expect? Explain. Water would have been detected; water is a waste product of respiration.
11. If you repeated part B, C, and D of the experiment but this time tested to see if oxygen was given off, what results might you expect? Explain. No oxygen would be detected; oxygen is taken in during cellular respiration, not given off.

Conclusion: Do living systems release carbon dioxide? Living systems release carbon dioxide.

Name ______________________ Date ______________

Solving the Mystery of Food Poisoning

Food poisoning is caused by a toxic substance produced by several kinds of bacteria. When the bacteria contaminate food, they begin to grow and produce a toxin. One kind of bacteria, *Clostridium botulinum,* causes a specific form of food poisoning known as botulism. This type of food poisoning usually involves improperly smoked or uncooked meat or fish, canned vegetables, or low-acid foods. When the contaminated food is eaten, the toxin in the food is absorbed through the gastrointestinal tract into the blood stream and attacks the nerves. As a result, a person with botulism usually experiences weakness, double vision, uncoordinated eye movement, and difficulty in swallowing and speaking. Death is not uncommon and may be caused by respiratory failure or cardiac arrest. Fortunately, not all forms of food poisoning are deadly. The symptoms of food poisoning that are caused by toxins produced by other bacteria include nausea, vomiting, colicky pain, and diarrhea. These symptoms usually appear 8 to 12 hours after eating the contaminated food. Almost all people fully recover within one to several days.

You are the head of a research team assigned to investigate an outbreak of food poisoning in a city. You interview those people who have been diagnosed as having food poisoning. Through your interviews you made the following observations:

1. All of the victims experienced symptoms of food poisoning within 24 hours. The symptoms varied in severity, but included nausea, vomiting, colicky pain, and diarrhea. There were no reported deaths associated with the food poisoning.
2. All of the victims ate at the same restaurant for lunch or dinner within 24 hours of the onset of food poisoning symptoms.
3. All victims had ordered a lunch or dinner entree with the salad bar or they had ordered only the salad bar.

Questions:

1. How would you interpret your observations at this point? Give a reason for your answer. Some students may say that some or all of the foods at the salad bar served by a particular restaurant (Restaurant X) were contaminated by the bacterial toxin that caused food poisoning. Eating foods from the salad bar was a factor common to all victims.
2. What would your hypothesis be? One possible hypothesis is that one or more salads served by Restaurant X on Day X contained bacterial toxin that causes food poisoning.
3. How would you rewrite your hypothesis to make it very specific? Answers will vary. Students may rewrite their hypothesis to state that one or more salads served by Restaurant X on Day X contained bacterial toxin that caused food poisoning. Accept any answer that specifies a particular ingredient.
4. How would you design an experiment to prove your hypothesis? Answers will vary. Students may choose to test a sample from every available batch of salad containing the specified ingredient from question 3. These samples should come from the salads served by Restaurant X on Day X. Students may test for any of the known bacteria that produce toxins that cause food poisoning.

Name ________________ Date ________________

Problem: How does one test a hypothesis? (text page 34)

Data and Observations:

TABLE 2-1. RADISH SEED GROWTH						
	Individual Results			Class Results		
Treatment	Number of Seeds Used	Number of Seeds Growing	Number of Seeds Not Growing	Number of Seeds Used	Number of Seeds Growing	Number of Seeds Not Growing
Water	20	20	0	500	463	37
Water and aspirin	20	0	20	500	2	498

Questions and Conclusion:

1. Define: (a) hypothesis (b) control (c) variable. (a) relates and explains observations and predicts new facts (b) a group identical to the experimental group except for the variable being tested (c) a factor being tested in an experiment
2. Which part of this experiment represents the: (a) data (b) control (c) variable? (a) the number of seeds (b) seeds soaked in water (c) seeds soaked in water and aspirin
3. Based on your original hypothesis, does the class data appear to support it? Explain. no; The data shows that fewer seeds grew with aspirin than with water alone.
4. Restate a new hypothesis based on experimental findings for the class. Use the "if-then" format. If aspirin is added to seeds while they are soaking in water, then these seeds will not grow as well as those soaked only in water.
5. Explain why testing or experimentation is needed before one can accept a hypothesis. Experimentation will supply facts that will support or reject the hypothesis.
6. Suggest a reason why it was best to use class totals rather than only your data when drawing conclusions about your hypothesis. The more data one gathers, the more reliable.
7. A hypothesis helps to predict new facts. Determine if the following could possibly be predicted based on your corrected hypothesis regarding aspirin and seed growth. Explain.
   (a) Aspirin added to pea seeds will reduce amount of growth. Since radish seeds soaked in aspirin show reduced growth, perhaps growth of pea seeds would also be reduced.
   (b) Aspirin added to soil will help house plants to form greener leaves. Data for radish seeds is unrelated; therefore, no prediction could be made.
   (c) Aspirin added to corn seeds will increase amount of growth. Since radish seeds soaked in aspirin show reduced growth, perhaps aspirin added to corn seeds will decrease growth.

Conclusion: How does one test a hypothesis? by experimentation

Name ________________ Date ________________

Models of an Atom

The model of the atom can be illustrated in two ways. One way is based upon the theory of an atom developed by Danish physicist Niels Bohr in 1913. In this model, an electron travels in a specific orbit around the nucleus. In Figure 3–1, a single hydrogen atom, indicate what represents the nucleus and what represents the electron's orbit.

Another way that the atom can be illustrated is using what is called a probability cloud. This model is based upon discoveries made a decade after Bohr developed his theory of the atom. These discoveries make up the quantum of the atom. Simply put, this theory states that the electrons move about within a probability cloud that forms a certain pattern in space. Figure 3–2 is of a probability cloud for a single hydrogen atom. Indicate where the nucleus is located and where there would be a high probability of finding the electron.

FIGURE 3–1.

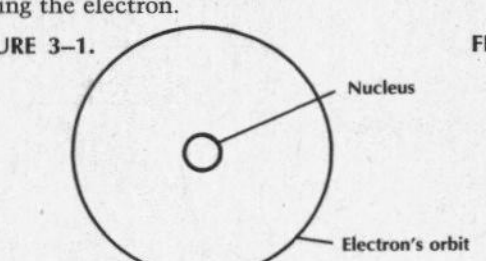

FIGURE 3–2.

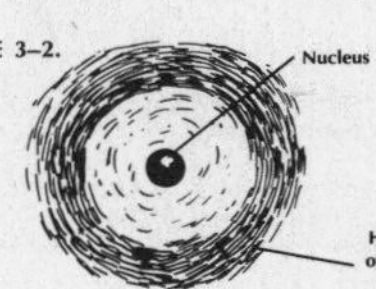

Questions:

1. What are the three particles of an atom and where are each found? The three particles of an atom are the neutron, proton, and electron. The neutron and the proton are found within the nucleus of the atom. The electron is found in an orbit or a probability cloud that surrounds the nucleus.
2. How are the two models of the atom described above similar? Both models have a nucleus that is surrounded by electrons.
3. How are the two models of the atom described above different? The Bohr model indicates that electrons are to be found in a definite orbit. The probability cloud indicates that electrons are most likely to be found within an area surrounding the nucleus.
4. Why is it important to understand the structure of an atom? Answers will vary. Students may say that it is important to understand the structure of an atom so that one can understand how atoms combine to form molecules and thus how elements combine to form compounds. Accept any reasonable answer.
5. Which model would you say is more accurate, Bohr's model or the probability cloud model? Explain. Answers will vary. Students may say that the probability cloud model is more accurate because it was based upon discoveries made about the atom many years after Bohr developed his model. Accept any reasonable answer.

Name ________________ Date ________________

Ionic Compounds and Electricity

Ionic compounds are made up of charged particles—ions—that are tightly bound together. If the attractive forces between the ions are weakened, the ions are free to move. Freely-moving, charged particles such as ions conduct electricity. To learn more about ionic compounds and electricity, work through the following activity.

Materials:

250-mL beaker	light bulb
dry cell	light bulb holder
electrical wires	distilled water
switch	salt
masking tape	glass stirring rod

FIGURE 3–1.

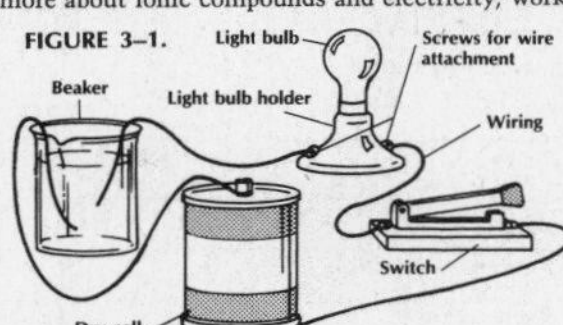

Procedure:

1. Set up a series circuit like the one shown in Figure 3–1. Do not add anything to the beaker until your circuit is set up completely. Make sure the switch is open. You will need to remove a short length of insulation from the ends of the wires that come into contact with the switch, the dry cell, the light bulb holder, and the distilled water. To help keep the wires along the side of the beaker, you may wish to use masking tape to hold the wires in place. **CAUTION:** *Do not touch both ends of the wire in the beaker with your bare hands at the same time that the switch is closed, as you may receive a mild shock.*
2. Add distilled water to the beaker until the bare ends of the wire are covered with the water. Close the switch. Observe what happens to the light bulb. Open the switch.
3. Now, add about 5 to 10 grams of salt to the distilled water. Using the glass stirring rod, gently stir the water so that the salt dissolves. Close the switch. Observe what happens to the light bulb. Open the switch before you disassemble your series circuit.

Questions:

1. What happened to the light bulb when there was only distilled water in the beaker and you closed the switch? Nothing happened. Distilled water must not have any free-moving charged particles in it; therefore, the circuit was not complete and the light bulb did not light up.
2. What happened to the light bulb when you dissolved salt in the distilled water and then closed the switch? Give a reason for the result. The light bulb lit up. The dissolved salt must have added freely-moving charged particles to the distilled water. The freely-moving charged particles conducted electricity, thus closing the circuit and causing the light bulb to light up.
3. How does distilled water differ from a saltwater solution? Distilled water does not have freely-moving charged particles, but the saltwater solution does have freely moving charged particles.
4. How would you classify distilled water and salt in terms of ionic compounds? Distilled water is not an ionic compound, but salt is an ionic compound.

Name ________________ Date ________________

Problem: How does one determine if a solution is an acid or a base? (text page 58)

Part A Answers:

3(a) 1–6 (b) 8–12 (c) 7 (d) 1 (e) 12 (f) 6 (g) 8

Data and Observations:

TABLE 3-4. pH OF KNOWN SUBSTANCES	
Solution	pH
Known Acid	1–6*
Known Base	8–14*
Known Neutral	7

*Answers will vary.

TABLE 3-5. pH OF UNKNOWN SUBSTANCES					
	A	B	C	D	E
Sample Number	Sample Name	Your Guess Acid, Base, Neutral	pH	Actual Results Acid, Base, Neutral	Did your guess match results?
1					
2					
3		Student answers will vary			
4		according to teacher selections			
5		of solutions.			
6					
7					
8					
9					
10					
11					
12					

Investigation Worksheet — Chapter 3

Name ______________________ Date ______________

Questions and Conclusion:

1. Define: (a) acid (b) base (c) neutral solution (d) pH scale (e) ion.
   (a) solution that has a greater concentration of hydrogen ions than hydroxide ions (b) solution that has a greater concentration of hydroxide ions than hydrogen ions (c) solution that has an equal number of hydrogen and hydroxide ions (d) a scale which indicates the relative concentration of ions in acids and bases (e) charged atoms or groups of atoms
2. Using numbers of the pH scale, describe how you can indicate if a solution is (a) acid (b) base (c) or a neutral solution. (a) 1 to less than 7 (b) 7 to 14 (c) 7
3. Identify these symbols: (a) OH^- hydroxide ion (b) H^+ hydrogen ion
4. Of the solutions tested, name: (a) the weakest acid (b) the strongest acid (c) the weakest base (d) the strongest base (e) any that were neutral. Answers will vary.
5. (a) What was the expected pH of the drinking water? 7
   (b) What was the actual pH of the drinking water? Answers will vary.
   (c) List several factors that may affect the pH of the drinking water. chemicals added to water at the filtration plant, chemicals such as iron present in the pipes through which water flows

Conclusion: How does one determine if a solution is an acid or a base?
One will use pH paper and the pH scale to determine if a solution is an acid or a base.

Essay — Chapter 4

Name ______________________ Date ______________

Prokaryotes and Eukaryotes

Biologists have come to realize that the differences between plants and animals are not as significant as the differences between two basic cellular types—prokaryotic and eukaryotic. The eukaryotic cell is the structural unit of all modern, or higher, organisms, including humans. Bacteria and cyanobacteria are the only known prokaryotic cells. It is generally thought that eukaryotic cells represent a more advanced stage of evolution than the prokaryotic cells. As a result of genetic evolution, there are fewer similarities between prokaryotic cells and eukaryotic cells than there are between plants and animals.

The nature of cellular organization and reproduction in prokaryotic cells is quite different from that of eukaryotic cells. The nuclear material of a prokaryotic cell is found in an irregular mass in the cytoplasm called a nucleoid, while that of a eukaryotic cell is enclosed within a nuclear membrane. Prokaryotic cells also lack the mitochondria, endoplasmic reticulum, golgi bodies, and lysosomes found in eukaryotic cells. When chlorophyll is present in prokaryotic cells, it is not organized into chloroplasts as it is in eukaryotic cells that contain chlorophyll. In addition, the cell wall of prokaryotic cells, when present, is made up of a different chemical composition than the cell wall of eukaryotic plant cells. Prokaryotic cells reproduce simply by dividing in half while the reproductive process of eukaryotes is made up of several steps that involve the nucleus and often the combining of gametes, or sex cells.

Another striking difference between prokaryotes and eukaryotes is the fact that the cytoplasm of typical eukaryotes constantly moves and is said to "stream". This results in the motility of many protists, such as in the amoeba. The cytoplasm of prokaryotes, on the contrary, exhibits no apparent streaming.

At one time the prokaryotes were grouped together with all other microorganisms into the kingdom Protista. This kingdom was proposed in 1866 by Ernst Haeckel in order to include in a classification system the growing body of knowledge about microorganisms. The members of Protista were distinguished from members of the plant and animal kingdoms on the basis of a single characteristic: that they existed as unicellular (single-celled) organisms.

It is thought that prokaryotic cells exhibit a very primitive structure. Because of this primitive structure and their supposed ancient origin (bacteria are believed to be the first living things to have developed on Earth), these two groups were placed together by R. H. Whittaker, in 1969, into the Kingdom Monera.

Questions:

1. Why are prokaryotes considered to be primitive when compared to eukaryotes? Prokaryotes possess less internal organization (no organelles other than ribosomes), they do not have cytoplasmic streaming, and their reproduction does not involve the combining of gametes.
2. At one time there were only two kingdoms, Plantae and Animalia. Then, a third kingdom was formed. What was this third kingdom? Why was it formed? The third kingdom was called the Protista and was formed in order to provide a group composed of all the newly discovered unicellular microorganisms.
3. In time, a fourth kingdom—Monera—was formed. Why? Is it necessary to have this kingdom? The Monera was formed in order to officially recognize the importance of the relatively primitive structure of the bacteria and cyanobacteria and to distinguish them from the eukaryotic Protista. It is necessary in the sense that it recognizes the radical differences that exist between the bacteria (and cyanobacteria) and all other, more advanced, forms of life on Earth.

Critical Thinking — Chapter 4

Name ______________________ Date ______________

Osmosis

Osmosis is the passage of a solvent through a semipermeable membrane from a region of greater concentration to a region of lesser concentration. In an organism, the solvent is usually water and the semipermeable membrane is usually the cell membrane.

Because cell membranes are more permeable to water molecules than to other molecules or ions, cells will swell when placed in dilute solutions and shrink in solutions more concentrated than themselves, as a result of the osmotic movement of water. For example, a sea urchin egg is normally shed into seawater. The egg does not change size because the seawater has the same concentration of water and ions as the fluid within the cell. If the egg is placed in dilute seawater, the egg will swell as water enters the egg. The swollen egg will eventually burst. On the other hand, when placed in seawater to which excess salt has been added, the egg will shrink as water leaves the egg. Human red blood cells placed in solutions more dilute or more concentrated than blood do the same thing.

Solutions that have a concentration of water and ions different from that of a cell are given special names—hypo-osmotic and hyperosmotic. In a hypo-osmotic solution, or dilute solution, the cell swells and its contents become more dilute. In a hyperosmotic solution, or a concentrated solution, the cell shrinks and its contents become more concentrated. A solution that has the same concentration of water and ions as the cell is called an isosmotic solution. Because there is no difference in osmotic pressure, the cell stays the same size in an isosmotic solution.

Explain the following in terms of osmosis:

1. Slugs are perhaps the gardener's worst enemy. These creatures are fond of tender young leaves and shoots. Because slugs are slimy and considered repulsive by most gardeners, they prefer not to pick the slugs up with their hands to dispose of them. Instead, many gardeners kill the slugs by sprinkling salt on them. The salt sprinkled on the slugs is much more concentrated than the salt within the cells of the slug. Therefore, the salt causes water to move out of the cells, the cells shrink in size, and their contents become more concentrated. Since the slug cannot carry out its life functions with its cells in this state, the slug
2. You enjoy eating a delicious ham dinner. But you get very thirsty (indicating that your body cells are low on water) after eating the salty meal. Salt from the meal enters the body fluids and makes them slightly hyperosmotic, thus causing water to be withdrawn from body cells. The body tries to correct this imbalance by having you drink more water to dilute the amount of salt ions in the body fluids, thus bring the body fluids back into osmotic balance with the body cells.
3. When growing living cells in test tubes, biologists are very careful to use a medium known as Ringer's solution. This solution has a salt concentration exactly equal to the salt concentration found in body and cellular fluids. If the solution had too much salt, or was hyperosmotic, the cells would shrink, their contents would become too concentrated, and they would die. If the solution had too little salt, or was hypo-osmotic, the cells would expand, perhaps burst, and die. The cells would stay the same size and maintain osmotic pressure in the Ringer's solution, which is isosmotic.

Investigation Worksheet — Chapter 4

Name ______________________ Date ______________

Problem: How does one measure cells within the microscope? (text page 84)

Question 3 Answers:

(a) 1350 µm (b) 14 200 µm (c) .4 mm (d) 0.12 mm

Data and Observations:

TABLE 4-2. ESTIMATING CELL SIZE

	Frog red blood cells		*Paramecium*		*Elodea*	
Viewing under low or high power	Low power	High power	Low power	High power	Low power	High power
Number of cells that fit side-by-side	38	10	6	1.5	9	20
Diameter of field of view	1500	375	1500	375	1500	375
Cell size in micrometers	39*	37.5*	250‡	250‡	165★	180★

*Values should be very close ‡Values should be very close ★Values should be very close

Questions and Conclusion:

1. Define: (a) millimeter (b) micrometer (c) field of view. (a) 1/1000 of a meter (b) 1/1000 of a millimeter (c) circle of light seen through eyepiece of microscope
2. Compare the cell size of your frog blood cells under low and high power. Are they very close or far apart? Explain. They are very close. An object does not change size when viewed under low and high power magnification. Only the magnification has changed.
3. Repeat question 2, comparing *Paramecium* measurements. Then compare *Elodea* measurements. Both *Paramecium* and *Elodea* measurements appear very close. An object does not change size when viewed under low and high power magnification. Only its magnification has changed.

Conclusion: How can cells be measured with the microscope? One must estimate the number of cells that can fit across the diameter of the field of view. This number is then divided into the diameter of the field of view to obtain cell size.

Skills — Chapter 5

Name ______________________ Date ______________________

Activation Energy and Catalysts

If a chemical reaction is to occur, it is necessary for the reacting molecules to collide with one another as they move about in a random way. However, unless the temperature is high enough, most molecules simply rebound from collisions without reacting. An example is the reaction between hydrogen and oxygen that forms water. The reaction will take place explosively if the temperature is high enough. But in a mixture of hydrogen and oxygen at room temperature, the molecules collide repeatedly with one another and rebound without change. The situation is similar to that shown in Figure 5–1.

A ball that is resting in a depression on a hillside will give energy if it can roll down the hill. The ball will not roll down the hill unless its energy is first raised enough to get it out of the depression.

In the case of hydrogen and oxygen molecules in a container at room temperature, the molecules will not have enough energy to form the transition state. If a lighted match is placed in the container, the molecules near the flame gain enough energy to react when they collide with one another. The overall energy released is transferred to nearby molecules causing the reaction to spread quickly to all parts of the container. The added energy molecules must have to form the transition state is called the activation energy of the reaction.

In chemical reactions that have high activation energies, the reacting molecules can be lifted over the energy barrier by raising the temperature. Frequently, however, it is undesirable to carry out a given reaction at high temperatures. Another approach is to find a way to lower the energy barrier. The energy barrier can be lowered by a substance called a catalyst. A catalyst binds with certain molecules that form an intermediate compound. The intermediate compound has a transition state that has a lower energy. The reaction can then occur at lower temperatures and thus at a faster rate.

FIGURE 5–1.

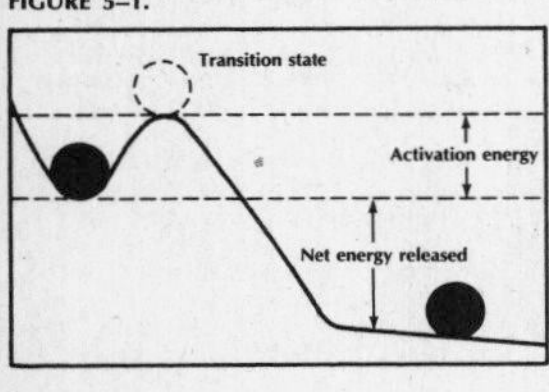

FIGURE 5–2.

Questions:

Use Figure 5–2 to answer questions 1–4.

1. Which letter represents the transition state when a catalyst is absent? A
2. Which letter represents the transition state when a catalyst is present? C
3. The activation energy is represented by which letter when a catalyst is present? D.
4. The activation energy is represented by which letter when a catalyst is absent? B.
5. Chemical reactions within biological systems rarely take place without a catalyst. The catalysts are specific proteins called enzymes. Why are enzymes so beneficial (and necessary) to metabolic reactions? They help to lower the amount of energy needed to start a reaction. They also help to speed up reactions.

Essay — Chapter 5

Name ______________________ Date ______________________

The Metabolism of Alcohol

Alcohol, when swallowed, is completely absorbed by the stomach and intestines, passing directly into the blood. From the blood, alcohol diffuses into all the body organs and has a marked effect on the central nervous system. Eventually, 95 percent of the alcohol taken into the body is broken down in the liver. The remaining 5 percent is excreted unchanged in the urine and the breath. This latter fact forms the basis for the use of the "Breathalyzer Test" in the detection of drunken drivers. Most alcoholic beverages contain little or no proteins or vitamins and therefore have little nutritional value.

The liver is the major organ that removes alcohol from the blood and converts the alcohol into other chemicals. The liver metabolizes alcohol in a two-step process. In the first step, two hydrogen atoms are removed from the alcohol molecule. In the second step, oxygen is added to the dehydrogenated molecule, producing the nontoxic acetate. Acetate leaves the liver, enters the blood and is eventually converted to carbon dioxide and water in other body tissues. These two steps are illustrated in Figure 5–1.

Each of the two steps are catalyzed by an enzyme. The enzymes are found in the cytoplasm of the liver cells. The hydrogen atoms that are removed from the alcohol molecules are carried by a substance known as NAD (nicotine adenine dinucleotide) to the mitochondria. There, the hydrogen atoms combine with oxygen atoms to form water.

The capacity of the liver to break down, or metabolize, alcohol is limited. Consuming large quantities of alcohol over a short period of time can be fatal. A high level of alcohol in the blood system can cause death, often from severe depression of the breathing centers at the base of the brain. Heavy drinkers can suffer from permanent physiological changes. These changes may negatively affect the intestines, circulatory system, lungs, kidneys, pancreas, and nervous system.

The organ most affected by heavy use of alcohol is the liver. Fat tends to accumulate in the liver's cells, producing a "fatty liver." Continued long term drinking causes cirrhosis, a condition in which parts of the liver degenerate and normal cells become replaced by scar tissue. Chronic cirrhosis can lead to death.

FIGURE 5–1.

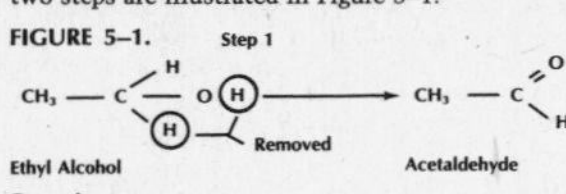

Questions:

1. How does alcohol enter the circulatory system? Alcohol is absorbed into the circulatory system directly from the stomach and the intestines.
2. What metabolic fact has permitted the development and use of the "Breathalyzer Test"? Approximately 5 percent of the alcohol taken into the body is excreted unchanged in the urine and the breath.
3. How does the liver metabolize alcohol? Alcohol is broken down in a two step process. First, hydrogen atoms are removed from the alcohol molecule, forming acetaldehyde. Secondly, an oxygen atom is added to the acetaldehyde, forming acetate.
4. Why can drinking a lot of alcohol over a short period of time be harmful? Since the liver is limited as to how fast it can metabolize alcohol, excess alcohol will continue to circulate throughout the body. High levels of alcohol can depress the breathing centers of the brain and result in death.

Investigation Worksheet — Chapter 5

Name ______________________ Date ______________________

Problem: How does the amount of catalase enzyme compare in different tissues? (text page 100)

Part A Answers:

6. (a) catalase (b) living cells of plant and animal tissue (c) hydrogen peroxide (d) water and oxygen gas (e) Bubbles of oxygen formed in the tube containing the enzyme and substrate, while no bubbles appeared in the tube with only the substrate.

Data and Observations:

TABLE 5-1. COMPARISON OF THE AMOUNTS OF CATALASE IN DIFFERENT TISSUES

Cell Type	Unboiled		Boiled	
	Chunk	Chopped	Chunk	Chopped
Carrot	*2	3	0	0
Potato	2	4	0	0
Liver	8	10	0	0
Muscle	7	9	0	0

*Student answers will vary. Values in the table show relative amounts of bubbling for each type of cell.

Investigation Worksheet — Chapter 5

Name ______________________ Date ______________________

Questions and Conclusion:

1. List four properties of all enzymes. unique three-dimensional shape, composed of amino-acids, proteins, act as catalysts within cells, remain unchanged during the chemical reaction, destroyed by heat
2. How were you able to judge if the enzyme was or was not working in this activity? No bubbles meant no enzyme action, while much bubbling indicated much enzyme action.
3. In general, do plant or animal cells contain more catalase? Give evidence from your data. Animal cells contain more enzyme because bubbling observed in liver and muscle was greater than in potato and carrot.
4. (a) In general, do chunk, unboiled cells release more, less, or about the same amount of catalase, as chopped, unboiled cells? Give evidence from your data. (b) Offer a possible hypothesis to explain your data. (a) less; The chopped cells showed more bubbling. (b) Chopped cells exposed more cell contents and thus provided more enzyme.
5. In general, do chunk, unboiled cells release more, less, or about the same amount of catalase as chunk boiled cells? Give evidence from your data. more; All boiled, chunk cells showed a value of 0 or almost zero for enzyme activity while unboiled showed moderate activity.
6. In general, do chunk, boiled cells release more, less, or about the same amount of catalase as chopped boiled cells? Give evidence from your data. about the same; All chunk or chopped, boiled cells showed a value of 0 or almost zero for enzyme activity.
7. Offer possible hypotheses to explain the data you obtained in questions 5 and 6. Heat destroys or denatures the enzyme. Thus, boiled cells had no enzyme activity.

Conclusion: How does the amount of catalase enzyme compare in different tissues? In general, the amount of catalase in animal cells is greater than in plant cells; boiled cells will show little enzyme activity; cells that have been chopped will release more enzyme than those in chunk form.

Skills Chapter 6

Name ______ Date ______

Radiation and Mutations

For more than 50 years it has been known that X rays and the energy emitted by the decay of radioactive elements can be dangerous to humans and plants. At extremely high dosages of such radiation, there is massive destruction to the animal nervous system and death occurs almost instantly. But most of the effects of radiation appear gradually and usually are due to the genetic damage, or mutations, of individual cells. A single, low exposure to radiation may not cause immediate symptoms, but permanent damage to body cells can occur. These harmful types of radiation are said to be mutagenic.

When mutations occur in the germ cells of the gonads, the parts of the body that produce either sperm or eggs, the mutations can be passed on to future generations. If mutations occur in other body cells, they can interfere with the normal genetic controls, causing cells to undergo rapid and uncontrolled divisions. These uncontrolled growths of cells are called cancers.

There are two types of radiation. One type is electromagnetic radiation. This type of radiation includes sunlight, radio waves, X rays, and microwaves. High-energy radiation, such as X rays, are capable of penetrating deep into living tissue. Sunlight, however, only affects the surface of the skin. The other type of radiation is called particulate radiation. This type of radiation is released as radioactive elements disintegrate. Uranium and radium are two well-known examples of elements in Earth's crust that are radioactive.

The amount of damage to the cells of a tissue by harmful radiation depends upon the amount of radiation that is absorbed by the tissue. Bone, for example, is a dense tissue and will absorb more of a certain radiation than will muscle, kidney, or brain tissue. Health physicists, scientists concerned with the biological effects of radiation, have established a unit that takes into account the biological effectiveness of radiation in humans. This unit is known as a rem. It indicates a standard amount of biological damage resulting from various sources. For example, people receive about 100 to 110 mrems (a mrem represents a millirem, one-thousandth of a rem) per year from natural background radiation such as sunlight and radioactive elements in Earth's crust.

The amount of radiation a person may receive safely depends on many factors. One of these factors is the rate at which radiation is received. About 60 percent of the people who are exposed to a single dose of high-energy radiation equivalent to 100 rems will develop moderate radiation sickness. The same dose, spread out over an entire lifetime, will not produce illness, but will probably shorten one's life by about 1 percent, or 8 months.

1. How many total rems of radiation must be absorbed in order for about 60 percent of the population to experience radiation sickness? 5
2. A 100 rem dose of radiation spread over a lifetime may shorten a person's life by how much? 8 months
3. The effects of radiation are cumulative. If a person were to receive 110 mrems of natural radiation per year, how many mrems would that add up to in 70 years? 7700 mrems How many rems would that be? 7700 mrems/1000 = 7.7 rems
4. With knowledge of the relationship between radiation and mutations, how might you explain the relationship between exposure to the sun and skin cancer? Sunlight is composed of different types of radiation, including the harmful UV radiation. Exposure to the sun for long periods of time can cause mutations in the skin cells. These mutations can lead to rapid, uncontrolled cell division and growth, causing various forms of skin cancer.

6–2

Essay Chapter 6

Name ______ Date ______

The Genetic Peril of the Cheetah

The cheetah is truly one of nature's marvels. A virtual running machine, its skull is small and lightweight, its limbs are long and slender, and its spinal column is unusually flexible. The cheetah's heart, lungs, and adrenal glands are all enlarged, enhancing the animal's ability to accelerate during a high-speed chase—a chase often clocked at up to 112 kilometers per hour. Unlike other cats, the cheetah's claws are always extended like cleats, enabling it to grip the ground. These adaptations have made the cheetah an effective hunter on the flat, open savannahs of central and southern Africa.

In spite of the cheetah's skill as a runner and hunter, the species seems to be headed for extinction. While the cheetah's body structure is superbly adapted to a running existence, the cheetah has traits that are considered maladaptive. It is extremely vulnerable to disease, and there is a high infant mortality rate. Although the cheetah is the world's fastest mammal, it can run rapidly for only a few hundred yards before it tires. After a typical chase, the cheetah collapses for half an hour in order to regain its strength. During this time, it is vulnerable to attack by other predators and can lose either its life or its catch. Cheetahs are rather timid creatures, with some 50 percent of their kills snatched away by more aggressive lions, leopards, and hyenas. The cheetah is now limited to a few, small areas in Africa. There are about 20 000 cheetahs left on Earth today.

Research over the last six years suggests that the cheetah has somehow lost most of its genetic variation. Scientific studies have revealed that, genetically, each cheetah is nearly identical to every other cheetah. In other words, the species exhibits genetic uniformity. Genetic uniformity hampers the ability of a species to adapt to environmental changes, such as temperature shifts, drought, glaciation, and even the emergence of new viruses or bacteria. Such uniformity is usually the result of intensive inbreeding.

Scientists have recently puzzled over the causes for the probable inbreeding and resultant genetic uniformity in the cheetah. The most plausible hypothesis to date is that at some point in the past the cheetah went through a severe population reduction. The population reduction was followed by inbreeding, which diminished genetic variability. How severe would the population reduction have to be in order to lead to genetic uniformity? Studies have shown that a population reduced to only seven individuals will retain about 95 percent of its original genetic variation. The population can retain that variation only if the survivors reproduce rapidly enough to expand the size of the population. Slow reproduction in a small population decreases the likelihood that different genetic types will survive. Scientists suspect that at least once in the past the cheetah's population dropped to only a few individuals. What caused the cheetah population to dwindle is not known. The possibilities include catastrophic climatic changes, viral or bacterial plagues, and even hunting by humans.

Several other animals have gone through severe population reductions and seem to be recovering. One example is the northern elephant seal. This population was reduced to about 20 animals. Yet after the passage of protective legislation, the seal population grew. Today the number of elephant seals reaches into the tens of thousands. Can the cheetah have the same good fortune?

Questions:

1. Provide a definition of genetic uniformity. Genetic uniformity refers to a population composed of individuals that are nearly genetically identical.
2. How does genetic uniformity occur? Genetic uniformity occurs when a population is 130 severely reduced in size, and reproduction by the survivors does not quickly increase the size of the population.
3. How does genetic uniformity hamper the survival of the cheetah? Due to genetic uniformity, the cheetah is unlikely to survive major environmental changes because there would not be enough genetic diversity to allow for new adaptations to develop.

6–3

Investigation Worksheet Chapter 6

Name ______ Date ______

Problem: How can one observe chromosomes in cells? (text page 124)

Data and Observations:

TABLE 6-2. CHROMOSOME APPEARANCE

Organism	Diagram of Chromosomes	Phases of Mitosis Seen
Bean root tip	Student drawings go into these spaces.	Answers will vary.
Bean root tip		Answers will vary.
Drosophila salivary gland		

Questions and Conclusion:

1. Define the following terms: (a) chromosome (b) mitosis (c) interphase (d) cell cycle. (a) structures in the nucleus that contain DNA and protein (b) equal distribution of replicated chromosomes to new nuclei (c) period between mitotic divisions during which chromosomes are replicated (d) life cycle of a cell consisting of interphase and mitosis
2. (a) Using your data from Table 6-2, list the phases of mitosis you observed in the bean root tip. (b) Were there more cells undergoing a particular phase of the cell cycle than any other phase? If so, which phase did you observe most often? (a) Answers will vary. (b) yes; interphase
3. How did the following help in the observations of the chromosomes: (a) staining (b) squashing? (a) made chromosomes more visible (b) separated the cells
4. Why did you use the tip of the root and not the entire root when preparing your slide? The root tip is composed of actively dividing cells.
5. The term chromosome is derived from chromo- (meaning color) and -some (meaning body). How is the term chromosome an appropriate one? The chromosome is a body within the cell that easily becomes stained, or colored.
6. If human skin tissue instead of root tips had been used in part A: (a) how many chromosomes would you expect to find in each cell? (b) would the skin cells have been undergoing mitosis? (c) explain your answer to (b). (a) 46 (b) yes (c) Skin tissue contains cells that divide rapidly.
7. (a) Consider the tissue from the salivary glands of *Drosophila*. How do the chromosomes from one cell compare to those from any other cell? (b) How does the situation described in 7(a) illustrate genetic continuity? (a) They are identical. (b) Cells have the same chromosomal makeup as one another and as the parent cells from which they originated.

Conclusion: How can you observe chromosomes in cells? Chromosomes can be observed when cells are rapidly dividing, stained, and squashed.

6–6

Skills Chapter 7

Name ______ Date ______

Punnett Square

One way to quickly calculate the possible genotypes and phenotypes of offspring is to use the so-called checkerboard or Punnett Square method. Use of the Punnett square is quite easy when dealing with one pair of genes for each parent. When dealing with several pairs of genes, the probability method for calculating genotypes and phenotypes becomes easier.

To use the Punnett square, the genotype of one parent is written above the checkerboard and the genotype of the other parent is written along the left side of the checkerboard. The new gene pairs of the offspring are obtained by combining the parent's genes that are above each row of the checkerboard with those along the side of the checkerboard.

A Punnett square for leaf shape in *Coleus*, a plant of the mint family is provided below. In *Coleus* deep-lobed leaves are dominant over shallow-lobed leaves. One parent is homozygous dominant (and deeply-lobed) and its genotype is *DD*. This genotype is written above the checkerboard. The other parent is homozygous recessive (and is shallowly lobed). It's genotype is *dd* and is written along the left side of the checkerboard. The possible genotypes of the possible offspring are determined by multiplying the parent's gene (located along the top of each row of boxes) by the parent's gene located along the side of each row of boxes. In square 1 the genotype would be *Dd*. By using the same method, the genotype of square 2 would also be *Dd*. Complete the Punnett square in Figure 7–1 by filing squares 3 and 4.

The Punnett square you have completed represents the possible genotypes and phenotypes of the first filial (or F_1) generation. Based on your understanding of this Punnett square, answer questions 1 and 2.

Complete the Punnett square (still dealing with *Coleus* leaf shape) in Figure 7–2 using the two offspring from the F_1 generation above as parents. Remember that the dominant gene is always written first. This new Punnett square represents the second filial (or F_2) generation. Use the information gained from the F_2 generation to answer questions 3–6.

FIGURE 7–1.

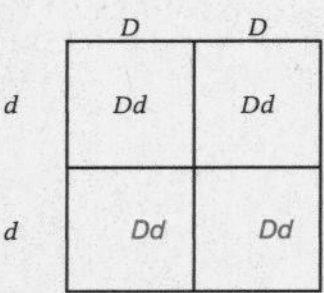

FIGURE 7–2.

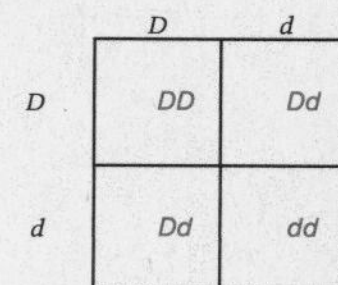

Questions:

1. What is (are) the genotype(s) of the F_1 generation? *Dd*
2. What is (are) the phenotype(s) of the F_1 generation? deeply-lobed leaves
3. What is (are) the genotype(s) of the F_2 generation? *DD, Dd, dd*
4. What is (are) the phenotype(s) of the F_2 generation? deep-lobed leaves and shallow-lobed leaves
5. What ratio expresses the possible relative numbers of the genotype(s) of the F_2 generation? 1 *Dd*: 2 *Dd*: 1 *dd*
6. What ratio expresses the possible relative numbers of the phenotype(s) of the F_2 generation? 3 deep-lobed leaves: 1 shallow-lobed leaves

7–2

Essay **Chapter 7**

Name ______________________ Date ______________

Pedigrees

Human geneticists and animal breeders apply Mendelian principles and laws when analyzing pedigrees, the family diagrams that represent the phenotypes of offspring. Pedigrees are useful because traits with simple patterns of inheritance can often be traced accurately. For many traits prediction can be made about the likelihood of expression of a trait in future generations.

A stumbling block to the use of human pedigrees is that most human traits are too complex to be identified as dominant or recessive, and many that are do not have simple patterns of inheritance. For some traits, phenotypes (for example, deafness) may behave as dominant in some families while as recessive in other families. This can occur if several genes are responsible for a particular phenotype. Recessive genes in families are sometimes difficult to keep track of in a pedigree because they remain hidden by their dominant alleles generation after generation. It may not be known if an individual actually carries a recessive allele.

A few human traits, however, have been associated with specific genes and their patterns of inheritance are well known. For these traits, pedigrees can be helpful in determining the genetic patterns within a family. The usefulness of a pedigree to determine the genotypes and phenotypes of a known trait for a particular family is illustrated in the following example. In this pedigree, attached earlobes result from a double-recessive genotype *(aa)*. Study the pedigree and, with your knowledge of genetics, answer the questions that follow.

FIGURE 7–1.

Female, free earlobes
Female, attached earlobes
Male, free earlobes
Male, attached earlobes

I
II 1 2 3
III 1 2 3 4
IV 1 2 3 4 5

Questions:

1. In generation II, one male offspring has attached ear-lobes. (A = free ear-lobes, a = attached ear-lobes). What are the genotypes of his parents? *Aa.*
2. In generation II, what are the possible genotypes of children 2 and 3? Explain. *AA or Aa. They would have received these possible genotypes from their parents because they are heterozygous for the trait.*
3. What must the genotype of the wife of child 1 in generation II be in order to have a child in generation III that has attached ear-lobes? Explain. *Aa. She must carry a recessive gene for attached ear-lobes.*
4. What is (are) the genotype(s) of children 1, 2, and 3, in generation III? Explain. *Aa. They have the phenotype of free ear-lobes, yet they must carry a recessive gene for attached ear-lobes because their father is homozygous for the trait.*
5. What would be the possible genotype(s) and phenotype(s) of the offspring in generation V if one of the children in generation IV were to marry a person who was homozygous for free ear-lobes? Explain. *Aa. Each child would receive a gene for free ear-lobes from one parent and a gene for attached ear-lobes from the other parent. Their phenotype is free ear-lobes.*

7–3

Investigation Worksheet **Chapter 7**

Name ______________________ Date ______________

Problem: How similar are traits of offspring to those of the parents? (text page 142)

Data and Observations:

TABLE 7-3. PHENOTYPES OF PARENTS AND CHILDREN					
Trait	Father	Mother	1st Child	2nd Child	3rd Child
Fingers					
Hair color					
Teeth					
Earlobes					
Rh blood type			Answers		
Tongue rolling			will		
Mid-digit hair			vary.		
Height					
Huntington's disease					

Questions and Conclusion:

1. (a) In this simulation, how many chromosomes did each child receive from each of the parents? (b) If this were an actual situation, how many chromosomes would each child receive from each parent? *(a) 2 (b) 23*
2. Explain how the element of chance enters into inheritance of traits. *There is no way to predict which chromosomes will end up in the sex cells of the parent.*
3. Using the data you generated for the first child, determine: (a) the number of traits it inherited that were exactly like those of the father (b) the number of traits it inherited that were exactly like those of the mother. *Answers will vary for (a) and (b).*
4. (a) Using your data from the second child, answer questions 3(a) and 3(b). (b) How many traits does the second child have in common with the first child? *Answers will vary for (a) and (b).*
5. (a) Using your data from the third child, answer questions 3(a) and 3(b). (b) How many traits does the third child have in common with the second child? *Answers will vary.*

Conclusion: How similar are traits of offspring to those of the parents? *It is possible for a child to share a number of traits similar to its parents, but it would be impossible because of chance to find a child that looks like only one parent.*

7–6

Essay **Chapter 8**

Name ______________________ Date ______________

Sex-Related Traits in Humans

The fact that human males have an X and a Y chromosome, and females have two X chromosomes and no Y chromosome, raises some interesting genetic possibilities. This is especially so when it is realized that the sex chromosomes carry genes other than those that determine sex. One should expect to discover that inheritance patterns are related to the sex of an individual. Genes located exclusively on the X chromosome are said to be sex-linked. Genes located exclusively on the Y chromosome are said to be holandric. Because holandric genes appear only on the Y chromosome, these genes produce their effect only in the males. Other mechanisms produce traits that are limited to one sex or another. The genes responsible for these traits are said to be sex-limited. The dominance of a given allele may depend upon the sex of the bearer. The trait that is expressed is said to be sex-influenced.

There are more than 60 sex-linked traits that have been identified in humans. Most of these appear to be due to recessive genes. Red-green color blindness was the first sex-linked trait to be described, and it is the most commonly encountered sex-linked trait. Hemophilia, a well known disorder in which blood clotting is deficient, is also controlled by a sex-linked gene. Other sex-linked traits in humans include two forms of diabetes, nonfunctional sweat glands, absence of central incisors, certain forms of deafness, night blindness, juvenile glaucoma, juvenile muscular dystrophy, and white forelock (a patch of light hair on the front of the head).

There are not many clearly established, holandric genes. One common to the population of India, however, is one that causes excessive hair development on the ears.

Sex-limited genes are different from sex-linked genes. Sex-linked genes may be expressed in either sex, although they may be expressed more in one sex than the other. Sex-limited genes express their effects only in one sex or the other, and their action is clearly related to the production of sex hormones. Sex-limited traits are mostly responsible for secondary sex characteristics. Beard development is such a sex-limited trait. Men normally have beards while women usually do not.

Sex-influenced genes are those whose dominance is influenced by the sex of the bearer. Pattern baldness exhibits such a genetic relationship. In pattern baldness, hair gradually thins on the top of the head. This characteristic is more common in males but may occur in females due to the fact that the gene for pattern baldness is dominant in males but recessive in females.

Questions:

1. Defective tooth enamel is due to a dominant sex-linked gene (E). A female homozygous for defective tooth enamel and a male with normal tooth enamel have three children, 2 girls and 1 boy. What are the possible genotypes and phenotypes of these children? *The genotypes of the girls has to be Ee. They received a dominant gene from their mother. They will have defective tooth enamel. The boy also must have defective tooth enamel because he has to carry the single dominant gene on his X chromosome.*
2. A female is heterozygous for hemophilia (Hh). Her husband does not have hemophilia. Could they produce a hemophiliac son? Could they have a hemophiliac daughter? Explain. *A son could inherit a recessive, sex-linked gene from his mother and so develop hemophilia. Since daughters have two X chromosomes, one from each parent, they will carry at least one dominant gene for normal clotting and so they will not be hemophiliacs.*
3. A male and a female are both heterozygous for pattern baldness. Will both be bald? Explain. *No. The male will be bald because the gene for pattern baldness is dominant in males. The female will not be bald because the gene for pattern baldness is recessive in females.*

8–2

Investigation Worksheet **Chapter 8**

Name ______________________ Date ______________

Problem: How does a genetic disease affect red blood cells? (text page 162)

Part A Answers:

3(a) *S'S* (b) *sickle-cell anemia* (c) *SS* (d) *SS'* (e) *sickle-cell trait*

Data and Observations:

TABLE 8-2. OBSERVATIONS OF RED BLOOD CELLS		
	Appearance	Description
Normal red blood cells		disc-shaped
Sickled red blood cells		sickle-shaped

Questions and Conclusion:

1. Explain why sickle-cell trait and sickle-cell anemia illustrate the inheritance pattern known as incomplete dominance. *One allele is not dominant to the other, resulting in a third, intermediate phenotype.*
2. (a) Where is hemoglobin found? (b) What is the job of hemoglobin? (c) Explain why abnormal, sickled hemoglobin is a problem. *(a) red blood cells (b) oxygen transport (c) Sickled red blood cells cannot carry the needed amount of oxygen.*
3. Explain why sickle-cell trait is less severe than sickle-cell anemia. *A person with sickle-cell trait has some normal red blood cells, while a person with sickle-cell anemia has no normal red blood cells.*
4. How might it be possible to check one's phenotype for normal red cells, sickle-cell trait, or sickle-cell anemia? *Examine a blood sample.*
5. Once the phenotype is determined for one's hemoglobin type, is the genotype also determined? Explain. *yes; In traits showing incomplete dominance, each phenotype has a unique, corresponding genotype.*
6. Assume that you are a genetic counselor as you complete the following problems. Show the parents how you have arrived at your answers by using Punnett squares. (a) A mother has normal red blood cells and the father has all sickled red blood cells. What are the chances of their children being born with sickle-cell trait? Sickle-cell anemia? (b) A mother has sickle-cell trait and the father has sickle-cell anemia. What are the chances of their children being born with sickle-cell trait? Sickle-cell anemia? *(a) All of the children will have sickle-cell trait (b) 50%; 50%*

Conclusion: How does a genetic disease affect red blood cells? *The oxygen-carrying ability of hemoglobin, and thus the shape of the red blood cell, is affected in the sickle-cell disorder.*

8–5

Skills — Chapter 9

Name ______________________ Date ______________

The Genetic Code

One major group of molecules in living cells is the nucleic acids. The nucleic acids include deoxyribonucleic acid (DNA) and ribonucleic acid (RNA). DNA makes up the chromosomes and contains information that is passed from generation to generation. RNA is the messenger molecule that takes the information coded for in the DNA and uses it to make proteins. It is through these proteins that the contents of the chromosomes, the genes, are expressed and metabolism is controlled.

The exact organization and structures of the nucleic acids were first described in 1953 when Rosalind Franklin, James Watson, and Francis Crick, among others, discovered DNA to be a double helix that consists of two strands (made of a five-carbon sugar called deoxyribose, nitrogen bases, and phosphate groups) spiraled about one another and weakly joined by specific pairing of the nitrogen bases. Messenger RNA (mRNA) was shown to be a single-stranded molecule with a structure comparable to half of the structure of the DNA molecule, but containing a different sugar (ribose) and a different nitrogen base (uracil).

The expression of genes occurs through a process called protein synthesis. This is a complex process that involves two steps, *transcription* and *translation*. Transcription begins with the temporary splitting of the DNA molecule. The nitrogen bases of one-half of this DNA molecule then serve as a template for the creation of an mRNA molecule. In translation, the nitrogen bases of mRNA pair with transfer RNA (tRNA) molecules and produce protein molecules. These pairings are precisely governed by the relative ability of the nitrogen bases to form bonds with one another. The rules for base-pairing are summarized in Table 9-1.

TABLE 9-1. PAIRING OF NITROGEN BASES

DNA with DNA	DNA with mRNA	mRNA with tRNA
A–T	T–A	A–U
T–A	A–U	U–A
G–C	C–G	G–C
C–G	G–C	C–G

Use the information in Table 9-1 to fill in the missing nitrogen bases (the blanks) in Figures 9–1, 9–2, and 9–3.

The information in the DNA is transcribed and translated in groups of three bases, called triplets. A triplet of mRNA is called a codon, while a triplet of tRNA is called an anticodon. DNA triplets pair with codons of mRNA, mRNA codons then pair with tRNA anticodons, and the amino acids carried by the tRNA molecules are joined to form long chains. These long chains are proteins. Each tRNA molecule carries a specific kind of amino acid, and different proteins are the result of different amounts and different arrangements of amino acids. Selected triplets and the amino acids they code for are presented in Table 9-2.

TABLE 9-2. DNA TRIPLETS AND AMINO ACIDS FOR WHICH THEY CODE

DNA	mRNA Codon	tRNA Anticodon	Amino Acid
AAA	UUU	AAA	phenylalanine
TTT	AAA	UUU	lysine
AAC	UUG	AAC	leucine
GGC	CCG	GGC	proline
TGG	ACC	UGG	threonine

FIGURE 9–1.

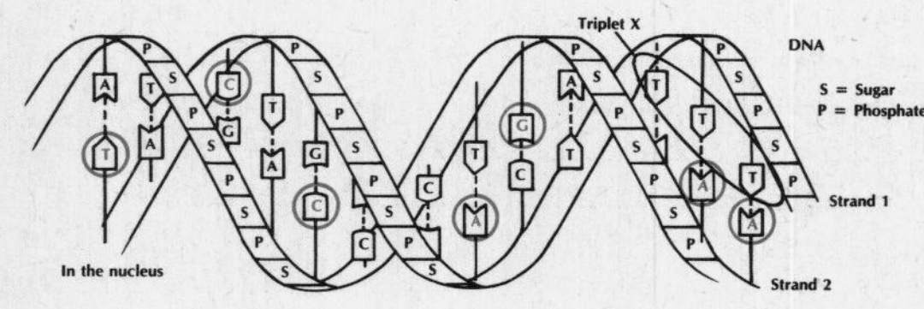

FIGURE 9–2.

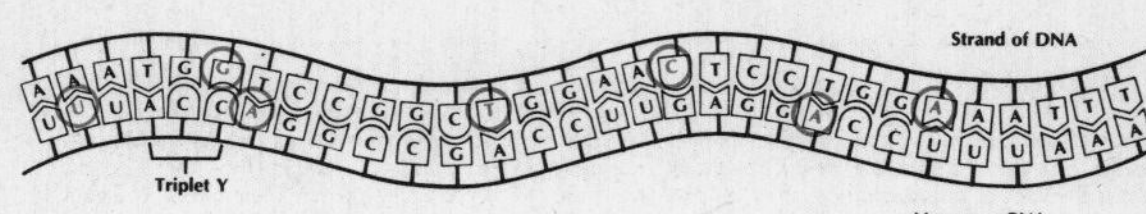

FIGURE 9–3.

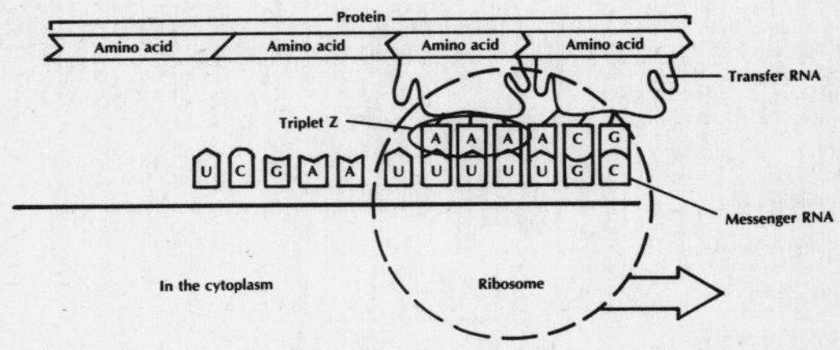

Questions:

1. The DNA triplet labeled X in Figure 9–1 codes for what amino acid? lysine
2. In Figure 9–2, what amino acid is coded for by the mRNA codon labeled Y? threonine
3. In Figure 9–3, what amino acid is carried by the tRNA molecule whose anticodon is labeled triplet Z? phenylalanine
4. The DNA triplet TCC codes for the amino acid arginine. By using the base-pairing rules expressed in Table 9-1, with what codon does this triplet pair? For what anticodon does this DNA triplet code? AGG; UCC

Investigation Worksheet — Chapter 9

Name ______________________ Date ______________

Problem: What is a method for extracting DNA from cells? (text page 184)

Data and Observations:

FIGURE 9–17.

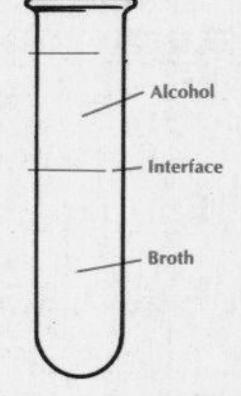

Questions and Conclusion:

1. What is the role of DNA in living cells? It contains the genetic blueprint for life.
2. Describe the structural and chemical makeup of DNA. It is composed of deoxyribose, phosphoric acid, adenine, thymine, cytosine, and guanine in a ladder-like configuration. Deoxyribose and phosphoric acid alternate to form the sides, while adenine joins with thymine, and cytosine joins with guanine to form the rungs.
3. What was the source of DNA in this lab? bacterial cells
4. What might have been the role of lysozyme (an enzyme) in this lab? to break open bacterial cells
5. Would your results have been different if carrot, chicken, or mushroom cells had been used instead of bacterial cells? Explain. no; All cells contain DNA.
6. How might the interface have appeared if you had used only frog cell cytoplasm? Little or no DNA would have been seen.
7. How might the concentration of DNA have compared between two test tubes if human sperm were placed in one tube and equal numbers of human body cells were placed in another? Explain. The concentration of DNA in the tube containing sperm cells would be half that of the DNA in the tube containing body cells because sperm cells contain half the chromosome number of body cells.

Investigation Worksheet — Chapter 9

Name ______________________ Date ______________

8. How might the concentration of DNA have compared between two test tubes if human sperm were placed in one tube and equal numbers of human eggs were placed in another? Explain. The DNA would be equal. Human eggs and sperm have the same number of chromosomes.
9. Study the chart below.

Organism	Percentage of Each Nitrogen Base Contained in DNA			
	A	T	G	C
human	30.2	29.8	19.9	19.8
wheat	27.3	27.1	22.7	22.8
bacteria	36.9	36.3	14.0	14.0

(a) Why is the percent adenine (A) always nearly equal to the percent thymine (T) in an organism? (b) Why is the percent cytosine (C) always nearly equal to the percent guanine (G) in an organism? (a) Adenine can pair only with thymine. (b) Cytosine can pair only with guanine.

Conclusion: What is a method for extracting DNA from cells? Cells are split open with an enzyme. The DNA then reacts with the alcohol to form a series of white strands.

Skills — Chapter 10

Name ______________________ Date ______________________

The Evolution of the Horse

The fossil records of a number of organisms, although incomplete, demonstrate a progression of changes from an initial form (ancestor) to that of the modern descendants. An especially well-documented case history of such evolution has been described for the horse. As the horse evolved, numerous evolutionary side branches developed and became extinct. There is also a major evolutionary line in which changes led from a terrier-sized, four-toed, forest-dwelling *Eohippus* to the larger, one-toed, plains-grazing species of *Equus*. The changes that have taken place during the evolution of today's horse represent adaptations to new habitats and living conditions. These adaptations arose as a consequence of random mutations that have become fixed by natural selection.

Questions:

1. What is the earliest ancestor of the modern horse, and when did it first appear? The earliest ancestor of the modern horse is *Eohippus*, which first appeared approximately 58 million years ago.
2. How does the foot structure of *Merychippus* differ from the foot structure of *Equus*? *Merychippus* has three toes on each of its forefeet and hind feet. *Equus* has one toe on each of its forefeet and hind feet.
3. How does the skull of *Miohippus* differ from the skull of *Equus*? The skull of *Equus* is larger and has a longer snout than the skull of *Miohippus*.
4. What obvious evolutionary changes have taken place between *Eohippus* and *Equus*? Obvious evolutionary changes include a reduction in the number of toes and an increase in size.

FIGURE 10–1.

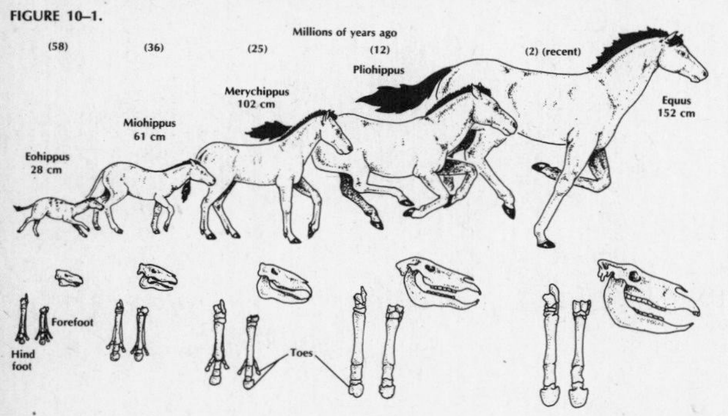

Essay — Chapter 10

Name ______________________ Date ______________________

Death of the Dinosaurs— How Did It Happen?

Approximately 65 million years ago an event of such magnitude took place that it ended the 160 million year reign of the dinosaurs. In 1980 a team of scientists composed of physicist Louis Alvarez and his son, Walter, a geologist, and two associates proposed a theory that attempts to explain the sequence of events that led to the extinction of the dinosaurs.

The Alvarez team had discovered a rare substance, iridium, in a thin layer of sedimentary clay deposited over a layer of rock that belonged to the same period of time as the rock layers bearing dinosaur fossils. Iridium, although nearly nonexistent in Earth's crust, is about 10 000 times more abundant in extraterrestrial rocks and is common in meteorites and asteroids. The iridium layer was found in two parts of the world in clay deposits of exactly the same age, thus prompting the Alvarez team to propose that the iridium had come from an asteroid that hit Earth with enough force to vaporize and scatter iridium atoms into Earth's atmosphere.

A controversial aspect of the team's theory was the idea that the impact of the asteroid blasted so much dust into the atmosphere that it prevented much of the sunlight from reaching Earth. In the darkness, photosynthesis would have been severely impaired, if not impossible, and many of the plants would have died. The deaths of large numbers of plants would have been followed by the extinction of plant-eating dinosaurs and then flesh-eating dinosaurs. Other scientists have suggested that the blocked sunlight would have also precipitated a global freeze, making the world fiercely hostile for the giant beasts that were well-adapted to a tropical world.

No one knows how long the dark, winterlike conditions might have lasted if they did indeed occur. They may have lasted only a few weeks, but significant environmental disruptions could have occurred that may have persisted for thousands of years. In any case, the result was the mass extinction of many plants and animals in many parts of the world.

Most evolutionary theorists have declared themselves supporters of this impact theory. Some scientists have modified or expanded the theory. They believe that perhaps a comet, instead of an asteroid, struck Earth. A comet could have been routed toward Earth by the gravitational pull of a hypothetical companion star to our sun, called Nemesis. Others speculate that a tenth planet, Planet X, might have upset the normal orbit of comets and sent one or more of them toward Earth. A few scientists do not accept the impact theory at all. They assert that no single, catastrophic event was responsible for the extinction of the dinosaurs because the dinosaurs (and other organisms) did not disappear from Earth as rapidly as is presently believed. These scientists maintain that only our faulty interpretation of the dinosaur fossil record supports the idea of rapid, mass extinctions, and that the extinctions occurred gradually over a longer period of time.

Whether the mysteries surrounding the death of the dinosaurs are ever solved, the fact remains that the dinosaurs no longer walk Earth. The event or series of events that closed the dinosaur era also permitted the rapid evolution of a class of animals that have replaced the dinosaurs on Earth. These animals were the mammals, a prolific group that has produced many highly complex animals, including humans and other primates.

Questions:

1. Dinosaurs were the dominant life form on Earth for how many years? 160 million years
2. Who were the scientists behind the current, and most popular, theory on how the dinosaurs became extinct? Louis Alvarez, his son Walter, and two associates
3. Summarize the impact theory. An asteroid struck Earth, vaporized, and sent so much dust into the atmosphere that sunlight could not reach the surface of Earth. Photosynthesis was inhibited, plants died, and the plant-eating and animal-eating dinosaurs soon followed.

Investigation Worksheet — Chapter 10

Name ______________________ Date ______________________

Problem: How does comparative biochemistry support the theory of evolution? (text page 216)

Data and Observations:

TABLE 10-2. COMPARISON OF RNA NITROGEN BASE SEQUENCES

	Number of RNA Sequences in Common With Each Organism														
Organism	1	2	3	4	5	6	7	8	9	10	11	12	13	14	15
1		22	20	16	15	15	14	14	9	7	7	6	7	7	9
5	15	15	15	12		25	17	15	8	7	8	10	8	10	10
10	7	7	7	9	7	7	9	10	18		7	6	6	8	8
15	9	9	11	10	10	10	8	10	7	8	10	13	12	8	

Questions and Conclusion:

1. Define: (a) mRNA (b) tRNA (c) DNA (d) nitrogen base (e) comparative biochemistry (f) homologous. (a) a single strand of nucleotides that carry the DNA message from nucleus to ribosomes (b) a clover-leaf-shaped molecule of nucleotides that brings specific amino acids to ribosomes in preparation for protein formation (c) nucleic acid with the genetic message (d) compound in nucleic acid that forms the rungs of DNA and RNA (e) study of chemical similarities in organisms (f) parts in organisms that have the same structures and therefore the same origin
2. What do the following letters represent in an RNA nitrogen base sequence: (a) A (b) U (c) C (d) G? (a) adenine (b) uracil (c) cytosine (d) guanine
3. In closely related organisms, the sequences of nitrogen bases in the RNA of each organism are very similar. Thus, they are thought to have evolved from a common ancestor. (a) Which two organisms show the most similar RNA sequences? (b) Which two organisms show the most similar biochemistry? (c) Which two organisms may have evolved from a common ancestor? (d) Which two organisms may have the most similar genetic material? (e) Which two organisms may have the most similar DNA? All answers are 5 and 6.
4. Reading down column 2, (a) which two organisms are the most related biochemically? Explain. (b) Which two organisms may show the most homologous chemical similarities? (c) Which two organisms may have evolved from the same ancestor? (d) Which two organisms are the least related biochemically? Explain. (a) 1 and 2; They have 22 similar nitrogen base sequences. (b) 1 and 2 (c) 1 and 2 (d) 2 and 10; They have only 7 similar nitrogen base sequences.

Investigation Worksheet — Chapter 10

Name ______________________ Date ______________________

5. Reading down column 9, (a) which two organisms are the most related biochemically? Explain. (b) Which two organisms may show the most homologous chemical similarities? (c) Which two organisms may have evolved from the same ancestor? (d) Which two organisms are the least related biochemically? Explain. (a) 9 and 10; They have 18 similar nitrogen base sequences. (b) 9 and 10 (c) 9 and 10 (d) 9 and 15; They have only seven similar nitrogen base sequences.
6. Closely related organisms often show many physical similarities. Which groupings would show the most physical similarities: (a) organisms 2 and 15 or 2 and 1 (b) organisms 3 and 15 or 3 and 5 (c) organisms 7 and 5 or 7 and 15? (a) 2 and 1 (b) 3 and 5 (c) 7 and 5
7. How might organisms 5 and 6 be expected to appear when compared to one another? Explain. very similar; The high number of similar nitrogen bases indicates they also have similar DNA.
8. How might organisms 1 and 12 be expected to appear when compared to one another? Explain. not very similar; The low number of similar nitrogen bases indicates they have different DNA.
9. An organism has the following mRNA nitrogen base sequence: ACCUCG. (a) Convert the mRNA base sequence into the proper corresponding DNA sequence of nitrogen bases. (b) Convert the mRNA base sequence into the proper corresponding tRNA sequence of nitrogen bases. (a) TGGAGC (b) UGGAGC
10. An organism has the following nitrogen base sequence: AUCCUG. (a) Convert the mRNA base sequence into the proper corresponding DNA sequence of nitrogen bases. (b) Convert the mRNA base sequence into the proper corresponding tRNA sequence of nitrogen bases. (a) TAGGAC (b) UAGGAC
11. When comparing a gorilla and a human, or a frog and a human: (a) which two animals show greater physical resemblance to each other? A lesser physical resemblance? (b) which two animals would have RNA sequences that are similar to each other? Not similar? (a) gorilla and man; frog and man (b) gorilla and man; frog and man

Conclusion: How does comparative biochemistry support the theory of evolution? The more nitrogen base sequences two organisms share, the closer their DNA is chemically. DNA similarity supports closeness of ancestry.

Investigation Worksheet — Chapter 11

Name ______________________ Date ______________

Problem: What evidence can be used to determine if an animal is or was a biped or a quadruped? (text page 243)

Data and Observations:

TABLE 11-1. COMPARISON OF QUADRUPED AND BIPED CHARACTERISTICS			
	Ape	Human	*Australopithecus*
Arm length	61	44	–
Leg length	51	52	–
Position of hind leg	bent	straight	–
Shape of lumbar region	straight	S-shape	–
Position of center of gravity	in front of pelvis	in center of pelvis	–
Location of weight-bearing axis	inside edge of lower portion of femur	outside edge of lower portion of femur	outside edge of lower portion of femur

Questions and Conclusion:

1. Define each of the following terms: (a) *Australopithecus* (b) natural selection (c) bipedalism (d) quadrupedalism. (a) most primitive hominids found in Africa (b) theory that the best adapted organisms survive and reproduce (c) locomotion on two feet (d) locc four feet
2. Compare arm and leg lengths in a biped. Leg length is greater than arm length.
3. Compare arm and leg lengths in a quadruped. Arm length is greater than leg length.
4. Explain how the position of the hind legs in bipeds differs from the position of the hind legs in quadrupeds. The hind leg is straight in bipeds, while bent in quadrupeds.
5. If the center of gravity is located above and in front of the pelvis of an animal, the animal has a tendency to fall over when standing on only two legs. Which animal that you studied in this investigation might have this problem? ape

Investigation Worksheet — Chapter 11

Name ______________________ Date ______________

6. An animal having more body weight in the upper trunk shows a center of gravity above the pelvis. (a) Describe how body weight is distributed in humans. (b) Explain how body weight distribution influences the ability of an animal to stand upright. (a) More body weight is below the pelvis. (b) More body weight above the pelvis causes an animal to fall over because its center of gravity is too high.
7. Explain how the shape of the lumbar region of a biped differs from the shape of the lumbar region of a quadruped. The lumbar region in quadrupeds is straight, while in bipeds it is curved.
8. Does the evidence indicate that *Australopithecus* was a biped or quadruped? Explain. biped; The location of its weight-bearing axis (in the legs) is similar to that in humans.
9. Explain if each of the following animals was bipedal or quadrupedal: (a) arm length = 452 mm; leg length = 520 mm (b) outside edge of knee joint worn more than inside edge (c) inside edge of knee joint worn more than outside edge. (a) biped; legs are longer than arms (b) bipedal; femur shows more weight toward outside edge of knee as in humans (c) quadruped; femur shows more weight toward inside edge of knee as in ape

Conclusion: What evidence can be used to determine if an animal is or was a biped or a quadruped? Quadrupeds have arms longer than legs, a straight lumbar region, bent legs, center of gravity above the pelvis, weight-bearing axis at inside edge of lower portion of femur. Bipeds have legs longer than arms, curved lumbar region, straight legs, center of gravity at pelvis, weight-bearing axis at outside edge of lower femur.

Skills — Chapter 12

Name ______________________ Date ______________

Identifying Unusual Mammals

Use the identification key that follows in order to determine the names of the unusual mammals illustrated to the right. For each mammal identified by a letter, record its name in the accompanying chart.

Identification Key

1a. Animal possesses hooves 2
1b. Animal lacks hooves 6

2a. Animal possesses long horns 3
2b. Animal possesses short horns or lacks horns 4

3a. Horns straight, not curved ....eland
3b. Horns curved ....sable

4a. Neck long and slender ....okapi
4b. Neck short and thick 5

5a. Lower back and rump of one color, without stripes ....takin
5b. Lower back and rump marked with stripes ....duiker

6a. Snout piglike 7
6b. Snout not piglike 8

7a. Ears greatly extended, like those of a jack-rabbit or donkey ....aardvark
7b. Ears shortened, not extended ....peccary

8a. Body covered by fur 9
8b. Body covered with horny scales ....pangolin

9a. Nose long and flexible ....coati
9b. Nose short, not flexible ....potto

TABLE 12-1. IDENTIFYING MAMMALS			
Unusual Mammal	Name	Unusual Mammal	Name
A	Aardvark	F	Pangolin
B	Coati	G	Okapi
C	Duiker	H	Sable
D	Eland	I	Potto
E	Takin	J	Peccary

Essay — Chapter 12

Name ______________________ Date ______________

Hydrothermal-Vent Tube Worms

A little over 10 years ago, geologists on the research submarine *Alvin* discovered a system of hydrothermal vents at a spreading ridge on the floor of the Pacific Ocean. Although the scientists were not surprised to find the spreading ridge, a place where Earth's crust is spreading apart, they were surprised and puzzled by the completely unexpected discovery of a thriving community of unusual invertebrate species. These species included giant tube worms as much as 1 meter long, large white clams 30 centimeters in length, and clusters of mussels. They also discovered shrimp, crabs, and fish.

The presence of such a rich community of organisms at a depth of such high pressure, low temperature (2°C–4°C), and darkness was bewildering. Every ecosystem on Earth must have a source of energy and, for the majority of Earth's communities, sunlight is that source. Plants transform sunlight into energy that is available to other members of the ecosystem. Here, in the perpetual darkness, there must be another source of energy. Observations made over the last 6 years have shown that while the water is very warm around the vents, ranging from 10°C to 20°C, the heat cannot supply enough energy to account for life at such depths. Scientists have known for years that sulfide-rich environments, such as terrestrial hotsprings, support bacteria that derive their energy from hydrogen sulfide, rather than the sun. Further study of the vent environment has shown that sulfur bacteria are present around the vents as well, and they serve as "green plants," turning the energy in hydrogen sulfide and other carbon compounds (the equivalent of sunlight) into a form usable by the tube worms and other organisms. The sulfur bacteria provide energy and support life around the hydrothermal vents.

The anatomy and metabolism of the tube worm, *Riftia pachyptila,* dominant life form around the vent, provides a remarkable model of the relationship between an organism and these sulfur bacteria. *Riftia* is an unusual creature. It is essentially a closed sac, without a mouth or a digestive system. At its tip is a bright red, gill-like plume through which oxygen, carbon dioxide, and hydrogen sulfide are exchanged with seawater. Below the plume, there is a ring of muscle, the vestimentum, that anchors the worm in its white tube. Most of the rest of the animal consists of a thin-walled sac that contains the worm's internal organs. The largest of the organs is the trophosome, which occupies most of the body cavity.

Microscopic studies of the trophosome indicate that it contains vast numbers of sulfur bacteria. *Riftia* seems to take in carbon dioxide, oxygen, and hydrogen sulfide from the water, thus supplying the bacteria with the materials they need for their metabolism. These substances are absorbed by *Riftia's* plume and are transported to the bacteria by way of the worm's circulatory system. The bacteria, in turn, produce the reduced carbon compounds that *Riftia* requires as food.

Riftia has the unusual ability to take in and transport hydrogen sulfide without poisoning itself. Hydrogen sulfide is toxic to most life forms. Research has shown that *Riftia* has a higher amount of hemoglobin in its blood than other invertebrates. Hemoglobin serves to bind with oxygen and transports it throughout the tube worm's body. Hemoglobin in *Riftia* is not a typical form of hemoglobin. It binds with hydrogen sulfide as well as oxygen. It is through this binding action that hydrogen sulfide can be transported to the bacteria in the trophosome without poisoning *Riftia.*

Questions:

1. How can the dark, isolated ecosystem around the hydrothermal vents supply itself with energy? The sulfur bacteria get their energy from hydrogen sulfide and supply energy to all of the other organisms around the vent.
2. What are three unusual features of *Riftia*? It lacks a mouth or digestive system; it has a unique relationship with sulfur-metabolizing bacteria; its hemoglobin is able to bind with hydrogen sulfide.

Investigation Worksheet — Chapter 12

Name ______________________ Date ______________________

Problem: What information can be gained from classifying living organisms? (text page 254)

Part B Answers:

TABLE 12-2. MATCHING SCIENTIFIC AND COMMON NAMES

Answer	I	II
g	*Beta vulgaris*	a. black pepper
l	*Salmo gairdneni*	b. perch
j	*Citrus limon*	c. rat
a	*Piper nigrum*	d. canary
k	*Ipomoea batatus*	e. penicillin
m	*Tarpor atlanticus*	f. herring
i	*Crocyodylus americanus*	g. beet
c	*Rattus norvegicus*	h. carrot
b	*Perca flavescens*	i. crocodile
h	*Daucus carota*	j. lemon
d	*Serinus canarius*	k. sweet potato
f	*Clupea harengus*	l. salmon
e	*Penicillium chrysogenum*	m. Atlantic tarpon

TABLE 12-3. MATCHING SCIENTIFIC AND COMMON NAMES

Answer	I	II
n	*Aralia quinquefolia*	a. dog
g	*Crotaphytus collaris*	b. seventeen-year locust
j	*Helianthus annus*	c. cat
i	*Eurycea bilineata*	d. paper birch
k	*Alytes obstetricans*	e. sea cucumber
l	*Urus horibilis*	f. sugar cane
h	*Magicicada septendecem*	g. collared lizard
d	*Betula papyrifera*	h. earthworm
m	*Secale cereale*	i. two-lined salamander
c	*Felis domesticus*	j. sunflower
f	*Saccharum officinarum*	k. midwife toad
h	*Lumbricus terrestris*	l. grizzly bear
e	*Cucumaria frondosa*	m. rye
a	*Canis familiaris*	n. five leaflet ginseng

Data and Observations:

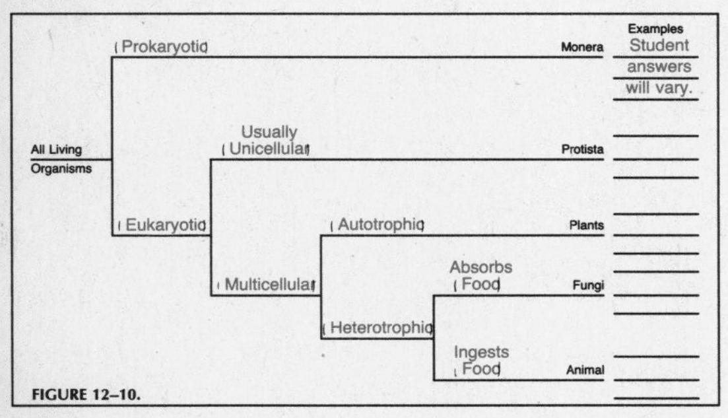

FIGURE 12–10.

Investigation Worksheet — Chapter 12

Name ______________________ Date ______________________

Questions and Conclusion:

1. Define: (a) binomial nomenclature (b) taxonomy (c) eukaryotic (d) prokaryotic (e) autotrophic (f) heterotrophic. (a) a two-word naming system used in classification of organisms (b) the science of classification (c) cells having a true nucleus (d) cells not having a true nucleus (e) an organism capable of making its own food (f) an organism incapable of making its own food
2. (a) What category of classification is used for the first term in a scientific name? (b) What category of classification is used for the second term in a scientific name? (a) genus (b) species
3. Describe three rules that are used in writing a scientific name. Do not use the information in question 2. Genus is written with a capital. Species uses lowercase. The entire name is either underlined or written in italics.
4. An organism is found to be eukaryotic and ingests food. Using completed Figure 12–10: (a) name the kingdom to which this organism belongs (b) list two other traits of this organism. (a) animal (b) It is heterotrophic and multicellular.
5. An organism is found to be prokaryotic. Using completed Figure 12–10, name the kingdom that this organism belongs to. Explain. Monera is the kingdom of classification for all prokaryotic organisms.
6. An organism belongs to the plant kingdom. Using completed Figure 12–10, list three traits that this organism will have. eukaryotic, multicellular, autotrophic
7. An organism belongs to the fungi kingdom. Using completed Figure 12–10, list three traits that this organism will have. absorbs food, heterotrophic, multicellular
8. List two reasons why there is a need for classifying organisms. (1) the need for order and organization (2) to provide a logical means for naming organisms
9. Explain why the language of classification is based mainly on Latin. in order to establish a universal nomenclature

Conclusion: What information can be gained from classifying living organisms? A scientific name is gained for all living things and specific traits can be assumed even though they are not seen directly when an organism is placed into a specific kingdom or group.

Essay — Chapter 13

Name ______________________ Date ______________________

Yeasts: New Research Tools

There are roughly 60 genera and 600 species of yeast. One species, *Saccharomyces cerevisiae*, better known as baker's yeast, is commonly used to swell bread, brew beer, and cause champagne to bubble. The bakers and brewers, however, are not the only people interested in this single-celled, colony-dwelling fungus. Biologists are also interested in *Saccharomyces cerevisiae*. Biologists are probing yeast cells to find out about the intimate details of genes, proteins, and the structure of living cells. Yeasts are helping biologists answer such questions as: How do you make a chromosome? What signals a cell that it is time to divide? What tells a cell to stop dividing?

Biologists apply to human cells what they learn from yeast because, in certain aspects, yeast cells and human cells are very similar. Like human cells, yeast cells have two genders and reproduce with cells similar to eggs and sperm; and each cell has a nucleus. A yeast cell has 17 pairs of chromosomes that behave remarkably like the 23 pairs of human chromosomes. During reproduction, the chromosomes in yeast cells can be involved in the same mistakes as those that cause genetic disorders such as Down Syndrome. Yeasts manufacture enzymes similar to those of humans and release and ferry them around in much the same way that the human pancreas, liver, and brain cells do. Yeast cells, like human cells, are vulnerable to mutagenic agents.

From a research standpoint, yeast cells have numerous advantages over cultured human or mouse cells. Yeast thrive in a petri dish. The cells divide about every two hours. Some mouse or human cells take 12 hours or more to divide. This means that experiments can be completed more quickly when using yeast cells. Since a yeast cell has about 10 000 genes and a human cell 40 000, yeast genes can be more easily mapped and analyzed than human genes. By exposing petri dishes of yeast cells to radiation or mutagenic chemicals, scientists can obtain a vast number of mutant strains of yeast. These strains can be studied for clues to the roles of genes in genetic defects.

Leland Hartwell, a geneticist at the University of Washington, has studied mutations in yeast cells. Some of the mutations did not allow yeast cells to divide. Hartwell wondered if a crucial gene controlling DNA synthesis could be involved. Some of the cells' buds would not separate from the mother cell. Over several years of research approximately 50 genes have been shown to control various stages of yeast cell division. It is thought that similar genes control cell division in human cells.

In 1985, Gerald Fink, a molecular biologist at the Whitehead Institute for Biomedical Research at Cambridge, Massachusetts, found in yeast something similar to the human AIDS virus. This virus does not make yeast immune-deficient, since there are no white blood cells for them to attack, but the virus is classified as a retrovirus, like the AIDS virus. A retrovirus carries its own nucleic acid to direct a cell's operations. It copies the genetic information it carries into the host cell's DNA. Fink hopes that understanding how the AIDS-like virus works in the yeast cell will lead to a better understanding of how the AIDS virus works in human cells.

Questions:

1. Why are scientists using yeast in order to better understand human cells? Yeast cells are similar to human cells in many respects.
2. What are some advantages of using yeast cells in research over human cells? Yeast cells grow easily in culture; they divide quickly; they have fewer genes; they are vulnerable to mutagenic agents.
3. How have mutant genes in yeast helped scientists better understand cell division? Mutant genes that affect certain stages of cell division have been identified. The scientists can study the mutant genes and compare them to healthy, normal genes.

Critical Thinking — Chapter 13

Name ______________________ Date ______________________

Is It a Plant or An Animal?

Before the advent of high-powered microscopes, biologists had little difficulty in classifying the forms of life that were visible to their naked eye. In these earlier times there were only two kingdoms, Animalia and Plantae. If an organism had green color and the presence of leaves, stems, and roots it was considered a plant. In contrast, if an organism had eyes, teeth, and legs, it was considered an animal. Plants were thought of as simple organisms that were nonmotile, or that did not exhibit movement. Animals were motile and were obviously more complex than plants.

With the use of early microscopes, new organisms were discovered. The biologists at that time tried to follow the same thoughts in differentiating between microscopic green (chlorophyll-containing) algae and the colorless, unicellular animals, yeasts, protozoans, molds, and bacteria. All of the microscopic algae, fungi, and bacteria were assigned to the plant kingdom because they were not motile, they had simple, plant-like structures, and they did not capture and eat solid food like animals. The protozoans, on the other hand, were classified as animals because of their complex structure, motility, and their ability to capture and eat solid food.

This simple classification soon encountered difficulties. The advances in scientific technique and microscopes made it more and more difficult to classify some organisms as either plant or animal. For example, it was discovered that plant cells contain cellulose, a molecule that provides structural support, while many animals, such as insects and crustaceans, have a supporting structure of chitin. Yet, many fungi (classed as plants) have cell walls of chitin, and certain primitive animals, the sea squirts, have an outer covering of cellulose. There are types of bacteria that are photosynthetic, and there are algae that produce mobile reproductive cells that resemble protozoans. The lines of distinction between plants and animals have become blurred.

Euglena is an example of an organism that exhibits a combination of overlapping characteristics of plants and animals. Plants contain chlorophyll that enables them to use sunlight as a source of energy for making their own food. Typical animal cells and fungi do not contain chlorophyll and they must have an external source of food. *Euglena*, an algal-like microorganism, contains chlorophyll in chloroplasts but also has the ability to engulf solid food. When food is available it takes it in, but when food is scarce it makes its own food. It also possesses a flagellum that gives it mobility. Some species of *Euglena* lack chlorophyll and are animal-like, while others are nonmotile and are plant-like.

The challenge facing today's biologists is to learn more about these organisms and continue to improve the criteria and methods for classifying organisms.

Questions:

1. How did the invention and improvement of the microscope create problems in classification? New organisms that did not fit existing classification schemes were discovered.
2. Why might *Euglena* be classified as a plant? As an animal? Some species contain chlorophyll and are nonmotile, like plants. Some are motile and consume food, like animals.
3. Why are *Euglena* and some types of bacteria difficult to classify? They have traits characteristic of more than one group.
4. Why was the two-kingdom classification system (Animalia vs. Plantae) abandoned? It was discovered that many organisms, fungi and bacteria, do not fit into either.
5. If scientists discover a new organism that clearly has characteristics of both fungi and protozoans (organisms, each in their own kingdom), how should the new organism be classified? Answers will vary. The new organism may be so different that a new kingdom is developed.

Investigation Worksheet — Chapter 13

Name ______________________ Date ______________

Problem: What are the traits of organisms in the kingdoms Monera, Protista, and Fungi? (text page 282)

Data and Observations:

FIGURE 13–29.

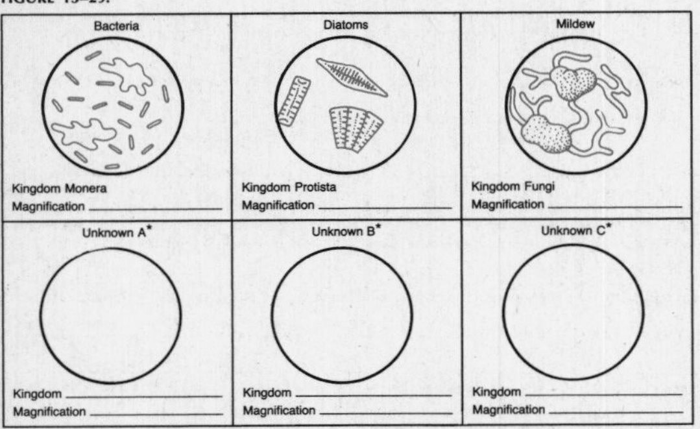

Answers will vary with the unknown used.

Questions and Conclusion:

1. List three traits of Kingdom Monera. Traits include prokaryotic cells, no nucleus, no mitochondria, chlorophyll possibly present but not located in chloroplasts.
2. (a) Distinguish between the two main groups of Eubacteria in Kingdom Monera. (b) Based on your answer to 2(a), to what group does the organism observed in Part A belong? (a) heterotrophic Eubacteria and autotrophic Eubacteria (b) Schizomycophyta
3. List three traits of Kingdom Protista. simple eukaryotic organisms, most unicellular, may be autotrophic or heterotrophic

Investigation Worksheet — Chapter 13

Name ______________________ Date ______________

4. (a) Distinguish among the seven phyla in Kingdom Protista. (Omit slime molds.) (b) Based on your answer to 4(a), to what phylum does the organism observed in Part B belong? (a) Three phyla are photosynthetic, but differ in their method of locomotion and color (Euglenophyta have a single flagellum and are green; Chrysophyta have no means of locomotion and are yellow-green to golden-brown; Pyrrophyta have two flagella and may be red). Four are heterotrophic and vary in their method of locomotion (sarcodines by pseudopodia; ciliates by cilia; flagellates by flagella; sporozoans have no means of moving). (b) Chrysophyta
5. List three traits of Kingdom Fungi. heterotrophic, either parasitic or saprophytic, cell walls with chitin
6. (a) Distinguish among the three phyla in Kingdom Fungi. (Omit lichens.) (b) Based on your answer to 6(a), to what phylum does the organism observed in Part C belong? (HINT: This fungus produces asci.) (a) Zygomycota produce sporangia; Basidomycota produce basidia; Ascomycota produce asci. (b) Ascomycota
7. List several traits that aided you in determining to which kingdom: (a) unknown organism A belonged (b) unknown organism B belonged (c) unknown organism C belonged. Answers will vary with the unknowns used.

Conclusion: What are the traits of organisms in Kingdoms Monera, Protista, and Fungi? Answers should reflect traits given in questions 1, 3, and 5.

Essay — Chapter 14

Name ______________________ Date ______________

Biotechnology: Growing Flavors in the Laboratory

At one time there were two flavors of ice cream from which to choose: vanilla and chocolate. Today we must make hard choices between common flavors like strawberry and unusual flavors like bubblegum. We must make the choice between the subtle, well-rounded natural flavor and its more intense, artificial, synthetically produced cousin.

Now we face other choices as biotechnology firms learn how to grow flavors in living plant cells. One California firm is harvesting vanilla flavor from cells that have been surgically removed from vanilla plants and cultured in a glass bioreactor. One of the key techniques of this technology is plant tissue culture, the growth of plant cells in the laboratory. For example, in order to make vanilla, scientists first remove cells from the vanilla plant and culture them in a laboratory dish. Various hormones are added to the cell culture to prevent the cells from differentiating into root or leaf cells. The cell culture is then submerged in a bath of nutrients that help the cells multiply. To turn on the cells' flavor-making factories, additional hormones are added. The cells are finally placed in a protected material and packed into a glass column through which more nutrients flow. Flavor that leaks out of the cells is collected.

The production of pure, natural vanilla flavoring is perhaps less complicated, but more expensive and time-consuming. The vanilla orchid grows primarily in the Malagasy Republic and Indonesia. Each flower of the orchid opens for only one day of the year and must be hand pollinated in order to produce the fruit, or bean. The vanilla bean is cured in a labor-intensive process that takes three to six months. Two kilograms of uncured beans produce approximately one-half kilogram of cured beans. The pure, natural vanilla flavoring extracted from the beans sells for around $2000 per kilogram.

Artificial vanilla flavoring is much less expensive than pure, natural vanilla. Artificial vanilla sells for $10 per kilogram and is made primarily of vanillin. Vanillin is an inexpensive by-product of the paper industry, extracted from wood pulp.

There is no question as to what is natural vanilla and what is artificial vanilla, but how do we treat the vanilla produced by vanilla plant cell cultures? Is it natural or artificial? The biotechnology firms claim that it is natural because it is produced by vanilla plant cells. The vanilla industry insists that it is artificial. They maintain that since pure, natural vanilla contains 150 constituents and the biotechnology firms product contains only eight or ten of these constituents, one of which is vanillin, it cannot be considered natural vanilla flavor. By 1990, the California biotechnology firms expect to produce several hundred thousand kilograms of vanilla flavor a year. This is about the same amount of vanilla that is currently produced by the vanilla bean industry.

Vanilla is not the only flavor that can be produced by plant cell tissue cultures. Similar techniques can be used to produce strawberry, raspberry, grape, and nearly any other fruit flavor. In the future, when you say "I'll take vanilla," what kind of flavor will you get?

Questions:

1. How are flavors produced through plant cell culture similar to natural flavors? The flavors come from living plant cells and are not synthetically produced.
2. Which type of vanilla flavoring would you prefer—natural, artificial, or that produced through biotechnology? Explain your reasoning. Answers will vary. Some may choose the natural because it comes directly from the vanilla bean.
3. If the laboratory-produced vanilla flavoring is accepted and approved for sale, what effect might this product have on the vanilla bean industry in the Malagasy Republic? (The cost of the laboratory-produced vanilla would be less expensive than pure, natural vanilla but slightly more than artificial vanilla.) Answers will vary. Students may say that the vanilla bean industry in the Malagasy Republic may suffer because there will not be as large a demand for pure, natural vanilla.

Investigation Worksheet — Chapter 14

Name ______________________ Date ______________

Problem: What are the characteristics of gymnosperms? (text page 304)

Data and Observations:

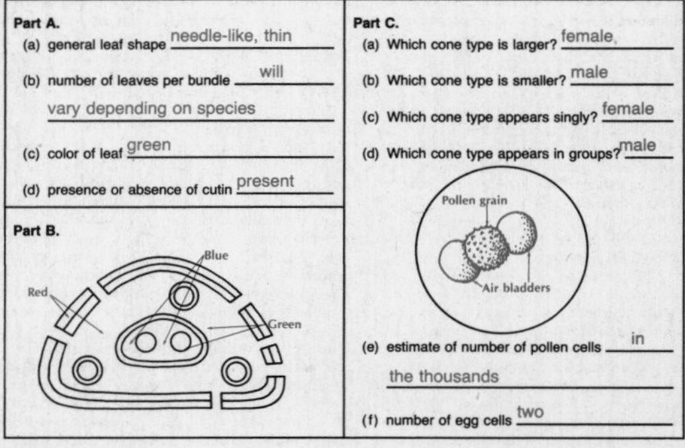

Questions and Conclusion:

1. Define: (a) gymnosperm (b) pollen grain (c) cone. (a) plants with naked seeds that develop on the scale of cones (b) structure that contains the male sex cell (c) seed-bearing or pollen-bearing structure of gymnosperms
2. Refer to Appendix A and determine the kingdom, phylum, subphylum, and class for a pine tree. kingdom Plantae; phylum Tracheophyta; subphylum Pteropsida; class Gymnospermae
3. Compare the number of pollen grains (male sex cells) on one scale to the number of egg cells (female sex cells) on one scale. More pollen grains are present than egg cells.
4. Pollen cells are carried by the wind to female cones where fertilization of egg cells occurs. Explain the adaptive advantage of air bladders on the pollen grains. aid the wind in carrying pollen

Conclusion: What are the characteristics of gymnosperms? green needle-like leaves with a photosynthetic spongy layer, layers of cutin, epidermis, and endodermis; vascular bundles; male cones appear in groups—form millions of pollen grains; female cones are singular—form two egg cells on each cone scale

Essay — Chapter 15

Name ______________________ Date ______________

Medicinal Leeches

To scientists a leech is an annelid and a close relative of the earthworm. It is also a hermaphrodite, having both male and female sex organs. To many of us, however, a leech is a repulsive, slimy creature with a notorious past. We relate leeches to the outdated medical practice of "leeching." The use of leeches for medicinal purposes was based on the belief that disease was caused by an excess of "bad" blood or by an imbalance in body humors (fluids). The medicinal leech, *Hirudo medicinalis*, was used to withdraw the bad blood or to readjust the body humors.

Leeching was most popular from 1820 to 1850, when the enthusiasm for leeching bordered on madness. A French doctor, Francois Broussais, once treated his own indigestion with 15 applications of 50 to 60 leeches over an 18-day period. Leeches were applied, up to 50 at a time, to patients having every disorder from nosebleeds to obesity.

Today, there is a resurgence in the medicinal use of leeches. It has promising potential for yielding new knowledge and new medical therapies. One such therapy was used in 1985 to save a reattached ear.

On August 16, 1985 in Medford, Massachusetts, a dog attacked a five-year-old boy and bit off his right ear. In a previous operation, an adult's ear had been reattached by surgeons. A child's ear, however, never had been. Not only did the ear have to be reattached, but the artery and veins that would supply blood to the ear had to be reconnected. Dr. Joseph Upton, who performed the operation, worked for 10 hours while looking through a surgical microscope. Artery reconnection is relatively easy, but reattachment of the smaller veins is more difficult: it takes a period of time before the veins are healed well enough to return blood from the ear. During this time, the tissues are subject to damage and infection. Within a few days, the boy's ear began to discolor. It first turned blue and then purple as blood pooled in the ear. Dr. Upton searched for a way to relieve the blood congestion in the ear while the veins healed, and he chose to return to the practice of leeching. He found the medicinal leech to be unavailable in the United States, but a series of phone calls led him to a company called Biopharm in Swansea, Wales. The firm sent a package of 30 medicinal leeches. Upon application, the first leech fastened itself to the upper part of the boy's ear and began to pulse slightly, the sign that bloodsucking had begun. Eight leeches and a few days later, the boy was released from the hospital and returned home with an intact, healthy ear. The leeches had given the ear time to heal itself.

Leeches have also become a model for research. The medicinal leech has large and accessible nerve cells. With a leech, one can pick out a particular neuron under the microscope and study it in detail. Scientists are interested in several biochemicals that have evolved in the leech as a means of obtaining blood. Scientists hope that these biochemicals may one day be used to treat circulatory problems and other disorders. One substance is an anticoagulant, a substance that prevents blood from clotting. Another biochemical secreted by the leech dilates the veins. Still another chemical, called a spreading factor, breaks down the cement that binds cells together. These biochemicals helped keep the boy's ear clear of congested blood until the veins could heal.

The giant Amazon leech secretes an anticoagulant that also may be used in medicine. Roy Sawyer and Andrei Budzynski discovered this biochemical and named it hemetin. Sawyer is a research scientist and owner of Biopharm. Budzynski is a biochemistry professor at Temple University. Hemetin is unusual in that it not only prevents coagulation, but also dissolves blood clots after they form. It is hoped that hemetin can one day be used to dissolve blood clots.

Questions:

1. What is leeching? It is a method of placing leeches on the body in order to withdraw blood.
2. How were leeches recently used to help save a reattached ear? Leeches were placed on the reattached ear. They removed congested blood.
3. Why are leeches of interest to medical scientists today? Leeches are useful in treating surgical grafts; they are helping researchers understand the human nervous system; they produce biochemicals that may someday be used to treat circulatory problems.

15–2

Investigation Worksheet — Chapter 15

Name ______________________ Date ______________

Problem: What does the pork worm *Trichinella spiralis* look like and what is its life cycle? (text page 324)

Data and Observations:

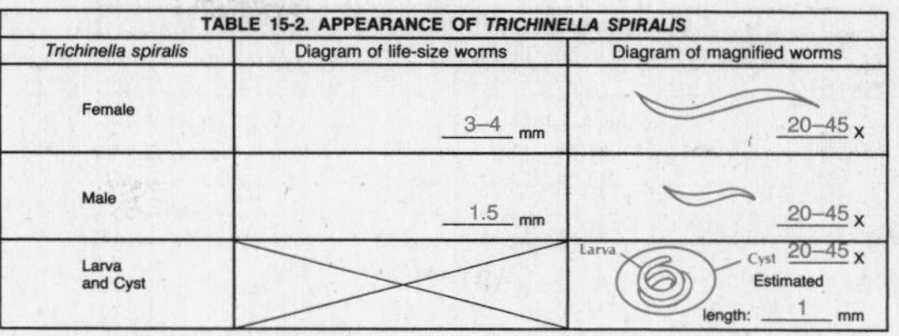

TABLE 15-2. APPEARANCE OF *TRICHINELLA SPIRALIS*		
Trichinella spiralis	Diagram of life-size worms	Diagram of magnified worms
Female	3–4 mm	20–45 x
Male	1.5 mm	20–45 x
Larva and Cyst		Larva; Cyst; 20–45 x; Estimated length: 1 mm

Questions and Conclusion:

1. Define the following terms: (a) parasite (b) host. (a) organism that lives in or on a host and gets nourishment from the host (b) organism from which another organism benefits
2. Classify *Trichinella spiralis* according to kingdom, phylum, genus, and species. Animalia, Nematoda, *Trichinella*, *spiralis*
3. List several characteristics for the phylum to which this animal belongs. round body shape, separate sexes, internal fertilization, external development, parasitic
4. What evidence do you have to support the observation that these worms are not hermaphrodites? A male and female were examined.
5. List the stage in the life cycle of the worm in which infection of other pigs could be prevented. Explain your answer. 2; Do not feed pig scraps containing the larvae to other pigs.
6. List the stage in which infection of humans could be prevented. Explain your answer. 6; Make sure pork is cooked thoroughly, thus destroying the larvae.
7. List the stage at which each of these symptoms may occur: (a) extreme weakness and muscle soreness (b) internal bleeding and infections (c) diarrhea, abdominal pain, and nausea. (a) 9 (b) 8 (c) 8 and 9
8. To find evidence of pork worms in a human, would you look for larval or adult worms? Explain your answer. larval; The appearance of the adult worm is rather short and the larval stage is easily detected.

Conclusion: What does the pork worm *Trichinella spiralis* look like and what is its life cycle? worms are small (female 3–4 mm, male 1–2 mm); body is round with two openings to the digestive tract; life cycle is completed within a pig or human host.

15–6

Skills — Chapter 16

Name ______________________ Date ______________

A Comparison of a Crustacean and an Insect

One characteristic that crustaceans and insects share, along with all other arthropods, is an exoskeleton, or external skeleton. The exoskeleton is composed of a substance called chitin. It may seem strange to find the skeleton on the outside of an animal's body, but whether the skeleton is internal or external, it serves the same functions. The skeleton gives the body form, protects delicate internal organs, and aids movement by serving as a place of attachment for muscles. The nature of the exoskeleton, however, limits the size and affects the development of an organism. The exoskeleton required to support a large insect would be very heavy, much more so than an internal skeleton supporting the same weight. It would make movement on land cumbersome. That is why most insects are relatively small. Flying would be even more difficult, although the fossil record reveals that at one time dragonflies with three-foot wingspans were common. The growth in size of an organism is also somewhat limited by an exoskeleton. Once the exoskeleton of an organism forms, it does not increase in size. Further growth of the organism depends upon molting, which is the splitting, shedding, and regrowth of the exoskeleton. The organism is vulnerable to predation during this molting process.

The exoskeleton is only one external characteristic that all arthropods share. Another is the segmented body. In addition to the external similarities, arthropods also share some internal features. You will discover several of these characteristics by studying the diagrams of a lobster and a grasshopper in Figure 16–1.

Questions:

1. Locate and label the cephalothorax and the abdomen on the lobster diagram.
2. Locate and label the head, the thorax, and the abdomen on the grasshopper diagram.
3. What types of internal parts do the lobster and the grasshopper share? the brain, heart, dorsal blood vessel, ovary, and ventral nerve cord
4. How does the digestive system of the lobster differ from that of the grasshopper? The lobster has a stomach and a digestive gland. The grasshopper has a digestive tube and stomach pouches. It also has a salivary gland.
5. The location of the heart in all arthropods is the same. Locate the heart in the lobster and in the grasshopper. Write a statement about where the heart is located with respect to the digestive system. (HINT: *Dorsal* means located near or on the back of an animal; *ventral* means located on the lower, or anterior, surface of an animal.) Arthropods have a dorsal heart, one that is located above the digestive system.

FIGURE 16–1.

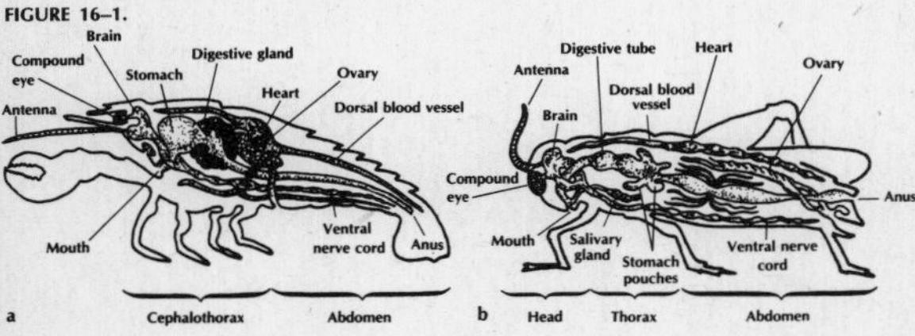

16–2

Critical Thinking — Chapter 16

Name ______________________ Date ______________

The Horseshoe Crab

Despite its name, the horseshoe crab is not a crab at all. It is an arthropod, but it is related to spiders and scorpions. All species of horseshoe crabs belong to the class Merostomata. The best known species of horseshoe crab, *Limulus polyphemus*, can be found from Maine to the Yucatan peninsula.

The remarkable, tanklike horseshoe crab is a hardy creature. It has existed on Earth for over 300 million years. Its anatomical structure enables it to walk the ocean floor, drift in the ocean waters, and burrow into the sand. The horseshoe crab has an exoskeleton that is tough but flexible. The exoskeleton, also called the shell, ranges in color from dark to light brown with subtle hues of green or yellow. A horseshoe crab can grow as large as 0.6 meter long and can have a mass of over 4.5 kilograms. In the adult crab, two compound eyes are located on the upper part of the shell. Scientists believe that the eyes can perceive movement, but not images.

Five pairs of legs are located on the underside of the horseshoe crab. Each leg has a clawlike pincer. The last pair of legs also have a fanlike structure that is used for burrowing into the sand. The other four pairs of legs are used for walking and for handling prey.

In the center of the legs, on the underside, is the mouth. It has a powerful gizzard with small teeth for grinding food. Near the mouth are two small pincers, called chelicerae. These are used for feeding. Directly above the mouth is the brain. The elongated heart is located along the back.

Toward the rear of the horseshoe crab is the abdomen. The abdomen is followed by the telson, or long, spikelike tail. The telson is used to help the horseshoe crab burrow into the sand. Burrowing is very important if the horseshoe crab is stranded by a tide. By burrowing into the sand, the horseshoe crab keeps moist until the next tide. The telson is also used to upright the horseshoe crab should it become inverted.

In the spring, usually in late May or June, an unusual phenomenon takes place. Thousands of horseshoe crabs converge on the beaches along Delaware Bay to mate. This mating episode always takes place at the new or full moon. At these times, the spring tide is at a high level. This enables the horseshoe crab to deposit its eggs high up on the beach.

During the mating episode, the large females crawl out of the water. Each female has a smaller male attached to her. The male holds onto the female with his first pair of walking legs. Once on the beach, the female digs 10 to 15 holes in the sand. She deposits from 200 to several thousand pearl-like eggs in each hole. The male is dragged across the eggs and emits sperm over them. After 24 hours, the horseshoe crabs cover their eggs and slip back into the ocean.

For 2 to 10 weeks, the fertilized eggs develop in the sand. The waves of the next high tide filter through and stir the sand, helping the newly hatched larvae reach the surface. The larvae then float out with the tide. A young horseshoe crab grows and molts several times a year for the first 2 to 3 years. At 10 to 12 years it becomes a sexually mature adult, and it may live for another 7 years.

The population of horseshoe crabs on the east coast of the United States has dwindled since 1900. The decrease in population can be attributed to fishermen who have, historically, destroyed the horseshoe crab because it eats clams. The horseshoe crab also has been harvested for fertilizer and eel bait. More recently, the horseshoe crab has been harvested for the processing of foods and for medical research. If the decline in the horseshoe crab population continues, we may see the disappearance of one of the world's last-remaining living fossils.

Questions:

1. What might happen to a horseshoe crab that has no telson and has been left inverted on the beach? It probably would die from lack of moisture, oxygen (since it is aquatic).
2. What might signal the horseshoe crab that it is time to mate? day length, water temperature
3. Why does the female horseshoe crab lay so many eggs? to ensure that some will survive
4. For what reasons is the horseshoe crab harvested today? Which reasons are acceptable to you? Why? medical research, food processing; Answers will vary.

16–3

Name ______________________ Date ______________

Problem: How do poisonous and nonpoisonous snakes compare? (text page 352)

Data and Observations:

TABLE 16-4. LOCATIONS OF SOME POISONOUS SNAKES

	Your State	California	Florida	Maine	Texas
Eastern coral	Check the		✓		✓
Southern copperhead	map to		✓		✓
Northern copperhead	determine				✓
Eastern cottonmouth	if each		✓		
Western cottonmouth	snake is				✓
Eastern massasauga	found in				
Western rattlesnake	your state.	✓			✓

Questions and Conclusion:

1. (a) List five traits of Subphylum Vertebrata.
   (b) List three traits of all reptiles. (a) internal skeleton, dorsal nerve cord, ventral heart, complex outer covering, paired appendages (b) lungs, ectotherms, dry, scaly skin
2. List three ways that most poisonous snakes may be distinguished from nonpoisonous snakes. vertical pupil, fangs, scale pattern on underside
3. Explain how the coral snake may be distinguished from nonpoisonous snakes. fangs, red bands touch yellow bands forming complete rings around body
4. Which states listed in Table 16-4 have the: (a) fewest poisonous species (b) most poisonous species? (a) Maine (b) Texas

Conclusion: How do poisonous and nonpoisonous snakes compare? They differ in shape of the pupil, presence or absence of fangs, and scale pattern on the underside of the tail.

FIGURE 16–27.

FIGURE 16–28.

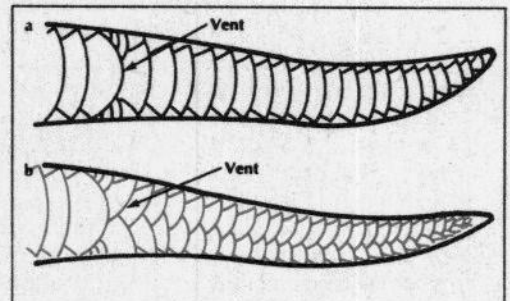

FIGURE 16–29.

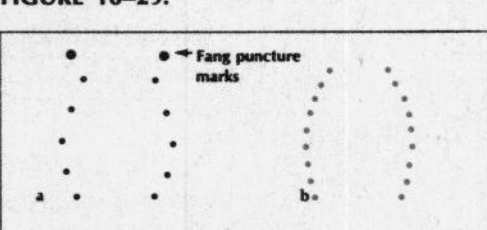

Name ______________________ Date ______________

Four Types of Sexual Spores

Fungi usually exhibit two different phases of growth. One phase is asexual and involves the growing, vegetative part of the fungi. The other phase is the sexual, or reproducing, phase. During the sexual phase, nuclei fuse or two gametes join together to produce spores. Different types of sexual spores are produced by fungi. The types of sexual spores formed are used to help differentiate the major groups of Eumycotina, the true fungi.

One type of sexual spore is called a *zygospore.* It is produced by a simple process in which there is a chance contact of the tips of two hyphae. Once in contact, the ends of the two hyphae swell and form two gametangia. A gametangium is a structure that forms gametes. The gametes are similar in appearance and structure and are not easily distinguishable as either male or female. The walls of the gametangia that make contact dissolve, permitting the protoplasts to fuse. The zygote that results from this union is called a zygospore. One fungus that reproduces sexually by zygospores is *Rhizopus stolonifer,* the common bread mold.

A second type of sexual spore is the *oospore.* This type of spore is formed by the fusion of two unlike gametes. The gametes are formed at the ends of hyphae. In *Saprolegnia,* an aquatic mold, a structure called an oogonium forms at the end of the hyphae. Within each oogonium, several female gametes, or eggs, form. Also formed at the end of other hyphae are structures called antheridia. Male gametes, or sperm, form within each antheridium. One antheridium presses close to the wall of an oogonium. A fertilization tube forms and penetrates the wall of the oogonium until it reaches an egg. Fertilization results from the fusion of sperm and egg. The fertilized egg that results is called an oospore.

Sexual spores that are enclosed in a sac, or ascus, form a third type of spore. These spores are called *ascospores.* In forming ascospores, the tips of certain hyphae form reproductive structures that contain similar gametes. Because these gametes are so similar and they cannot be identified as sperm or egg, they are referred to simply as + and −. When the two reproductive structures meet, the cell walls between them dissolve. The nucleus of each + hypha passes into a − hypha. Pairs of + and − nuclei fuse. Meiosis then occurs, followed by mitosis. In the process, each nucleus receives some of the cytoplasm of the original − hypha and surrounds itself with a thick wall, forming an ascospore. All of the ascospores that are formed are enclosed in the same sac, or ascus. Among the familiar molds that produce ascospores are those species that are sky-blue or green in color and are commonly seen on old bread, cheese, and oranges. These species of mold belong to the genus *Penicillium.*

The class Basidiomycetes is familiar to almost everyone as mushrooms, rusts, smuts, and shelf, or bracket, fungi. A distinctive feature of this class is that members develop spores called basidiospores. During a common form of reproduction, two cells of any two hyphae come together, after which the walls between them dissolve. The nucleus from one cell passes into the other cell. The cell now contains two nuclei and is said to be dikaryotic. Fusion of the two nuclei, followed by meiosis, takes place in special cells called basidia. The basidia are often club-shaped. The spores formed by these basidia are called *basidiospores.* The basidiospores are not enclosed in any structure, such as an ascus. Rather, the basidiospores are attached to each basidium by short stalks, each called a sterigma. Most basidia have four sterigmata.

Questions:

Label the parts of the various sexual spores in Figure 17–1.

FIGURE 17–1.

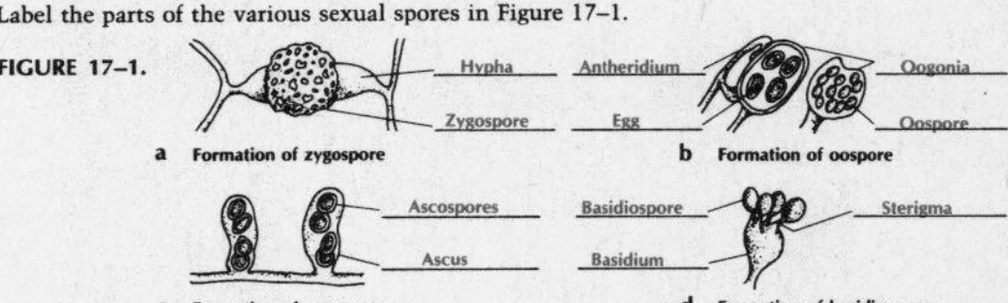

Name ______________________ Date ______________

Problem: How do different organisms reproduce asexually? (text page 370)

Data and Observations:

TABLE 17-1. OBSERVATIONS OF ASEXUALLY REPRODUCING ORGANISMS

Organism	Single Organism	Organism Reproducing
Paramecium		
Yeast		Bud
Oscillatoria		Heterocysts
Rhizopus nigricans		Sporangium; Spores

Questions and Conclusion:

1. Define: asexual reproduction, fission, budding, fragmentation, spore. reproduction in which a single parent produces offspring by mitosis; asexual reproduction in which one organism divides into two small organisms of equal size; asexual reproduction in which an outgrowth forms on parent and later separates, forming a new organism; asexual reproduction in which part of an organism breaks off, forming a new organism; special cell that gives rise to a new organism

Name ______________________ Date ______________

2. Explain why the four types of reproduction studied are asexual and not sexual. Include features such as parent number and type of cell reproduction. Only one parent was used and the process of meiosis was not used.
3. To which kingdom does each of the following organisms belong: paramecium, yeast, *Oscillatoria, Rhizopus nigricans?* Protista; Fungi; Monera; Fungi
4. Explain how the cells formed during budding differ from those formed during fission. Fission produces two cells of equal size, while budding usually results in a single small cell.
5. How do the number of cells formed by budding or fission compare to the number of spores formed by *Rhizopus nigricans?* Millions of spores are formed by *Rhizopus nigricans,* but only one or two cells are formed by budding or fission.
6. How may the number of spores formed be important to the survival of the bread mold? Chance for survival of spores is low, therefore, many spores will guarantee some surviving.
7. (a) How do offspring formed during asexual reproduction compare to the parent? (b) How may this be helpful to the offspring? (a) They are identical. (b) Helpful traits of the parent will be passed to the offspring.

Conclusion: How do different organisms reproduce asexually? by fission, budding, fragmentation, and spores

Skills Chapter 18

Name ______ Date ______

Bacterial Flagella

Some, but not all, species of bacteria move by means of flagella. The flagellum of a bacterium has no definite covering membrane and it consists of a single, small filament. This filament is made up of three or more longitudinal fibers. In some cases, the fibers are parallel to one another. In other cases, the fibers are intertwined. Some flagella, and perhaps all, appear to be attached to a structure called the hook. The hook is attached to a structure called the basal body. Flagella move with a wavelike motion that propels the bacterium.

Chemical analyses of flagella show that they are made up of a single protein. This protein has been named flagellin. Although all flagella are composed of flagellin, bacterial flagella take many forms. These forms include coiled, curly, wavy, and straight. Several forms can be found in a single cell. The flagella also may be arranged in various ways on bacterial cells. If only one flagellum is located on one end of the cell, the flagellation is said to be *monotrichous*. The flagellation is said to be *lophotrichous* if several flagella are located at one end. *Amphitrichous* flagellation describes the condition when at least one flagellum is located at each end. The flagellation is said to be *peritrichous* when the flagella protrude from all parts of the bacterial surface. It should come as no surprise that bacteria have been classified based on their flagellation.

In addition to flagella, some bacteria have very fine appendages that extend outward from the surface of the cell. These appendages are called fimbriae, or pili. Like flagella, the pili are made up of a single protein. This protein is different from flagellin and is called *pilin.* Each pilus is made of a single rigid filament. Unlike the flagella, the pili are small, short, and very numerous. Pili are also rigid and immobile. The function of pili is not well understood. It is known that bacteria with pili have a strong tendency to adhere to one another and to various other particles, such as animal cells (including red blood cells), plant cells, and yeast cells. It has been suggested that the ability to adhere to particles may be important for the bacteria in terms of fixing themselves to tissues from which they can obtain nutrients.

Questions:

1. Write the type of flagellation on the blank below each figure.

FIGURE 18–1.

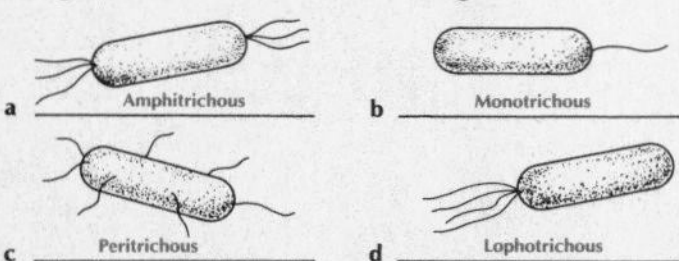

2. How are flagella and pili similar? Both are single filaments and are made up of protein.
3. How do flagella and pili differ? Flagella are long and motile. Sometimes there is only one flagellum present. Pili are small, short, and immobile. Pili, when present, are numerous.
4. Figure 18–2 is a drawing of *Escherichia coli.* Identify the flagellum and a pilus.

FIGURE 18–2.

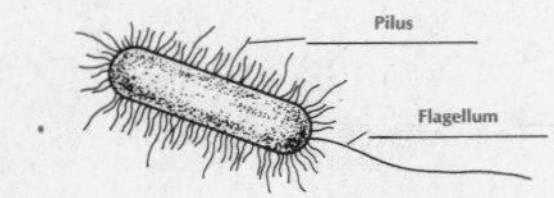

Critical Thinking Chapter 18

Name ______ Date ______

Termites and Protozoans

Termites live in colonies that range in size from a few hundred to several million individuals. This insect society consists of several castes, including the winged and sighted queen and king and the wingless and usually blind workers and soldiers. The termites have a social structure similar to that of ants. They not only feed, groom, and protect one another, but the offspring of one generation assist the parents in raising the next generation. This behavior is remarkable since termites evolved much earlier than, and quite independently from ants.

Termites belong to the only order of insects that have the general ability to digest cellulose. Like their close relatives the cockroaches, termites harbor protozoans in their gut. The protozoans produce the enzymes that termites need to digest cellulose, the main chemical constituent of all plants. Most of the protozoans live in a vesicular appendix of the termite's gut. Ingested wood, ground up in the termite's proventriculus, or gizzard, is broken down into a sugar called dextrose. Dextrose is the same kind of sugar found in grapes. The termites also digest a great many of the rapidly multiplying protozoans, thereby obtaining protein. The protozoans, in turn, have a place to live and a steady supply of food.

The presence of protozoans in the gut, as in the primitive Darwin termite, is a characteristic of all primitive termites. Most primitive termites feed on dead wood, making them especially dreaded by people whose homes are made of wood. Termites not only destroy the supportive structure of homes, but also eat wood furniture, books, packing cases, leather, cloth, and crops that include fruit trees, stem crops such as sugarcane, and a wide variety of underground crops such as potatoes and yams.

The advanced termites lack special gut protozoa. They do, however, maintain a sophisticated association with bacteria and/or fungi. In three of the four subfamilies of advanced termites, large cultures of bacteria grow in the hindgut. The bacteria help ferment plant material, thus making nutrients available to the termites.

Both advanced and primitive termites, except those belonging to the fungus-growing subfamily, also have bacteria in their gut that can fix atmospheric nitrogen. These bacteria can take nitrogen from the air and incororate it into amino acids, the building blocks of proteins. The only other insect known to harbor such bacteria is the brown-hooded cockroach.

Most termites prefer to eat dead plant material that has been attacked by fungi. The fungi break down the plant cells and release nutrients. In the savannah regions of Asia and Africa, the long dry seasons slow the activities of the fungi. This often results in a food shortage for the termites. One group of termites, however, has solved this food-shortage problem. The fungus-growing subfamily, Macrotermitinae, has developed a unique relationship with the fungi of genus *Termitomyces.* As a matter of fact, this fungus is found nowhere else except in the nest of termites. The termites cultivate the fungus on fungus combs. These combs are made by the termites from their own feces. The fungus feeds on and breaks down the feces, releasing nutrients the termites can then consume. The fungus-growing termites are of great ecological importance. Their activities account for most of the decomposition process in the hot, dry savannahs.

Questions:

1. Termites have a general ability to digest cellulose. How are they able to do so? with the help of protozoans, bacteria, and/or fungi
2. How are the primitive and advanced termites similar? With the exception of members of Macrotermitinae, both primitive and advanced termites have gut bacteria that can fix nitrogen.
3. In what way is *Termitomyces* important to termites? *Termitomyces* help break down the feces of the termites, releasing nutrients needed by the termites.

Investigation Worksheet Chapter 18

Name ______ Date ______

Problem: How can you measure respiration rate in yeast?

(text page 384)

Data and Observations:

TABLE 18-2. READINGS OF HEIGHT OF LIQUID IN TUBES

	Starting Height	Height After 5 Minutes	Height After 10 Minutes	Height After 15 Minutes	Height After 20 Minutes	Total Distance Liquid Moved
Tube 1	73 mm	73 mm	73 mm	73 mm	73 mm	0 mm
Tube 2	70 mm	70 mm	72 mm	71 mm	69 mm	−1 mm
Tube 3	74 mm	80 mm	83 mm	87 mm	92 mm	18 mm
Tube 4	75 mm	76 mm	78 mm	78 mm	82 mm	7 mm

*Sample data

Questions and Conclusion:

1. Define cellular respiration. process in which cells release the energy of food such as glucose
2. (a) What gas is released by yeast cells as they carry out cellular respiration? (b) What is the role of sucrose in the experiment? (a) carbon dioxide (b) It serves as a food source.
3. As the yeast cells released gas, pressure within the test tube increased. This pressure forced the liquid within the test tube to rise into the glass tube. (a) Which tubes showed evidence of gas release? (b) How were the contents of those tubes alike? (a) 3 and 4 (b) Both tubes contained a food source (sucrose) and yeast.
4. What experimental evidence do you have that: (a) yeast without food does not carry out cellular respiration (b) food itself is not responsible for gas release? (a) tube 1 (b) tube 2
5. Yeast is used in several baking processes. Dough rises due to the trapping of gas within the dough. (a) What gas is trapped within the dough? (b) Where does this gas come from? (a) carbon dioxide (b) It is a waste product of cellular respiration.

Investigation Worksheet Chapter 18

Name ______ Date ______

6. Unleavened bread is made without yeast and is usually very flat. Explain why. The dough will not rise because there are no yeast cells to produce carbon dioxide.
7. (a) What chemical produced by yeast cells is used in the production of beer and wine? (b) Why do yeast cells produce this chemical? (a) ethanol (b) Ethanol is a waste product of cellular respiration.
8. Design an experiment to test these hypotheses: (a) Temperature influences the respiration rate of yeast cells. (b) The pH of a liquid influences the respiration rate of yeast cells. (a) Fill one flask with warm water and a second flask with cold water. Prepare test tubes with yeast and sucrose. Note which tube generates more carbon dioxide. (b) Add acid to one tube that contains yeast and food, and base to a second tube that contains yeast and food. Note which of the tubes generates more carbon dioxide.

Conclusion: How can you measure respiration rate in yeast? Yeast solution in a closed test tube releases carbon dioxide, thus increasing pressure in the tube. The increase in pressure and thus the increase in carbon dioxide is a means of measuring the rate of cellular respiration by yeast.

Skills **Chapter 19**

Name ______________________ Date ______________________

Bone Marrow—Where Immunity Begins

Bone marrow can be thought of as a massive factory that makes the materials the body needs to defend itself from foreign invaders. The bone marrow is one of the largest and most active tissues in the body. For example, the average half-life of a white blood cell called a neutrophil is about 6 hours. To maintain a normal level of neutrophils it is necessary that the bone marrow produce over 100 billion neutrophils a day. In addition, the bone marrow forms red blood cells (erythrocytes), platelets, and various other white blood cells (leukocytes).

The production of cells begins with a pluripotent stem cell. This stem cell differentiates into a myeloid stem cell or a lymphoid stem cell. The myeloid stem cell goes through a preliminary process that prepares it for becoming a red blood cell, a megakaryocyte, a myeloblast, or a monocyte. Red blood cells help supply oxygen to all the body's tissues. Megakaryocytes break apart to form platelets. Platelets work with blood proteins to help in blood clot formation. The myeloblast develops into an eosinophil, basophil, or neutrophil, all of which are white blood cells. Eosinophils help combat allergies and chronic parasitic infections and possibly detoxify foreign proteins to which the person is allergic. The basophils contain heparin, an anticoagulant. But the role of basophils in maintaining a balance between the clotting and anticlotting systems is uncertain. Neutrophils seek out, ingest, and destroy bacteria and have been referred to as the body's first line of defense against bacterial infections.

Monocytes, which are another type of white blood cell, often follow neutrophils into an infected area of the body. The monocytes ingest bacteria, other foreign matter, and dead cells. Monocytes make up a second line of defense. After monocytes circulate in the blood for about 24 hours, they enter tissue and become macrophages. Macrophages ingest foreign invaders and work with special lymphocytes to fight infections and cancer.

Lymphoid stem cells are responsible for the formation of certain lymphocytes. Lymphocytes are formed in the bone marrow, lymph nodes, thymus, and spleen. Lymphocytes include B cells and three kinds of T cells: K cells, or killer T cells, helper T cells, and suppressor T cells. B cells are primarily responsible for humoral immunity, or immunity due to circulating antibodies. B cells create antibodies that bind to bacteria and viruses. The antibodies either neutralize these foreign objects or make them vulnerable to attack by other immune cells. B cells often complete their formation in the spleen. Cellular immunity is directed by T cells. Cellular immunity is responsible for delayed allergic reactions, rejection of transplanted foreign tissue, and the breaking apart of tumor cells. T cells also attack viruses, fungi, and bacteria. T cells often complete their development in the thymus.

Questions:

Complete the chart, which shows how various blood cells are formed from bone marrow.

FIGURE 19–1.

- Pluripotent Stem Cells
  - Myeloid stem cells
    - Myeloblasts
      - Eosinophils
      - Basophils
      - Neutrophils
    - Erythrocytes
    - Monocytes → Macrophages
    - Megakaryocytes → Platelets
  - Lymphoid stem cells
    - Suppressor T cells
    - Killer T cells, or K cells
    - Helper T cells
    - B cells

Essay **Chapter 19**

Name ______________________ Date ______________________

PNI—Psychoneuroimmunology

Is it coincidence that people have fewer colds when they are content with their lives than when they are under stress? A theme of folklore and literature hints that the mind can influence the body's vulnerability to infection and disease. Just 10 years ago, most specialists in communicable disease would have scoffed at such a suggestion. But today, research by immunologists and neurologists is giving credibility to such ideas. The idea that the mind can influence the body's immune system has developed into a new discipline—psychoneuroimmunology, or more simply, PNI.

There is overwhelming evidence for chemical and anatomical links between the brain and the immune system. First, there is evidence that neurotransmitters, chemicals released by nerves, bind to immune cells. The neurotransmitters then alter the immune cell's ability to multiply and kill foreign invaders. Second, there are reports that hormones, which are regulated by the brain, could affect the immune cell's ability to fight disease. Hormones known as hematologic growth factors stimulate immune cell production. Finally, there is evidence that nerve fibers in immunological organs, such as the thymus, bone marrow, and lymph nodes, are associated with lymphocytes. Together, the nerves and hormones that carry messages to the immune system activate the immune system by turning it on and off.

Further research shows that neuropeptides, small proteinlike chemicals made by brain cells, can possibly latch onto macrophages and change the speed or direction of their movement. Macrophages are large ameboid white blood cells that gather at the sight of an infection. They rebuild damaged tissues and devour bacteria, viruses, and other foreign particles.

Candace Pert and Michael Ruff, both of the National Institute of Mental Health, have carried out a study concerning neuropeptides and macrophages. In this study, they showed that when people felt helpless, their macrophages moved more sluggishly than usual. The sluggishness was probably caused by changes in neuropeptides. This finding suggests why seriously ill patients who give up hope often fare worse than those who remain optimistic.

With growing evidence that the brain and immune system are linked, Gérard Renoux of the University of Tours in France decided to find out which areas of the brain were responsible for controlling the immune system. Renoux found that if he damaged the left side of the cortex in a mouse, the structure and activity of the mouse's immune system would change. The number of white blood cells in the spleen dropped and the ones that remained became less efficient at killing tumors and responding to foreign cells. Renoux concluded that the right side of the cortex must be responsible for the slowing of the immune system. When Renoux damaged the right side of the cortex, the immune cells acted differently. The cells became slightly more active. Renoux concluded from his studies that the left side of the cortex stimulates the immune system and the right side suppresses it.

Renoux's theory provides a clue as to how emotions and mental imagery may help fight disease. Since formation of images seems to be controlled by the right side of the brain, it is possible that exercises involving imagery somehow keep the right side of the brain from suppressing the immune system. It also has been suggested that the left side of the brain processes emotions such as excitement, sense of control, and hope. Thus, the sense of control and hope experienced by optimistic patients might stimulate their brains to bolster their immune systems.

Questions:

1. Through which substances does the brain seem to affect the immune system? neurotransmitters, hormones, and neuropeptides
2. How does the left side of the brain affect the immune system? It stimulates the immune system.
3. How does the right side of the brain affect the immune system? It suppresses the immune system.

Investigation Worksheet **Chapter 19**

Name ______________________ Date ______________________

Problem: What are certain traits of bacteria? (text page 406)

Data and Observations:

TABLE 19-1. TRAITS OF BACTERIA

Part	Observations			
A. Shape	Species name		Shape	
	Answers will vary depending on samples.			
B. Pattern	Pattern 1	e	Pattern 6	b
	Pattern 2	c	Pattern 7	h
	Pattern 3	a	Pattern 8	i
	Pattern 4	f	Pattern 9	g
	Pattern 5	d	Pattern 10	j
C. Motility	Sample		Motile (yes or no)	
	A		Answers will vary depending	
	B		on samples. All motile	
	C		bacteria have flagella.	

Questions and Conclusion:

1. Define bacteria, flagellum, motility. very small, prokaryotic, unicellular organisms; long whiplike projection of a cell that is used for locomotion; ability of a cell to move on its own
2. Analyze the scientific names and descriptions of the following bacteria. Diagram and label these species of bacteria on a separate sheet of paper: (a) *Staphylococcus aureus*—nonmotile, causes infection of any body organ (b) *Streptococcus pyogenes*—nonmotile, causes sore throat, scarlet fever (c) *Clostridium tetani*—motile, bacillus, occurs in pairs and in chains, causes tetanus. (a) single coccus (b) chain of cocci (c) paired and chained bacilli with flagella

Conclusion: What are certain traits of bacteria? Bacterial cell shape may be either coccus, bacillus, or spirillum. Cells may occur singly or in groups ranging from two to clusters, or chains of many cells. Certain species are motile, while others are nonmotile.

Essay **Chapter 20**

Name ______________________ Date ______________________

Simple Fruits

The old question "Is it a fruit or a vegetable?" raises few problems, botanically. A fruit has its origins in the flower. By definition a fruit is a mature ovary that contains seeds. Botanically speaking then, a string bean, a kernel of corn, and a tomato are as much fruits as is a peach or a strawberry. The term vegetable is a nontechnical term and is rarely used by botanists.

The form, texture, and structure of fruits vary. Some fruits are fleshy, some are dry, some have many seeds, some have few or one. These and other characteristics help botanists classify fruits. Various types of simple fruits are discussed below.

Legume (or pod). This type of fruit is characteristic of nearly all members of the pea family, Leguminosae. The shell of this type of dry fruit generally splits in half revealing and releasing the seeds. Beans, peas (in their shell), and peanuts (in their shell) are all examples of legumes.

Achene. Buckwheat, the "seeds" on the surface of the strawberry, and sunflower "seeds" (shell and all) are parts of this group. All members of the sunflower family, the Compositae, produce achenes. These fruits are dry and since they are usually very small and contain only one seed, they are commonly called seeds. The seed in an achene can be separated easily from its shell. Unlike legumes, achenes do not split open.

Caryopsis (or grain). This fruit is found in members of the grass family, the Gramineae. This family includes important plants such as wheat, oats, barley, rye, corn, and rice. Like the achene, the caryopsis is a dry, one-seeded fruit that does not split open. Unlike the achene, the shell of the caryopsis is united all the way around and it is difficult to separate the shell (the fruit wall) from the seed except by a special milling process.

Nut. The term nut is often applied to a number of hard-shelled fruits and seeds. Botanically, a nut is a one-seeded, dry fruit that does not split open. The fruit wall is hard or stony. Chestnuts, walnuts, and acorns are all nuts.

Drupe. This is a fleshy fruit produced by some members of the rose family, the Rosaceae. Plums, cherries, almonds, peaches, and apricots are all drupes. The drupe usually is one-seeded and the seed is surrounded by a hard, stony structure, called the *pit*. Surrounding the pit is the edible flesh. Both the pit and the fleshy part of a drupe are parts of the ovary wall. In almond fruits, the seed is surrounded by a fleshy part of the ovary wall that becomes hard and dry and forms the hull as the seed develops.

Berry. Like the drupe, a berry is a fleshy fruit. But unlike the drupe, it contains many seeds and many compartments, or locules. A tomato is a common type of berry. Citrus fruits, such as lemons and limes, are a type of berry called a *hesperidium*. A hesperidium has a thick leathery fruit wall with oil glands, and many seeds surrounded by an edible flesh. Another berrylike fruit is the *pepo*. In this type of fruit, the fruit wall is a rind that surrounds a fleshy material. Pepos are produced by members of the Cucurbitaceae, the cucumber or pumpkin family. Watermelons, squashes, pumpkins, cantaloupes, and cucumbers are all types of pepos.

Pome. This fruit is characteristic of members of one subfamily of the Rosaceae that includes the apple and quince. Most of the ovary portion of the apple is found in the core. The fleshy part of the apple is a combination of part of the ovary wall and other floral tissues.

Aggregate Fruit. An aggregate fruit is formed from many ovaries of a single flower. Each one of these ovaries matures into an individual fruit which, individually, may be a small drupe *(drupelet)*, achene, or a number of other kinds of simple fruits. The raspberry and the blackberry are aggregates of drupelets. The strawberry, an aggregate of achenes, is made up of many small achenes that are attached to a large, fleshy receptacle. The receptacle is the base structure to which the flower parts are attached.

Questions:

Provide the technical term that applies to each of the following fruits. One has been done for you.

1. honeydew melon berry/pepo
2. zucchini squash berry/pepo
3. popcorn caryopsis
4. nectarine drupe
5. lima bean legume
6. pecan nut
7. grapefruit berry/hesperidium
8. strawberry aggregate of achenes

Investigation Worksheet — Chapter 20

Name ____________________ Date ____________________

Problem: How can you tell if a seed is still alive? (text page 428)

Data and Observations:

TABLE 20-1. PERCENTAGE OF SEEDS WITH LIVING TISSUE				
	Your Results		Class Results	
	Boiled	Unboiled	Boiled	Unboiled
Total number of seeds				
Number of seeds with living tissue	Students answers will vary. However, boiled seeds should show a very low percentage (possibly 0%) of seeds with living tissue.			
Number of seeds with no living tissue				
Percentage of seeds with living tissue				

Questions and Conclusion:

1. Define: (a) seed embryo (b) endosperm (c) cellular respiration. (a) part of seed that will germinate and form new plant (b) stored food within seed (c) process whereby living tissue releases energy from food
2. Which area of the seed turned blue when iodine was added? What does this tell you about that area within the seed? endosperm; It is the major food storage area of the seed.
3. In which area of the seed did the pink color of tetrazolium concentrate? What does this tell you about that area within the seed? embryo; Cellular respiration is occurring most rapidly in this area.
4. How do the class percentages of living tissue for boiled and unboiled seeds compare? What process was halted as a result of the boiling? unboiled seeds show the highest percentage of living tissue; cellular respiration
5. Explain why the presence of living tissue is an indication of which seeds will germinate. Living tissue must be present for germination to occur. Most seeds with living tissue will germinate if the proper environmental conditions are present.
6. How might the tetrazolium test be of value to farmers before they plant large batches of seeds? They can determine before planting whether or not the batch of seeds is alive.

Conclusion: How can you tell if a seed is still alive? Test a seed with tetrazolium. A pink color will indicate that the seed is alive.

Essay — Chapter 21

Name ____________________ Date ____________________

Variations on Photosynthesis

Most plants carry out the process of photosynthesis. In this process, light energy is used to combine carbon, oxygen, and hydrogen to form glucose. There are two phases of photosynthesis, the light reactions and the dark reactions. In the light reactions, energy absorbed by the chlorophyll molecule is used to produce two different energy molecules: ATP and $NADPH_2^+$. During the light reactions water also is split into hydrogen and oxygen. In the dark reactions, the energy molecules produced by the light reactions and CO_2 are used to drive reactions that form glucose.

The light reactions of photosynthesis are similar for all higher land plants; but, over the course of millions of years, three major variations of the dark reactions have evolved.

The most common variation is called C_3 photosynthesis. In C_3 plants, the first compound formed from CO_2 during the dark reactions is PGA, phosphoglycerate. This PGA then reacts to eventually form glucose.

A second variation, characteristic primarily of tropical plants, is called C_4 photosynthesis. In plants such as corn and sugarcane, the first molecule to be formed from CO_2 is oxalacetic acid, a four-carbon compound. This molecule then undergoes several changes to form PGA. The rest of the dark reactions continue as in C_3 plants. C_4 plants are able to carry out photosynthesis under conditions that are unfavorable for C_3 photosynthesis: high light intensity, high temperature, little available water, and low concentrations of carbon dioxide.

A third variation of photosynthesis has evolved in plants such as the cactuses, the jade plant, kalanchoe, and most succulents that inhabit hot, dry regions. In order to take in CO_2, these plants, called CAM plants, open their stomates at night. This enables them to conserve water. During the night, CAM plants use the CO_2 to form various acids, most commonly malic acid. The malic acid is stored until the daytime when it is converted to oxalacetic acid. Photosynthesis then continues in a way similar to that of C_4 plants. The acronym CAM stands for Crassulacean Acid Metabolism and was first identified among members of the Crassulaceae, the sedum family.

Questions:

1. How does photosynthesis in C_4 plants differ from that of C_3 plants? In C_4 plants, oxalacetate is the first compound formed from CO_2.
2. How does photosynthesis in CAM plants differ from that of C_4 plants? In CAM plants, malic acid is first formed from CO_2, and then oxalacetate is formed.
3. Crabgrass is considered a weed and can withstand droughts, intense light, and high temperatures. Which variation of photosynthesis would you expect this plant to have? C_4 photosynthesis
4. "Living stones" are succulents that grow naturally in the arid regions of South Africa. Which type of photosynthesis would you expect these plants to have? CAM photosynthesis

Investigation Worksheet — Chapter 21

Name ____________________ Date ____________________

Problem: How can you estimate the number of stomata on a leaf? (text page 444)

Data and Observations:

TABLE 21-2. ESTIMATION OF NUMBER OF STOMATA ON A LEAF			
		Sample Data	Your Data
Length and width of leaf		length = 140 mm width = 10 mm	Answers will vary.
Total area of leaf (length × width)		140 mm × 10 mm = 1400 mm²	
Number of stomata observed in:	Area 1	4	
	Area 2	6	
	Area 3	3	
	Area 4	5	
	Area 5	2	
	Total	20	
Average number of stomata observed		$\frac{20}{5} = 4$	
Number of high power fields of view on entire leaf (total area ÷ area of high power field of view – 0.07 mm²)		$\frac{1400 \text{ mm}^2}{0.07 \text{ mm}^2} = 20\,000$	
Number of stomata on entire leaf (number of stomata in one high power field of view × number of high power fields of view on entire leaf)		20 000 × 4 = 80 000	

Questions and Conclusion:

1. Define (a) guard cell (b) stoma (c) leaf epidermis. (a) green cell that surrounds and controls the size of stomata in leaves (b) pore in the epidermis that functions in gas exchange (c) top and bottom layer of certain leaves, protective in nature, contains cells and stomata
2. (a) Name the gases that enter and leave a leaf by way of the stomata. (b) Where do these gases originate or come from? (c) How are these gases related to photosynthesis? (a) CO_2, O_2, H_2O; (b) CO_2 and H_2O are released from a plant during respiration. O_2 enters the leaf from the air or is released during photosynthesis. (c) CO_2 and H_2O are used during photosynthesis, while O_2 is released.

Investigation Worksheet — Chapter 21

Name ____________________ Date ____________________

3. Explain the relationship between stoma size and the action of guard cells. Guard cells swell during the day resulting in opening of the stoma. Guard cells lose water at night and collapse, thus causing closure of the stoma.
4. Name two places in the procedure in which the accuracy of your final count of stomata for the entire leaf could be improved. a more exact measurement of the entire leaf and more than five counts of stomata
5. A student estimated the number of stomata on three different kinds of leaves. The data are shown here:

	Upper epidermis	Lower epidermis
A.	0 stomata/mm²	214 stomata/mm²
B.	27 stomata/mm²	31 stomata/mm²
C.	350 stomata/mm²	0 stomata/mm²

Use the following plant types to match with plant A, B, or C: water lily, cactus, oak tree. Explain your choices. A is oak tree; B is cactus; C is water lily. The upper epidermis of most deciduous trees has no stomata; cacti have a few stomata per leaf (needle) to help prevent water loss. A water lily grows on the surface of the water and would have no stomata on its underside, which is below the water's surface.

Conclusion: How can you estimate the number of stomata on a leaf? One must first calculate the area of an entire leaf, then determine the number of stomata by sampling several areas of the leaf. A few mathematical calculations will yield the number of stomata on the entire leaf.

Name ____________________ Date ____________________

Stems as Reproductive Structures

In plants, reproduction that does not involve the sexual process is called vegetative reproduction. Leaves, stems, and roots all may be involved in helping a plant reproduce vegetatively. Stems, however, are more often involved in vegetative reproduction than either leaves or roots.

Most plants derived through vegetative reproduction are genetically identical to the parent plant and are called clones. Sometimes mutations can occur during vegetative reproduction and the mutated individuals that result can be different from the parent.

There are five main kinds of stems that frequently carry out vegetative reproduction. These stems include the stolon, the rhizome, the tuber, the corm, and the bulb.

Stolon. Some plants, such as Bermuda grass, have above-ground, horizontal stems called stolons, or runners. The stolon, like a normal, erect stem, has nodes and internodes and usually leaves. The stolon of Bermuda grass has shoots and roots that arise at each node. The strawberry also produces stolons, however, shoots and roots arise from every other node.

Rhizome. A horizontal, below-ground stem is called a rhizome. Like the stolon, it has nodes and internodes at regular intervals. Shoots and roots may arise from each node. Rhizomes may be long and slender, as in Kentucky bluegrass, or they may be thick and fleshy as in the iris.

Tuber. Some slender rhizomes have thickened, fleshy segments, especially at the tip. These thickened parts are called tubers. The potato is a common type of tuber. On the potato tuber there are buds which are called "eyes." These eyes represent groups of buds at the nodes of the stem and have the potential to develop into shoots.

Corm. A corm is a thickened, food-storing underground stem that develops in preparation for a plant's dormant period. The corm remains alive in the soil while the above-ground portions of the plant dies. At the beginning of a new growing season, the corm sprouts roots and the terminal bud grows, eventually forming a flowering stem. During the growing season, axillary buds develop into new corms and it is these new corms that survive the dormant period. The crocus is a common plant that produces corms.

Bulb. A bulb is an underground, modified stem in which food is stored in thickened leaves that surround a short, erect stem. The stem has at least one central terminal bud that will produce a single, upright, leafy stem and flower. There is usually at least one axillary bud that has the potential to develop into a new bulb. The onion is a commercially valuable bulb.

Questions:

1. How do stolons differ from long, slender rhizomes? Stolons grow above-ground, while rhizomes grow below the soil surface.
2. How are corms and bulbs similar? Both are below-ground stems that store food.
3. What is the relationship between rhizomes and tubers? Slender rhizomes may form thickened segments that are called tubers.

Name ____________________ Date ____________________

Plant Movements

Plants seem so changeless and still, yet they are in continuous motion. Time-lapse photography shows that stems actively twist and turn, and flowers and leaves often repeat a series of movements like a well-rehearsed, stately dance.

Most movements of plants can be classified according to the mechanism involved. Two different types are growth movements and turgor movements. Growth movements result from the differential growth of cells. That is, cells in one part of the plant grow faster than those in another part of the plant. Turgor movements of plant parts result from the differential changes in turgor of some cells. In this type of movement, water moves in or out of cells, causing cells to either swell and become turgid or to shrink and collapse. Turgor movements are readily reversible while growth movements are irreversible.

A tropism is a type of growth movement that results from an external stimulus. The stimulus must come from a single direction, and it affects the direction of growth of a plant. Two familiar tropic movements are geotropism (response to gravity) and phototropism (response to light). Others include thigmotropism (response to touch), chemotropism (response to chemicals), and hydrotropism (response to water).

Tropisms can be either positive or negative, and a plant's response to the same stimulus may differ from plant part to plant part. For example, the primary root is usually positively geotropic, growing in the direction of gravity. The stem, however, is negatively geotropic, growing away from the pull of gravity. A plant's geotropic movements enable a seed that is planted "upside down," with root end pointing upward, to germinate and grow normally. The stem tip will turn as it grows so that it points upward and the root tip will turn and grow deeper into the soil.

Phototropic responses occur in most plants. Commonly, the stems are positively phototropic, bending toward the light as they grow. The stems of some plants, such as English ivy, are negatively phototropic. This negative response can be observed if a pot of English ivy is placed in a sunny window. The stems of the English ivy turn and grow away from the light and into the room.

Different intensities of light may evoke opposite phototropic responses. The stems of Bermuda grass and a few other plants are negatively phototropic at low-light intensities. Such plants grow close to and along the ground when they grow in open places with full sun exposure. These same plants exhibit a positively phototropic response when they grow in the shade. They grow more erect, or away from the ground.

The most familiar examples of positive thigmotropism are shown by the tendrils or stems of some climbing vines. A slightly rough or uneven surface providing two or more sources of stimuli is needed. The immediate reaction of the tendrils or stems to the surface is probably due to changes in turgor, but the changes are irreversible and followed by growth so that the tendril or stem wraps around the supporting object.

An example of chemotropism is found in angiosperms. The chemotropism involves the pollen tube. The pollen tube, in response to chemical stimuli, grows unerringly downward through the style into the embryo sac in the ovule. Hydrotropism may be thought of as a special type of chemotropism, since water is a chemical substance. Curvature of roots in response to water is observed in several kinds of plants. However, hydrotropism is not as common as was once believed. The evident hydrotropism of roots is due to the more rapid growth that takes place in roots in moist soil and not to the curvature of existing roots toward water.

Questions:

1. Liverworts usually grow close to the ground. However, they can be observed growing at an angle in a terrarium that is exposed to little light. What type of growth does the liverwort exhibit? negative phototropism
2. Just after germinating, vines in tropical forests grow toward darker places, usually the shadows of large trees. Once they make contact with the tree they grow up the trunk toward the canopy of the forest. What tropisms are involved? Explain and identify each tropism as either negative or positive. negative phototropism—growth toward the tree trunk; then positive phototropism and negative geotropism as growth extends to the canopy

Name ____________________ Date ____________________

Problem: How do different environmental conditions alter transpiration rate? (text page 466)

Data and Observations:

TABLE 22-1. MEASURING THE RATE OF WATER LOSS

	Normal Conditions			High Humidity (Plastic Bag over Plant)			Low Humidity (Cool Air Blowing over Plant)		
Trial	Starting mark	Ending mark	Distance moved	Starting mark	Ending mark	Distance moved	Starting mark	Ending mark	Distance moved
1	3 mm	150 mm	147 mm	2 mm	83 mm	81 mm	5 mm	180 mm	175 mm
2	7 mm	141 mm	134 mm	5 mm	60 mm	55 mm	0 mm	206 mm	206 mm
		Total	281 mm		Total	136 mm		Total	381 mm
		Average	140.5 mm		Average	68 mm		Average	190.5 mm

Questions and Conclusion:

1. (a) Define xylem. (b) What is its function? (c) Where are xylem cells located in this experiment? (a) vascular tissue present in plants (b) transport water and minerals through a plant's roots and stem to its leaves (c) throughout the plant
2. (a) Define stomata. (b) What is their function? (c) Where in your experiment were stomata found? (a) pores on the surface of most leaves (b) gas exchange and transpiration (c) on the pine leaves
3. (a) Define transpiration. (b) Explain how xylem and stomata are related to the process of transpiration. (a) process in which water is constantly brought up through a plant and escapes through stomata via evaporation (b) Xylem provides a pathway for water transport. Stomata are the points of exit for the water as it evaporates from the leaf.
4. How was the transpiration rate measured in your experiment? Movement of water along the glass tube was an indication of water loss from the plant.
5. What three different conditions were used to influence transpiration rate? normal surroundings, high humidity, and low humidity
6. (a) Using specific numbers from your data table, explain how each condition influenced transpiration rate. (b) Make a hypothesis about why transpiration rate is influenced by the changed conditions. (a) High humidity should show the lowest rate, while low humidity should show the highest rate of transpiration. (b) High humidity will reduce evaporation rates, and low humidity will increase evaporation rates.

Conclusion: How do different environmental conditions alter transpiration rate? Low humidity speeds up transpiration; high humidity slows it down.

Name ____________________ Date ____________________

The Life Cycle of the Spadefoot Toad

It is late June in the Sonoran Desert of Arizona. The ground is parched because there has been little rain since March. The midafternoon temperature on bare ground reaches 65°C. Rumbling storms herald the arrival of moist air. The inevitable summer monsoon is about to begin.

The summer monsoon is made up of small thunderstorms—usually about five kilometers in diameter—that sweep across the desert. The thunderstorms, although small, make their appearance known. They occur almost daily and can yield as much as 2½ cm of rain in an hour.

Each living thing in the desert waits for the rain in its own way. Perhaps one of the most amazing is the spadefoot toad. To escape the hot, dry desert environment, this toad lives in a dormant state deep in the desert soil—about one meter underground. A membrane covers the toad's skin and enables it to absorb moisture while preventing any moisture loss. Its very large stomach enables it to eat half its body weight. This amount of food provides enough energy and nutrients to sustain life for an entire year or two. The spadefoot toad is called into action by the summer monsoon. Within the limits of this short season—about three months—it must find a mate, reproduce, and eat.

On the evening of the first flooding rains, tens of thousands of spadefoot toads dig themselves out of their burrows. The males assemble at newly formed ponds, singing their mating songs. Breeding must take place on the first night that the spadefoot toads emerge from their burrows to give the tadpoles a chance to complete metamorphosis before the ponds dry up.

In Tucson, Arizona, there are two species of spadefoot toads—the southern spadefoot (*Scaphiopus multiplicatus*) and the larger Couch spadefoot (*Scaphiopus couchii*). The males of each species have unique mating calls that the females recognize. When the male encounters a female of his own species, he climbs onto her back and grasps her around the middle. This position is called amplexus. As the female moves through the water, she lays as many as 4000 eggs, which the male fertilizes. After mating, the toads leave the pond and dig shallow burrows in the moist soil. While the rains last, they emerge every night from their burrows to feed.

Depending on the temperature of the pond water, the eggs hatch into tadpoles in 13 to 48 hours. At first, they are blind and helpless. They are sustained by a small amount of yolk in their gut. After about one day, their eyes and mouths are fully developed. They become small eating machines, eating almost anything in sight—from bacteria to other tadpoles. Because the ponds are temporary, the tadpoles must undergo metamorphosis quickly. The Couch spadefoot has a brief larval life—as few as 8 days from egg to immature toad. The cost of this quick development is an extremely small and vulnerable toad. Several of them can sit on a quarter.

The southern spadefoot develops slower, taking about 21 days to become an immature toad. Although the southern spadefoot reaches a larger size than the Couch spadefoot, there may be a price to pay for slower development. If the rains do not continue, the ponds will not last for 21 days, and all the tadpoles will die.

There are other dangers faced by the spadefoot tadpoles. Several species of beetles and dragonflies also lay their eggs in the ponds. The larvae of these insects feed on tadpoles. Horsefly larvae that live in the mud at the bottom of the pond feed on the newly metamorphosed toads.

If a tadpole is able to find food, escape predators, and reach maturity, it still faces life in the desert. The young toads spend the rest of the summer struggling to capture enough food to triple or quadruple in size so that they can survive underground until the next summer rains. If the young spadefoot toads reach adulthood, they will be able to participate in mating activities in two or three years.

Questions:

1. Why is metamorphosis so short in the spadefoot toad? The tadpole must metamorphose before the pond dries up.
2. What are some difficulties that face the spadefoot tadpole? finding enough food, pond drying up, being eaten by several kinds of predators
3. What is amplexus? grasping of the female toad by the male during mating

Investigation Worksheet — Chapter 23

Name ____________ Date ____________

Problem: How does *Obelia* show sexual and asexual reproduction? (text page 484)

Data and Observations:

TABLE 23–1. COMPARISON OF SEXUAL AND ASEXUAL PHASES IN *OBELIA*

Letter	Structure	Sexual or Asexual Phase?
Figure 23–13 Parts		
A	Reproductive polyp	Asexual
B	Medusa bud	Asexual
C	Gastrovascular cavity	Asexual
D	Tentacles	Asexual
E	Mouth	Asexual
F	Feeding polyp	Asexual
G	Colony	Asexual
Figure 23–14 Parts		
H	Gonads	Sexual
I	Mouth	Sexual
J	Tentacles	Sexual
K	Medusa	Sexual
Figure 23–15 Parts		
L	Larva	Asexual
M	Sperm	Sexual
N	Male medusa	Sexual
O	Testes	Sexual
P	Female medusa	Sexual
Q	Ovaries	Sexual
R	Eggs	Sexual
S	Zygote	Asexual
T	Medusa bud	Asexual
U	Reproductive polyp	Asexual
V	Colony	Asexual
W	Feeding polyp	Asexual

Investigation Worksheet — Chapter 23

Name ____________ Date ____________

Questions and Conclusion:

1. Define: (a) asexual reproduction (b) sexual reproduction. (a) a single parent produces offspring without forming sex cells (b) reproduction involving two parents plus the forming and joining of sex cells (eggs and sperm)
2. Explain why (a) the colony form of *Obelia* is the asexual phase of the life cycle and (b) the medusae of *Obelia* are the sexual phase. (a) The colony is considered as one parent, and sex cells were not formed. (b) The medusae are either male or female. Thus, there are two parents that form sex cells.
3. (a) To what phylum does *Obelia* belong? (b) List several characteristics for this phylum that are shown by *Obelia*. (a) Coelenterata (b) hollow body with only one opening; mouth surrounded by tentacles

Conclusion: How does *Obelia* show sexual and asexual reproduction? *Obelia* has a life cycle that alternates between a sexual phase (the medusae) and an asexual phase (the colony).

Essay — Chapter 24

Name ____________ Date ____________

Reunited Twins

The reuniting of twins can produce fascinating results. In one such case, twins who did not know one another were reunited as adults. When they were brought together, many similarities were discovered. Both were firefighters, both had moustaches, sideburns, and the same glasses. Both drank the same kind of beer and held the bottle in the same way. Both were bachelors and were good humored. When reunited, they kept making the same remarks at the same time and using the same gestures.

Though the twins saw their similarities as wondrous curiosities, the scientific community sees things very differently. Behavioral researchers grapple with the old question as to whether it is our environments or our heredities that make us what we are. To these researchers, identical twins that have different upbringings are a rare opportunity to study this question.

A research group headed by psychologist Thomas Bouchard, Jr. is studying reunited twins. What this group hopes to discover is the heritability of certain human traits. Heritability is the degree to which a trait is influenced by genes, expressed in percentages.

The heritability of a specific characteristic, for example height, can be judged by looking at identical twins that were raised apart. Since these twins share 100 percent of their genetic material, any difference in height must be due to environment. By comparing twins, the researchers found that within the population, 90 percent of the variation in height is influenced by genetic factors. The remaining 10 percent is influenced by environment.

The researchers also found that one's ability to ward off illness is heritable. Identical twins reared apart appear to have similar immune systems. The researchers looked for nine key antibodies. They found that the twins usually had at least seven in common. Fraternal twins and nontwin siblings shared only four key antibodies on average.

Genes also seem to play a role in susceptibility to heart and lung disease. More remarkable is the fact that the timing of the onset of a disease is genetically encoded. Identical twins have developed glaucoma, diabetes, and heart attacks within a short time of one another.

Researchers stress, however, that identical twins inherit predispositions to diseases and that health habits influence those predispositions. For example, a nonsmoking twin with a family history of lung cancer will have a better chance of staying healthy than his or her identical twin who smokes a pack of cigarettes a day.

Research on twin psychology has not yielded substantial results. However, there is some evidence that identical twins reared apart have very similar brainwave patterns, react alike to stimuli, and process information at a similar speed. Identical twins also perform similarly on tests of verbal fluency and IQ. Results of IQ tests show that identical twins reared in the same family have IQ scores that correspond 86 percent of the time. Fraternal twins reared in the same family have IQ scores that correspond 60 percent of the time. But identical twins reared apart are generally much more similar than the fraternal twins, showing a 72 percent match in IQ scores. By contrast, nontwin siblings had similar IQ scores about 47 percent of the time.

Questions:

1. Why do you think identical twins that are reared apart are more similar in physical structure than in IQ? IQ is more influenced by environmental factors than physical structure.
2. Two identical twins were raised apart. When they met, they were identical in height, although one was several pounds heavier than the other. Do you think the difference in weight is influenced by genes or by the environment? Explain. The weight difference is most likely due to environmental influences. The heavier twin may eat more.
3. Two identical twins were reunited. One twin had just recently developed glaucoma. Would you expect the other twin to develop glaucoma? Why? Yes. Most identical twins develop the same diseases at nearly the same time.

Investigation Worksheet — Chapter 24

Name ____________ Date ____________

Problem: How does sea urchin egg development compare to human egg development? (text page 510)

Data and Observations:

TABLE 24-2. DEVELOPMENTAL STAGES OF THE SEA URCHIN

Stage a	Nucleolus, Nucleus — Unfertilized egg	Stage b	Fertilization membrane — Fertilized egg
Stage c	2-cell stage	Stage d	4-cell stage
Stage e	16-cell stage	Stage f	Blastula
Stage g	Morula		

Questions and Conclusion:

1. Define: (a) development (b) external development (c) internal development. (a) changes an organism undergoes in attaining its final form (b) development outside the female body (c) development within the female body
2. Based on your definitions in question 1, explain how development of a sea urchin differs from that of a human. Sea urchin development is external, while in humans it is internal.
3. Each time a cell divides by mitosis, two identical cells are formed. Describe the stage(s) that occur(s) between: (a) the 4-cell stage and the 16-cell stage (b) the 16-cell stage and the 64-cell stage. (a) 8-cell stage (b) 32-cell stage
4. (a) Does cell size increase or decrease with increasing number of cells? (b) What evidence do you have from your observations in Part A to support your answer to 4(a)? (a) decrease (b) Cells in each successive stage were smaller in size than in the preceding stages.
5. (a) In humans, how long does it take for a fertilized egg to reach the uterus? (b) Through what structure must the fertilized egg pass? (c) Describe the changes that take place in the fertilized egg between the ovary and the uterus. (a) four days (b) fallopian tube (c) Mitosis results in an increase of cells from 1 to many.
6. (a) In humans, what happens to the blastula after day 4 of development? (b) How does this differ from what happens in the sea urchin at the same time? (a) The blastula becomes attached to the uterus, and development continues with the mother supplying all the needs of the embryo. (b) The sea urchin embryo drifts in the water and is independent of the mother.
7. Why can diagrams for early sea urchin development be used to represent early stages of human development? Early stages of development are similar.

Conclusion: How does sea urchin egg development compare to human egg development? Development is similar to the blastula stage. After that, major differences exist.

Name ______________________ *Date* ______________

Digestion and Absorption of Nutrients

The main dietary carbohydrates are polysaccharides, disaccharides, and monosaccharides. Starches and their derivatives are the only polysaccharides that are digested by the human digestive system. The major disaccharides that are digested are lactose (milk sugar) and sucrose (table sugar). Fructose and glucose are two monosaccharides that are digested. All carbohydrates are eventually broken down into three monosaccharides—glucose, galactose, and fructose—which are rapidly absorbed across the wall of the small intestine.

Protein digestion begins in the stomach, where large polypeptides are broken down into smaller polypeptides. In the small intestine, the polypeptides are digested by enzymes that are secreted by the pancreas and small intestine. The two major kinds of amino acids, neutral and basic, are the result. Absorption of the amino acids is rapid in the duodenum and jejunum, but slow in the ileum.

Fat digestion begins in the duodenum, with the assistance of an enzyme from the pancreas. The end products of fat digestion are fatty acids, glycerol, and glycerides. Fat absorption is greatest in the upper parts of the small intestine, but a small amount is also absorbed in the lower small intestine.

Vitamins and minerals are not broken down or digested. They are absorbed directly through the small intestine. Water-soluble vitamins are absorbed rapidly. Absorption of fat-soluble vitamins, such as A, D, E, and K, is slowed if the pancreatic and bile enzymes necessary for fat absorption are in short supply. Vitamin B_{12}, however, is absorbed in the ileum. Vitamin B_{12} binds to a protein secreted by the stomach and the resultant complex is absorbed in the ileum.

Many minerals, including calcium and iron, are mostly absorbed in the upper small intestine. Calcium absorption is facilitated by lactose and protein. Most of the dietary iron is in the ferric (Fe^{+3}) state. The ferrous (Fe^{+2}) state of iron is the form of iron that is most readily absorbed. Ascorbic acid, or vitamin C, facilitates the conversion of ferric iron to ferrous iron.

Table 25–1 summarizes the absorption sites of the digested products of carbohydrates, proteins, fats, and selected vitamins and minerals.

TABLE 25-1. ABSORPTION SITES OF SELECTED SUBSTANCES

Substance	Site in Small Intestine: Upper (duodenum and first half of jejunum)	Middle (second half of jejunum)	Lower (ileum)
Sugars (glucose, etc.)	2	3	2
Neutral amino acids	2	3	2
Basic amino acids	2	2	2
Fatty acids	3	2	1
Water-soluble vitamins	3	2	0
Vitamin B_{12}	0	1	3
Calcium	3	2	1
Iron (Fe^{+2})	3	2	1

NOTE: Relative absorption is graded from 0 to 3. No absorption = 0; greatest absorption = 3.

Questions:

1. What substance(s) is (are) absorbed the most in the upper part of the small intestine? The lower part? fatty acids, water-soluble vitamins, calcium, and iron; vitamin B_{12}
2. What substance(s) is (are) not absorbed much or at all in the lower part of the small intestine? fatty acids, water-soluble vitamins, calcium, and iron
3. In what two parts of the small intestine are most nutrients absorbed? the upper and middle parts, or the duodenum and jejunum

Name ______________________ *Date* ______________

Problem: How is the milk sugar lactose digested?

(text page 528)

Data and Observations:

TABLE 25-4. LACTOSE DIGESTION

Lactose and lactase model joined together | Lactose model after digestion by lactase (Glucose, Galactose)

Circle	Contents	Resulting color of TesTape	Glucose present?
1	glucose solution	green	yes
2	milk	yellow	no
3	lactase	yellow	no
4	lactase and milk	green	yes

Questions and Conclusion:

1. Define: (a) enzyme (b) substrate (c) digestion (d) lactose (e) lactase. (a) a protein that activates a chemical reaction (b) molecule upon which a certain enzyme acts (c) the chemical change of food into useable form (d) a carbohydrate present in milk (e) an enzyme that changes lactose into glucose and galactose

Name ______________________ *Date* ______________

2. Use your models from Part A to answer these questions. (a) What carbohydrate molecule is present in milk before it is digested? (b) What two smaller molecules form a molecule of lactose? (c) Does the glucose in the lactose molecule exist as a separate entity before the digestion of milk? (d) What organ of the digestive system produces lactase? (a) lactose (b) glucose and galactose (c) no (d) small intestine
3. Use your experimental results from Part B to answer these questions. (a) Was glucose present in milk? (b) Was glucose present in lactase? (c) Was glucose present in milk after the enzyme lactase was added? Explain. (a) no (b) no (c) yes; The enzyme lactase digests or breaks down lactose into molecules of glucose and galactose.
4. Explain why it was helpful to test glucose with TesTape. to determine how and if the TesTape will react, and to confirm presence of glucose
5. Explain the role of the enzyme lactase in the digestion of milk. Lactase will digest lactose into simple sugars that the body can use as cellular food.
6. Some people cannot drink milk because their digestive systems do not produce lactase. If milk is drunk, it is not digested. This results in cramps, bloating, gas, and diarrhea. Suggest a treatment that would allow such a person to drink milk. Add lactase to the milk before the person drinks it.

Conclusion: How is the milk sugar lactose digested? It is digested by lactase and is broken down into glucose and galactose.

Name ______________________ *Date* ______________

Cyclosporine and Transplants

In 1970, microbiologists at a Swiss pharmaceutical firm, Sandoz, Ltd., were looking for microbes that might produce chemicals with antibiotic properties. They brought a fungus from southern Norway to the laboratory. The fungus produced a substance with some unusual chemical properties. Further research showed that the substance was not effective as an antibiotic. But Jean Borel, an immunologist at Sandoz, saw that this substance—cyclosporine—suppressed the immune response in an unprecedented way.

Most medications that suppress the immune response curb the activity of all types of immune cells. As a result, these medications leave the body susceptible to all sorts of infections. Cyclosporine functions differently. It selectively suppresses the activities of helper T cells.

Helper T cells are called into action when foreign substances, or antigens, are detected in the body. These antigens may be in the form of surface proteins on foreign tissue or invading microorganisms. When helper T cells detect antigens, they send out substances called lymphokines. Lymphokines signal other cells of the immune system to mount an attack. Cyclosporine inhibits helper T cells but leaves enough of the immune response intact to fight infections.

Borel's findings caught the attention of Cambridge scientist David White. White and transplant surgeon Roy Calne tried cyclosporine on animals that received organ transplants. They were impressed with the results of cyclosporine treatment. The transplanted organs were not rejected, and the animals' immune systems were not suppressed to the point of being unable to fight off ordinary infections.

Calne's first attempts at using cyclosporine for human organ transplants were highly successful. The transplanted organs were not rejected. Also, patients treated with cyclosporine were able to fight infections better than patients treated with traditional immunosuppressant medications.

As use of cyclosporine increased, two effects were noted. First, transplant patients receiving cyclosporine experienced fewer complications and recovered from surgery more rapidly than patients taking traditional immunosuppressants. Second, one-year survival rates for transplant patients improved. Use of cyclosporine increased the one-year survival rate for heart transplant patients from 63 percent to 83 percent. Perhaps the most dramatic improvement in survival rates can be observed in liver transplant patients. Treatment with cyclosporine has doubled the one-year survival rate for those patients to more than 70 percent. As a result, liver transplants are now considered therapeutic rather than experimental.

The beneficial effects of cyclosporine have not been limited to transplant patients. Cyclosporine also has been used to treat patients with juvenile-onset diabetes. When treated with cyclosporine, half of a group of patients who had just been diagnosed as diabetic were able to stop using insulin temporarily.

In 1984, the U.S. Food and Drug Administration approved cyclosporine for controlled trials in juvenile-onset diabetes patients. Clinical trials to test the effectiveness of cyclosporine on autoimmune diseases such as multiple sclerosis also are planned.

Although cyclosporine can be considered a breakthrough in the medical field, it does have a few drawbacks. Cyclosporine must be taken for an entire lifetime. No one knows what the long-term effects might be. Also, cyclosporine is not inexpensive. Annual costs for ongoing treatment range from $3000 to $5000.

Questions:

1. How does cyclosporine work? It suppresses the activity of helper T cells.
2. How is cyclosporine different from traditional immunosuppressants? Cyclosporine seems to focus on the helper T cells. Traditional immunosuppressants act on all types of immune cells.
3. What are some benefits of cyclosporine? Answers may vary. It has improved the survival rates of transplant patients; it does not suppress all types of immune cells.

Critical Thinking — Chapter 26

Name ______________________ Date ______________

Laser Canalization

A human heart has two thin-walled atria that receive circulating deoxygenated blood and two ventricles that pump blood. The atria and ventricles are completely separate. The heart of a reptile also has two thin-walled atria that receive circulating blood. However, the heart of a reptile has one ventricle that pumps blood. The ventricle is divided by a thin wall of tissue—the septum. The division of the ventricle is not complete (except in crocodiles) and allows some mixing of oxygenated and deoxygenated blood.

Of great interest to cardiovascular surgeons is the fact that the reptilian heart does not have well-developed coronary arteries. Coronary arteries supply the hearts of many other animals, including humans, with blood. These arteries are so important that when the flow of blood becomes partly blocked, heart damage can result. If blockage of the arteries is severe enough, the result may be a sudden, fatal heart attack.

For cardiovascular surgeons, the absence of coronary arteries in the hearts of reptiles raises an important question: How is the reptilian heart nourished without being fed by an elaborate arterial system? The answer to this question is that blood from the ventricle of a reptile seeps into the sinusoids, or tiny spaces in the myocardium. The myocardium is the wall of muscle that encases the heart. The blood that seeps into the sinusoids nourishes the heart. Human hearts have sinusoids, too. This fact provides the basis for a new method in cardiovascular surgery called laser canalization. The left ventricle is chosen for this procedure because it is the more powerful pumping chamber.

Laser canalization is an open-heart operation, but it is far less complicated than the bypass surgery that is employed currently. In bypass surgery, blood is shunted around coronary artery obstructions by attaching one end of a vein—usually taken from the leg or chest—to the aorta; the other end of the vein is attached to the blocked artery just beyond the obstruction. Bypass surgery often takes hours to perform. Laser canalization takes only minutes and involves tapping ventricular blood by boring 8 to 14 holes through the wall of the left ventricle with a hand-held, high-powered, carbon dioxide laser. Blood seeps through the tiny holes and into the sinusoids, thus nourishing the damaged area of the heart. Bleeding from the laser holes outside of the ventricle wall is minimal because the laser-bored holes seal at the surface by means of the natural clotting process.

Laser canalization is done in the United States, Japan, and the Soviet Union. Dr. Mahmood Mirhoseini of St. Luke's Hospital in Milwaukee, Wisconsin, has performed laser canalization on a number of patients. Because laser canalization is still a new procedure, eligible patients include those who have had at least one standard bypass operation and have areas of the heart that are too damaged for conventional grafts. All of Dr Mirhoseini's patients that underwent laser canalization are still alive and well. X rays of their hearts and blood vessels show that the operations were successful. In one patient, the areas of the heart that received laser canalization are receiving more blood than the sections that underwent traditional bypasses.

Questions:

1. What are some similarities and differences between reptilian and human hearts? Both have two atria; both have sinusoids; humans have two ventricles, reptiles have one ventricle; humans have separate atria and ventricles, reptiles have incomplete division of the ventricle; the human heart has well-developed arteries, the reptilian heart does not.
2. On what principle is laser canalization based? It is based on sinusoid structures of the reptilian heart.
3. What are some advantages and disadvantages of bypass surgery? Bypass surgery is an older, more proven method; it takes hours to perform the surgery.

Investigation Worksheet — Chapter 26

Name ______________________ Date ______________

Problem: How does one analyze pulse and heartbeat? (text page 546)

Data and Observations:

TABLE 26-1. PULSE RATES

Trial	Wrist	Neck	Running pulse for 15 seconds	Running pulse for 1 minute
1				
2				
3				
4				
5				
Total				
Average				

TABLE 26-2. TIME SEQUENCE DURING NORMAL HEARTBEATS

	Shown on ECG by which letter segments	Time needed to complete event(s)
Atria relaxed	T–P	0.3
	Q–T	0.4
Ventricles relaxed	T–P	0.3
	P–Q	0.2
Atria contracted	P–Q	0.2
Ventricles contracted	Q–T	0.4

Questions and Conclusion:

1. What is your pulse and what does it exactly agree with? It is a wave or surge of blood caused by the forceful contraction of the ventricles. It exactly agrees with the heartbeat.
2. Explain why you can feel a pulse in your wrist and neck. A pulse can be detected in arteries that lie close to the surface of the body.
3. Define: (a) systole (b) diastole. (a) contraction of atria or ventricles (b) relaxation of atria or ventricles
4. Using the ECG in Figure 26A, determine what line segment corresponds to each of the following normal heartbeat events: (a) atrium systole (b) ventricle systole (c) atrium diastole (d) ventricle diastole. NOTE: Keep in mind that when one set of chambers is contracting, the other is relaxing. (a) P–Q (b) Q–T (c) Q–P (d) T–Q

Conclusion: How does one analyze pulse and heartbeat? Pulse can be analyzed by counting the waves of blood passing through an artery. Heartbeat can be analyzed through the use of an ECG.

*Student answers will vary. The wrist and neck pulse rates should be essentially the same. The pulse rate calculated after exercise should be noticeably higher.

Skills — Chapter 27

Name ______________________ Date ______________

Choking and First Aid

The larynx is a highly specialized organ. Although it acts as a valve for preventing swallowed food and foreign objects from entering the lower respiratory passages, it is specifically designed for voice production. Movement of the cartilages in the larynx causes the size of the opening between the vocal folds, or vocal cords, to change, thereby producing sound.

The mucous membranes of the upper part of the larynx are very sensitive. If a piece of food or any other foreign body comes into contact with this part of the larynx, explosive coughing immediately follows. Although the person may appear to be in danger, the coughing itself is a reflex and indicates that he or she is not choking. If the person grabs the throat and is unable to speak, he or she may indeed be choking. Choking results when an object enters the larynx and muscles of the larynx go into spasms. These spasms cause the vocal cords to become tense. As a result, air cannot enter the trachea, bronchi, or lungs.

A first aid technique that has been proven successful in helping people who are choking is the Heimlich maneuver, developed by Dr. Henry J. Heimlich. This technique is effective if the choking person is still conscious and able to sit or stand. If a person suspected of choking cannot speak and nods "yes" when asked if he or she is choking, then life-saving measures, such as the Heimlich maneuver, are imperative.

First, the individual administering the Heimlich maneuver stands behind the choking person and wraps his or her arms around the person's waist. Next, a fist is made with one hand. The thumb knuckle of the fisted hand is placed next to the victim's abdomen, slightly above the navel and below the rib cage. Grabbing the fisted hand with the free hand, the person administering aid presses into the choking person's abdomen with a quick upward thrust. The thrust must be repeated several times, if necessary. The abdominal thrusts usually drive air from the lungs with enough force to dislodge the foreign object. Improper techniques include squeezing the chest or slapping the back. Squeezing the chest may result in broken ribs, and slapping the back may cause the foreign object to become lodged more tightly.

Questions:

1. A member of your family just took a swallow of milk. He or she begins coughing violently. Should you administer any first aid procedure? Why? No. Coughing does not interfere with his or her ability to breathe.
2. You are eating at a restaurant. A man at the next table quickly stands up and with a panicked expression begins to grab his throat. What should you do? Ask him if he is choking. If he cannot speak and nods "yes," begin the Heimlich maneuver.
3. Do you think it is important for everyone to know how to perform the Heimlich maneuver? Why? Answers will vary.

FIGURE 27–1. Heimlich maneuver

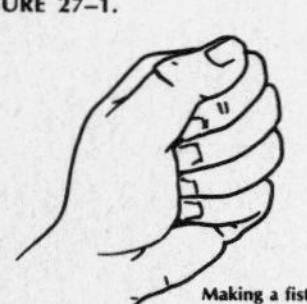

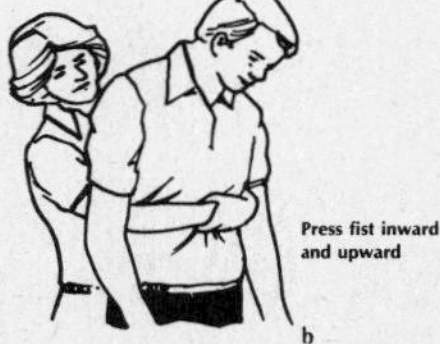

Investigation Worksheet — Chapter 27

Name ______________________ Date ______________

Problem: How is urine used to help diagnose diseases? (text page 580)

Data and Observations:

TABLE 27-2. RESULTS OF URINE SAMPLE TESTS

Sample	Specific gravity	pH	Acid, base, or neutral	Glucose
Distilled water	1.000	7	neutral	no
Urine A	1.018	3	acid	no
Urine B	1.035	5	acid	yes
Urine C	1.004	11	base	no

Questions and Conclusion:

1. Normal urine has a specific gravity of 1.010–1.025. A high specific gravity (over 1.025) means that many dissolved chemicals such as salt, glucose, and protein are present in the urine. A low specific gravity (below 1.010) indicates few dissolved chemicals. (a) What was the specific gravity of distilled water? (b) Offer an explanation for why it was so low. (c) Which urine samples were normal for specific gravity? (d) Which urine samples were abnormal for specific gravity? (a) 1.000 (b) No dissolved chemicals are present. (c) A (d) B, C
2. Normal urine has a pH of about 6. (a) What was the pH of distilled water? (b) Which urine samples were normal for pH? (c) Which samples were abnormal for pH? (a) 7 (b) none (c) A, B, C
3. Normal urine has no glucose present. (a) Was glucose present in the distilled water? (b) Which urine samples had glucose? (c) Which urine samples had no glucose? (a) no (b) B (c) A, C
4. These problems may show in the urine: diabetes mellitus is indicated by glucose and high specific gravity. Diabetes insipidus is indicated by a very low specific gravity. Basic urine indicates possible kidney infection, anemia, or kidney stones. Acid urine indicates fever or high protein diet. List the urine sample(s) that might be associated with each of these diseases or conditions: (a) diabetes insipidus (b) diabetes mellitus (c) fever (d) anemia (e) kidney infection. (a) C (b) B (c) A, B (d) C (e) C

Conclusion: How is urine used to help diagnose diseases? Certain diseases show changes from the normal values expected for urine. Measuring the specific gravity, pH, and presence or absence of glucose may indicate if the body is normal.

Essay **Chapter 28**

Name ______________________ Date ______________

The Pineal Gland

The pineal gland is a ductless gland located near the center of the brain. It is smaller than an aspirin, and there has been considerable debate over its function.

Much of what researchers know about the pineal gland comes from animal studies. In these studies, the gland was removed from various animals. Removal of the gland caused these animals to lose their seasonal instincts and habits. Birds lost the urge to migrate, and deer grew antlers at the wrong time.

Richard Wurtman, an endocrinologist, believes that the pineal gland acts as a neuroendocrine transducer, a system that converts a nerve-type signal into an endocrine signal. In this system, the hormone melatonin, which is produced in the pineal gland, is affected by the length of daylight.

In nonmammalian animals, such as the frog, the pineal gland senses light and dark. However, in mammals, the presence of light is first detected by the eyes. This information travels from the optic nerve to the spinal cord and from the spinal cord to the pineal gland.

In daylight, the pineal gland converts the amino acid tryptophan into serotonin. Serotonin is stored in the pineal gland. At night, nerve cells that are connected to the pineal gland release neurotransmitters, NAT (N-acetyltransferase) and HIOMT (hydroxyindole-O-methyltransferase). These enzymes increase in concentration and turn serotonin into melatonin, which then flows into the bloodstream. The level of melatonin in the bloodstream is converted into a time signal that gives an animal its sense of the seasons. The animal's ability to recognize seasonal changes helps its survival. Survival may depend on the seasonal habits of migration and reproduction, addition of winter fur, deposition of body fat, or winter hibernation.

In humans, the pineal gland may affect the sleep cycle. Studies show that melatonin makes people drowsy. Some researchers feel that it may influence the onset of puberty. The pineal gland also may be responsible for Seasonal Affective Disorder, or SAD. This disorder is characterized by the winter blues that many people experience from November until spring.

Norman Rosenthal, a psychiatrist at the National Institute of Mental Health, put several SAD sufferers in front of very bright lights twice a day for several hours. These people no longer experienced the winter doldrums, but what caused this change is unknown.

Questions:

1. To what system does the pineal gland belong? Explain. the endocrine system; The pineal gland is a ductless gland that secretes a hormone.
2. In what way is the pineal gland closely associated with the nervous system? The pineal gland converts a nerve-type signal into an endocrine signal.
3. What outside force seems to have a direct effect on pineal gland functions? the length of daylight
4. What does the pineal gland help regulate in animals? Answers will vary. Generally, students will list daily and seasonal activities and rhythms.
5. What effect might the pineal gland have on humans? It may influence the sleep cycle, the onset of puberty, and play a role in SAD.

Investigation Worksheet **Chapter 28**

Name ______________________ Date ______________

Problem: How does the body control calcium balance? (text page 598)

Data and Observations:

FIGURE 28–15.

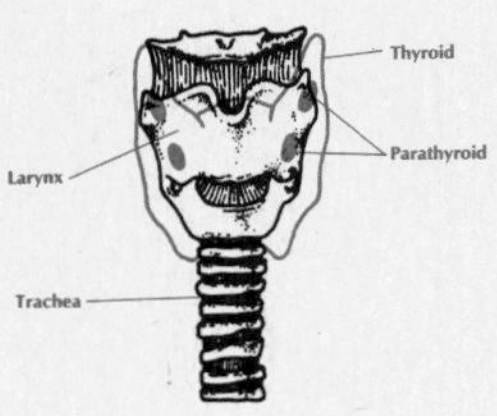

FIGURE 28–16.

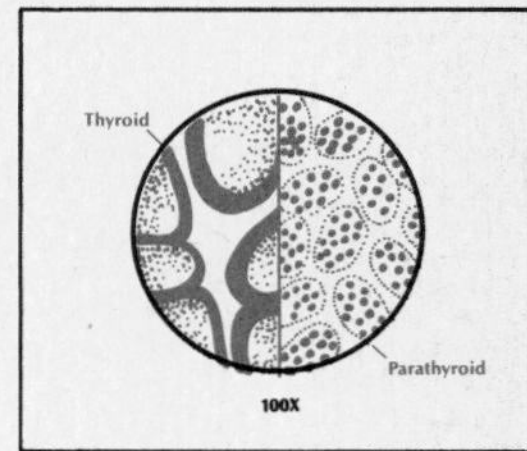

Questions and Conclusion:

1. When the calcium level in the blood increases, which hormone is released? Which is not? calcitonin; parathormone
2. When the calcium level in the blood decreases, which hormone is released? Which is not? parathormone; calcitonin
3. Is calcitonin or parathormone produced by the parathyroids? The thyroid? parathormone; calcitonin
4. Define endocrine system, hormone, and homeostasis. composed of ductless glands that secrete hormones directly into blood; a chemical regulator that is produced in one part of the organism and affects other parts; maintaining of a constant internal environment

Conclusion: How does the body control calcium balance? The calcium balance is controlled through the interaction of two hormones. Parathormone will remove calcium from the blood and store it in bone. When needed, calcitonin will remove the stored calcium from bone and place it into the bloodstream.

Skills **Chapter 29**

Name ______________________ Date ______________

Comparison of Vertebrate Brains

The central nervous system is a complex arrangement of communication cells. It is made up of the brain and spinal cord. In all vertebrates, the brain forms from an enlarged bulb of nervous tissue. The spinal cord develops posteriorly to the bulb and continues down the trunk of the animal.

Parts of the brain are developed to various degrees in vertebrates. This development is related to function. In Figure 29–1, one can see how brain development and function are related.

In fish, amphibians, reptiles, and birds, the optic lobes (the vision center) are large. This is because eyesight is important in these types of animals. Although vision is important in mammals, the optic lobes are not as large and are located just below the cerebrum.

The medulla oblongata, located at the base of the brain, is well developed in fish and amphibians. The lateral lobes of this brain section allow aquatic vertebrates to determine water pressure and current changes. The medulla oblongata contains neurons that act as regulatory centers for tail movements that are used for locomotion in the water.

When comparing vertebrate brains, one notices that olfactory lobes become less prominent in mammals and birds as compared to fish, amphibians, or reptiles. In contrast, one also notices that the cerebrum and cerebellum become noticeably larger and more complex in birds and mammals when compared to the same brain structures in fish, amphibians, or reptiles.

The cerebellum, which is responsible for motor coordination, is highly developed in birds and mammals. In both of these groups this brain area becomes folded. This folding allows more brain tissue to be accommodated in a small space.

The cerebral hemisphere (responsible for conscious and mental processes) makes up the largest parts of the avian and mammalian brains. In mammals the development of this section is more complex. This is illustrated by the convolutions, which are not present in the avian brain.

Questions:

Answer the following questions by examining Figure 29–1.

1. In which vertebrate would smell play a more important role, amphibian or mammal? Explain. amphibian, because it has larger olfactory lobes than the mammal
2. How does the cerebellum in a bird differ from the cerebellum in a fish? A bird's cerebellum is larger and more convoluted.
3. How does the cerebrum of a mammal differ from that of a reptile? A mammal's cerebrum is larger and convoluted.
4. Which vertebrate would have a higher ability for association and consciousness? Explain. the mammal; It has the largest cerebrum, which is associated with these two abilities.

FIGURE 29–1.

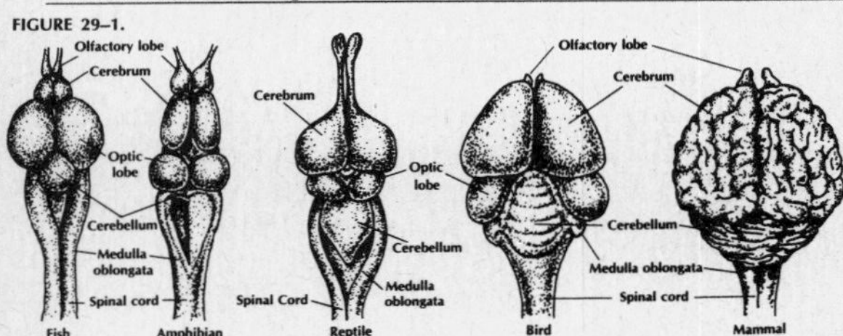

Essay **Chapter 29**

Name ______________________ Date ______________

Mapping Brain Activity

Physicians have various imaging techniques available to them to observe the physical structures of the brain. These techniques include X rays, computerized tomography (CT), magnetic resonance imaging (MRI), and positron emission tomography (PET). Compared to these imaging techniques, a new technique, known as magnetoencephalography (MEG), has the unique ability to indicate which parts of the brain are active, not just the structures of the brain. The difference between the older imaging techniques and MEG is like that between a detailed map of a city and a display that shows which telephones in the city are active at any given time.

Magnetoencephalography was made possible with the invention of a Superconducting Quantum Interference Device, or SQUID. SQUID is the most sensitive magnetometer known. It can detect magnetic fields less than one-billionth as strong as those of Earth. That is the strength of the magnetic fields generated within the brain by the electrical activity of the neurons.

The principles on which SQUID works were discovered by Brian Josephson in 1962. He was studying the current flow through a superconductor. A superconductor is a material that loses all electrical resistance when cooled below a critical temperature. Normally, electrical currents require a voltage, or a "push," in order to flow. But a supercurrent in a superconductor can flow without voltage.

Josephson wondered what would happen if he cut a superconductor in half and then joined the two pieces with a thin layer of electrical insulation. Would the electric current, or electrons, stop at the insulation? Josephson found that although the electrons were capable of passing through the insulation, their flow produced a weak magnetic field. The magnetic field, in turn, increased the insulating properties of the barrier between the two pieces of superconductor. Thus, whenever current was interrupted, Josephson knew that magnetic fields were being produced. From this idea came the SQUID.

Several SQUIDs are grouped together to map the magnetic field of the brain. Remember that weak magnetic fields are produced by the normal functioning of a neuron. During a nervous impulse, ions—electrically charged sodium or potassium atoms—flow along the nerve pathway. Such a flow simulates an electric current and generates a magnetic field. The group of SQUIDs can detect this magnetic field and thus map brain activity.

Until MEG, the only way to measure the brain's electrical activity was to attach electrodes to the skull or directly to the brain. This technique is known as electroencephalography, or EEG. However, the skull distorts the pattern of electrical activity, thus limiting EEG's usefulness. Cutting holes in a patient's skull to install electrodes directly on the brain is painful, risky, and costs $20 000 or more. MEG makes mapping the brain easier because the brain's magnetic fields pass through the skull without distortion, and surgery is not necessary.

Magnetic imaging of the brain with MEG is still considered an experimental technique. MEG is available at a few medical centers for research use only. Researchers have been focusing on treatment of epilepsy with this new technique. Epilepsy is characterized by seizures—uncontrolled movements of the arms and legs, abrupt memory loss, and/or loss of consciousness. For some people, medication is not effective in controlling seizures. Surgery is the only remedy. MEG now offers a way for neurosurgeons to precisely locate damaged neurons. Apart from its value in medical diagnosis, researchers are hopeful that MEG may offer insights into the working of the normal brain, such as how the brain responds to stimuli.

Questions:

1. What is magnetoencephalography, or MEG, based on? the magnetic fields produced by neural activity in the brain
2. What has made MEG possible? Answers may vary. Most students will say the development of a sensitive magnetometer known as SQUID.
3. What advantages does MEG have over EEG? There is no distortion of the magnetic field by the skull, and surgery is not necessary.

Name ______________________ Date ______________

Problem: What is the function of certain brain parts? (text page 622)

Data and Observations:

TABLE 29-2. BRAIN ANATOMY	
Area	Name
1	medulla oblongata
2	temporal lobe
3	frontal lobe
4	parietal lobe
5	cerebrum
6	occipital lobe
7	cerebellum
8	longitudinal fissure
9	right central fissure
10	right cerebrum half
11	left cerebrum half
12	left central fissure

Name ______________________ Date ______________

Questions and Conclusion:

1. In relation to the central fissure as well as the left and right cerebrum sides, describe the location of the brain tissue that controls each of the following functions: (a) muscle movement on right side of body (b) muscle movement on left side of body (c) sensations on right side of body (d) sensations on left side of body. (a) left side of cerebrum in front of left central fissure (b) right side of cerebrum in front of right central fissure (c) left side of cerebrum in back of left central fissure (d) right side of cerebrum in back of right central fissure
2. Cite evidence that: (a) most functions are evenly distributed on both sides of the brain (b) certain functions are controlled by only one brain side. (a) muscle movement and sensation of body areas involve both left and right brain sides (b) speech and comprehension of spoken words involve only left side of cerebrum
3. Damage to each of the following areas would probably interfere with what normal functions? (a) right cerebrum side: L-4, 5 (b) right cerebrum side: V-12, 13, 14 (c) left cerebrum side: L-7,8 (d) left cerebrum side: H-8,9 (a) movement of left arm and hand (b) ability to see objects in right field of view (c) ability to feel sensation on right side of face (d) ability to speak

Conclusion: What is the function of certain brain parts? Functions will depend on the brain area described. In general, the left cerebrum controls body muscles and sensation of the right side, while the right cerebrum controls body muscles and sensation of the left side.

Name ______________________ Date ______________

Bone Development

Bones develop from embryonic connective tissue. This tissue is apparent when a fetus is about 5 weeks of age. In a fetus, some of the embryonic connective tissue will ossify, or develop into bone tissue directly. Direct ossification takes place in bones that are needed for protection, such as the flat bones of the skull. In other parts of the fetus, which include most of the skeleton, the embryonic connective tissue is first replaced by cartilage. This process is almost complete when the fetus is about 6 weeks of age. The cartilage later undergoes ossification to be replaced by bone tissue.

Ossification in the cartilage of a long bone starts near the center of what will be the shaft. This area where ossification begins is called the diaphyseal, or primary center of ossification. Bone that originates at a primary center of ossification is called the diaphysis. Bones that form directly from embryonic connective tissue also have a primary center of ossification. Primary centers appear at different times in different bones. However, most primary centers appear when the fetus is 7 to 12 weeks old. Figure 30–1 shows the primary centers of ossification in an 11-week-old fetus. Almost all primary centers are present by birth. At this time, ossification has progressed almost to the ends of the long bones.

At birth or shortly after, another center of ossification may appear at the ends of the long bone. This secondary center of ossification is called the epiphyseal. The bone that originates at a secondary center is called the epiphysis.

Between the diaphysis and the epiphysis is a plate of cartilage known as the growth plate, or the epiphyseal cartilage plate. Continued lengthening of bone tissue takes place at the epiphyseal cartilage plate. This process takes place between puberty and the twenty-fifth year.

The endocrine system exerts an important control over bone growth. The growth hormone from the anterior lobe of the pituitary gland stimulates bone growth at the epiphyseal cartilage plates. Hormones from the gonads (testes and ovaries), on the other hand, bring about cessation of growth by causing the epiphyseal cartilage plate to ossify.

Questions:

1. The illustration below shows a femur of a young child. Identify the diaphysis, the two epiphyses, and the two epiphyseal cartilage plates.
2. Identify the primary tissue that makes up the long bone in a fetus that is 5 weeks, 6 weeks, and 12 weeks old. 5 weeks: embryonic connective tissue; 6 weeks: cartilage; 12 weeks: bone at primary centers of ossification and cartilage at the ends of bones
3. Why is an injury at the epiphyseal cartilage plate serious in a young child? Answers will vary. Students may say that damage to the epiphyseal cartilage plate could affect the growth of the bone.

FIGURE 30–1.

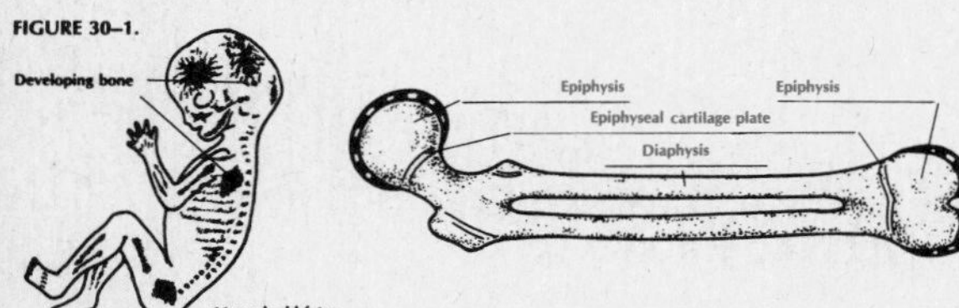

Name ______________________ Date ______________

Problem: How does muscle shorten when it contracts? (text page 642)

Data and Observations:

TABLE 30-1. PARTS AND AREAS ON FIGURE 30-20, PART A
1 I band
2 A band
3 H zone
4 Z line

SARCOMERE MEASUREMENTS, PART B		
Length of	Relaxed	Contracted
one thin filament	28 mm	28 mm
one thick filament	39 mm	39 mm
A band	39 mm	39 mm
I band (both together)	28 mm	12 mm
H zone	17 mm	0.5 mm
one sarcomere	74 mm	58 mm

Investigation Worksheet — Chapter 30

Name ______________________ Date ______________

Questions and Conclusion:

1. Define the following terms: (a) skeletal muscle (b) muscle fibril (c) sarcomere (d) relaxed muscle (e) contracted muscle. (a) striated muscle, most common body muscle type (b) small unit of muscle fiber (c) functioning unit of muscle fibril (d) muscle not doing work (e) muscle doing work
2. Describe briefly what provides skeletal muscle with its characteristic striated or banded appearance. the alternating bands of muscle protein present in each sarcomere
3. As muscle contracts, how does each of the following change? (a) thick filament length (b) thin filament length (c) sarcomere length (d) A band length (e) I band length (f) H zone length (a) does not change (b) does not change (c) gets shorter (d) does not change (e) gets shorter (f) gets shorter and disappears
4. When a muscle contracts, it shortens in length. (a) Which filaments are responsible for sliding when contraction occurs? (b) Over what do these filaments slide? (a) thin filaments (b) thick filaments
5. Explain how it is possible for a muscle to shorten during contraction when there is no actual change in the length of the thick and thin filaments. (This is called the sliding filament hypothesis.) The thin filaments compact as they slide over the thick filaments, and this action decreases length.
6. Explain how the thin filaments actually slide over the thick filaments. Myosin hooks onto actin in the presence of ATP. The chemical energy of ATP is then transformed into mechanical energy that moves the actin over the myosin.

Conclusion: How does muscle shorten when it contracts? Thin filaments present in the sarcomeres slide over the thick filaments causing the length of the sarcomeres to shorten.

Essay — Chapter 31

Name ______________________ Date ______________

Memory

Memory is considered to be a major factor in learning and depends on storage of information.

There appear to be two types of information storage—short-term memory storage and long-term memory storage. In short-term memory storage, memory lasts from a few minutes to a few hours. An example of short-term memory is memorizing a telephone number long enough to dial it correctly. Long-term memory storage often requires constant repetition of the learning experience or rehearsal. Therefore, to remember a particular telephone number permanently, you must look it up and dial it many times, or repeat it over and over to yourself. It is thought that once information becomes a part of long-term memory storage, the information, or memory trace, lasts a lifetime.

Just how information becomes a memory is still largely unknown. One of the biggest breakthroughs in this area occurred by accident in the early 1950s. A man known as H. M. had a particularly severe form of epilepsy. H. M.'s doctors decided on a drastic treatment. They removed a small section of his brain, which included most of the hippocampus, the amygdala, and some surrounding cortex. The surgery had the expected result—less severe epileptic seizures. However, H. M. could no longer learn new facts.

H. M.'s form of amnesia demonstrated that there are different types of memory connected with different parts of the brain. Declarative memory involves remembering facts such as names, dates, and places. For example, if you were to remember something and declare, "I know where the keys are," you would be using declarative memory.

The other type of memory is procedural memory. This type of memory is acquired by repetition or conditioning. It includes skills such as riding a bicycle. Procedural memory is not affected by damage to the hippocampus and amygdala as is declarative memory.

Mortimer Mishkin is chief of neuropsychology at the National Institute of Mental Health. He has been conducting elaborate experiments that are providing glimpses of how the brain processes information into declarative memory. What Dr. Mishkin has discovered is that the most important parts of the visual memory system are located in the hippocampus and amygdala. He also found that each structure performs a unique function. Removing the hippocampus destroys an animal's ability to remember how two objects are related spatially.

The amygdala serves to store information with emotional overtones. Removing the amygdala does not alter an animal's performance on spatial relationships.

Mishkin believes that emotions help determine what is stored in long-term memory. He believes that every memory cannot become a part of long-term memory storage; therefore, the brain must be able to discriminate between what must be stored and what does not need to be stored. Many people say that their strongest and clearest memories are connected with very emotional events.

Studies also have been done by Richard F. Thompson at Stanford University to determine the site of procedural memory. Working with rabbits, he has determined that procedural memory is stored in a different part of the brain than declarative memory. His studies show that procedural memory is stored in the cerebellum.

Questions:

1. How do short-term memory and long-term memory storage differ? Memories in short-term storage last from a few minutes to a few hours. Memories in long-term memory storage last a lifetime.
2. All memories can be stored as short-term or long-term. However, there are two major kinds of memory associated with different parts of the brain. What are these two kinds of memory? declarative and procedural
3. A person can remember which houses were on his or her block but cannot remember which houses are next to one another. Which part of this person's brain is associated with the inability to remember the houses' locations? hippocampus

Investigation Worksheet — Chapter 31

Name ______________________ Date ______________

Problem: How can you study the behavior of an animal? (text page 656)

Data and Observations:

TABLE 31-1. OBSERVATIONS OF VINEGAR EEL BEHAVIOR

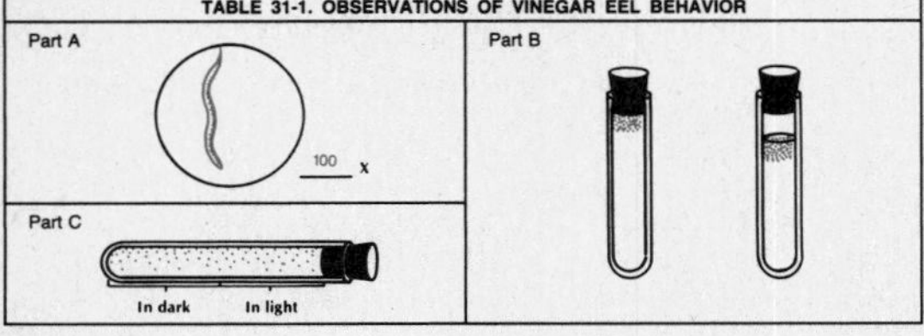

Questions and Conclusion:

1. Define: (a) behavior (b) positively geotropic (c) negatively geotropic (d) positively phototropic (e) negatively phototropic. (a) response of an organism to stimuli (b) moving toward gravity (c) moving away from gravity (d) moving toward light (e) moving away from light
2. Vinegar eels are roundworms. They are members of the phylum Nematoda. (a) List several characteristics of animals in this phylum. (b) Name those characteristics that you observed in vinegar eels. (a) round body, two openings to digestive system, male or female, internal fertilization (b) round body
3. Answer these questions based on your observations in Part B. (a) Are vinegar eels positively geotropic or negatively geotropic? (b) What evidence supports your answer to 3(a)? (c) What experimental evidence do you have that the animals are responding to gravity as opposed to the air at the top of the tube? (d) How do your observations and conclusions compare to those of your classmates? (a) negatively geotropic (b) Eels were on the top surface of tube. (c) Eels were present on top of the tube that had no air space. (d) They were the same.
4. Answer these questions based on your observations in Part C. (a) Are vinegar eels positively phototropic, negatively phototropic, or neutral with respect to light? (b) What evidence supports your answer to 4(a)? (c) How do your observations and conclusions compare to those of your classmates? (a) neutral (b) Eels were seen along the entire tube in both the presence and absence of light. (c) Answers may or may not agree.
5. Based on your answers to questions 3(d) and 4(c), are the experimental results obtained from studies of behavior easily interpreted? Explain. Answers will vary, but expected answer is no.

Conclusion: How can you study the behavior of an animal? Design and conduct controlled experiments on an animal.

Essay — Chapter 32

Name ______________________ Date ______________

Prairie Dogs

Prairie dogs are social animals that live in large groups known as prairie dog towns. The prairie dog towns range in size from about 0.5 hectare (1 hectare = 10 000 m^2) to over 100 hectares. The larger towns are subdivided by topography or vegetation into wards. A ward may be compared to a neighborhood and is usually less than 0.5 hectare.

Within each ward, the prairie dogs are united in a cohesive, cooperative unit called a coterie. The members of a coterie defend their ward against all trespassers. Breeding coteries usually contain only 1 adult male, 3 or 4 adult females, and their young up to one year of age. The breeding season is mid-March to mid-April and the gestation period is from 28 to 36 days. The size of a litter varies from 2 to 8 young, which are nursed by the mother for about 6 weeks. During May and the early part of June, the pups begin to emerge from their burrows for the first time.

Nonbreeding coteries may contain 2 to 30 members. The members may be all males, more males than females, or an equal number of both sexes. No social hierarchy exists, although one male, usually the most aggressive and the strongest defender of the ward, may dominate the rest.

Members of the coterie cooperate with one another. Competition for food and shelter is uncommon in a coterie. Social relations within a coterie are friendly and intimate. These relationships include grooming, play activities, and an identification kiss—a recognition display in which each individual turns its head and opens its mouth to permit contact with the other.

Vocal communication emphasizes the unity of the coterie. Vocal sounds include warning barks, territorial calls, defense barks, fighting snarls, tooth chattering, and fear screams. The sounds mean the same thing to each member of the coterie, and the members react the same to each sound. For example, the warning bark is given at the first sign of intrusion. If the intruder is a predator, all the prairie dogs react to the signal by repeating the bark and running toward their burrow. Many of the burrows are interconnected, so escape routes remain open even if a predator chases a prairie dog down a burrow. In addition to predator defense, prairie dogs within a coterie defend against intrusions by other prairie dogs.

Overpopulation in a coterie may force territorial expansion. In this case, the dominant, or defending, male of the adjacent coterie is driven out. The prairie dogs from the overpopulated coterie may then take over abandoned burrows in the adjacent coterie. Overpopulation may also result in social unrest and the eventual emigration of the yearlings. Adults may leave to escape the demands of the new pups or to seek more abundant food. When prairie dogs relocate, they may dig new burrows at the edge of the town. Or, they may go a few kilometers away to start up new towns.

Black-tailed prairie dogs are found in a 644-kilometer-wide zone that lies east of the Rocky Mountains and extends from southern Saskatchewan to southern Texas. Regarded as a nuisance by some people, the numbers of prairie dogs have been reduced drastically through attempts to eradicate them. Not only have the eradication measures affected the numbers of prairie dogs, they also have indirectly affected the black-footed ferret. The ferret's diet consists mainly of prairie dogs. The prairie dog's burrow provides shelter for the ferret during extreme temperatures and inclement weather. The decline of the prairie dog is partly responsible for endangering the black-footed ferret.

Questions:

1. Why are prairie dogs considered social animals? They live together in a cooperative unit.
2. What is the relationship between prairie dog towns and wards? Prairie dog towns are subdivided into smaller units called wards.
3. What makes up a ward? a small group of prairie dogs called a coterie
4. What are some behaviors that express social relationships in a coterie? grooming, play activities, identification kiss, and vocalization

Investigation Worksheet — Chapter 32

Name ______ Date ______

Problem: How do population changes alter population pyramids? (text page 688)

Data and Observations:

TABLE 32-4. STATIONARY POPULATIONS

Question	Answer
(a)	4.2
(b)	4.8
(c)	3.7
(d)	4.2
(e)	3.5
(f)	4.2
(g)	24.6

Questions and Conclusion:

1. Define: (a) population (b) prereproductive group (c) reproductive group (d) postreproductive group (e) stationary population (f) growing population. (a) group of organisms that naturally interbreed (b) portion of population that will be reproducing in future years (c) portion of the population reproducing at the present time (d) portion of the population that does not reproduce and will not in the future (e) one that is neither increasing nor decreasing (f) one that will increase
2. The graphs that you have constructed are called population pyramid graphs. Describe and compare the general pyramid shapes for the two population graphs. stationary—uniform width for all age groups with gentle taper at top; growing—very wide base with largest population at prereproductive level, sharp taper at top
3. Compare the following categories for a stationary population to those of a growing population. (a) percent of prereproductive groups (b) percent of reproductive groups (c) percent of postreproductive groups (a) percentage of prereproductive age is much greater in growing population: 25% to 44%; (b) percentage is about the same in both: 41% to 43%; (c) percentage of postreproductive is lower in growing population: 25% to 18%

Investigation Worksheet — Chapter 32

Name ______ Date ______

4. Based on your percentages in question 3 and the general pyramid shapes of question 2, explain what problems or trends may be seen in the future in terms of food supply, housing, waste disposal, and impact on the environment: (a) for a stationary population (b) for a growing population (c) explain your answers to (a) and (b). (a) Problems or trends will be about the same in the future as they are in the present. (b) Problems in a growing population will become serious in the future. (c) Population is not increasing or decreasing in a stationary population; population will be expected to increase as the prereproductive population increases, thus creating more need for housing, food, and other resources.
5. The following pyramid graph was prepared for a population. (a) Could it be considered as a stationary, growing, or declining population? (b) How does this population appear to differ from the others studied in regard to the percent of prereproductive groups? (a) declining (b) This group is the smallest seen in any population group.

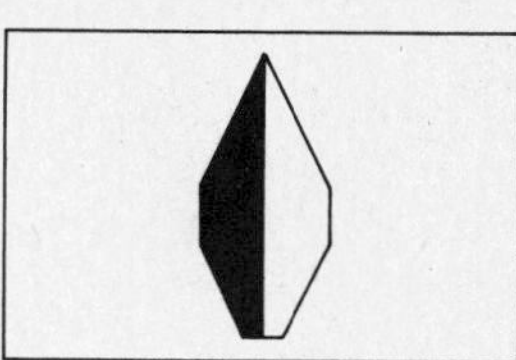

Conclusion: How do population changes alter population pyramids? The percentage of prereproductive, postreproductive and reproductive populations will change as the general trends of a population change.

Essay — Chapter 33

Name ______ Date ______

Living Together—Amensalism

Every plant or animal lives in a community and associates with many species. In certain cases, neither species is affected by the presence of the other. This kind of relationship is called neutralism.

Most people are familiar with the relationship characterized by two species benefiting from each other (mutualism). It is a positive, or helpful, interaction. Lichens, an alga and a fungus, are an example of mutualism. The alga provides food for the lichen, and the fungus provides the moisture.

In some relationships, one species suffers and the other species benefits. This type of interaction can be parasitism or predation. In parasitism, the parasite takes nourishment from its host, and leaves the host in a weakened state. In predation, the predator kills and eats its prey.

Another harmful interaction that many people are not aware of is amensalism. In this interaction, one species produces a chemical that inhibits the other and prevents it from sharing the same resources. The species that produces the substance is not affected by it. Amensalism is more common among plants and probably evolved long ago because the chemical compounds involved seem to be normal metabolic wastes. These chemicals are known as antimetabolites or antibiotics.

The resins in conifers and the latex in milkweeds are two examples of antibiotic compounds. These compounds are effective against most animals that may try to eat the plant. The giant coastal redwoods produce an antibiotic that is found in their bark. The compound inhibits the growth of lichens, mosses, and other plants that could otherwise live on the surface of the bark. This compound may be responsible for the ability of redwood lumber to resist rotting and termite destruction.

The walnut tree shows amensalism, but in an indirect way. The tree produces a nontoxic substance called juglone. It is present in the leaves, fruit, and tissues of the tree. The fruit and leaves fall to the ground and release juglone into the soil. In the soil, the juglone is oxidized to a substance that inhibits the growth of certain plants, such as heaths and broadleaf herbs.

Molds, fungi, and bacteria also produce antibiotics. In particular, soil fungi secrete antibiotics so powerful that only a small amount is needed to inhibit the growth of competing organisms. The products of amensalism also have medicinal purposes; they are used frequently to fight bacterial infections.

Questions:

1. What is amensalism? the interaction between two species in which one species inhibits the second
2. Why is amensalism considered a negative interaction? One species is prevented by another species from obtaining resources that it needs to survive.
3. In the desert shrub community, it is not unusual to see soft chaparral growing in the middle of a circular patch devoid of any other plant growth. At the edge of the circle, extending outward, plant life flourishes. How might you explain this phenomenon? What type of interaction does it represent? The soft chaparral must give off an antibiotic that inhibits the growth of other plants. The interaction is an example of amensalism.

Investigation Worksheet — Chapter 33

Name ______ Date ______

Problem: How does one measure soil humus? (text page 710)

Data and Observations:

TABLE 33-2. MEASUREMENT OF GAS PRODUCTION

Soil sample	Type/location of soil sample	Volume of gas formed by humus
A	Garden, top 10 cm	32 mL*
B	Garden, 30 cm below A	5 mL
C	Sand	3mL
D	Playground	8mL
E	Empty lot	22mL

*Student data may vary.

Questions and Conclusion:

1. Define: (a) soil (b) topsoil (c) humus. (a) upper covering of earth, composed of minerals, rock particles, and humus (b) uppermost and most fertile zone of soil (c) rich layer of soil containing decayed remains of living matter
2. Hydrogen peroxide (H_2O_2) reacts chemically with humus (mainly carbon) to form oxygen gas. In this investigation: (a) What gas was formed during the reaction? (b) What chemical was the source of this gas? (c) Where was the gas observed or collected? (a) oxygen (b) hydrogen peroxide (c) at the top of the cylinder
3. The amount of gas produced by a soil sample is directly related to the amount of humus contained in it. (a) Which sample produced the most gas? (b) Which sample contained the most humus? (c) Which sample produced the least gas? (d) Which sample contained the least humus? (a) Answers will vary. (b) Answer should agree with answer 3(a). (c) Answers will vary. (d) Answer should agree with answer 3(c).

Investigation Worksheet — Chapter 33

Name ____________ Date ____________

4. (a) Describe the source of humus in soil. (b) Considering your answer to 4(a), explain why samples A and B, even though they were both taken from the same place, had different amounts of humus present. (a) dead organic matter such as plants, animals, and microbes (b) Most organic matter is near the surface of the soil. Sample A was from the top of the soil, while B was from an area deeper in the soil.

5. Water retention and mineral availability to plants is improved by the amount of humus present in soil. (a) Which soil sample would possibly be best for growing plants? (b) Explain. (c) Which soil sample would possibly be worst for growing plants? Explain. (a) should be the sample showing the greatest volume of gas collected (b) This soil sample has the greatest amount of humus present. (c) should be sample showing the lowest volume of gas collected; This soil sample has the lowest amount of humus present.

Conclusion: How does one measure soil humus? Mix soil with hydrogen peroxide. The volume of oxygen gas produced will correlate with the amount of humus present in the soil sample.

Skills — Chapter 34

Name ____________ Date ____________

Factors Influencing Succession

Succession is characterized by progressive changes in species, structure, and energy flow. It involves a gradual and continuous replacement of species until the community is completely replaced.

Succession in areas that are not inhabited already is called primary succession. Rocks and bare cliffs are common sites of primary succession. Succession that continues from a state in which organisms are already present is called secondary succession. Secondary succession occurs in areas disturbed by humans, animals, or natural forces.

Fire. No matter what stage of succession a community is in, fire always retards succession. However, sometimes fire is vital to maintain a particular biome. For example, prairie fires often inhibit succession in grasslands by destroying any young hardwood trees. The fires burn the exposed parts of the grasses, but the roots survive. Shrubs and very young hardwood trees cannot survive the hot prairie fires. Thus, only the grasses grow and maintain the prairie biome.

Lumbering. Removal of a forest by methods such as clear-cutting returns the land to an earlier stage of succession. Because sunlight and nutrients are now available for the smaller plants, the cut area fills in with herbs, shrubs, and seedlings of trees. The shrub stage passes into the "even-aged pole forest," characterized by trees 10 to 20 centimeters in diameter. Eventually, the area becomes a mature forest again.

Grazing. Grazing by wild or domestic animals can stop succession or even reverse it. The first grasses in a prairie are short. Later, tall-grass species move into the area. American bison stop succession as they graze on the taller grass. Thus, the grazing bison permit the short grass to remain the dominant vegetative life form. Overgrazing by domestic animals also can change a grassland into a desert.

Cultivation. Cultivation turns back succession. If plots of grassland and young forests are turned into farmland but are not carefully managed, erosion by both wind and water can render the land useless. The water and wind can remove the nutrient-rich topsoil and expose the hard clay subsoil. Crops cannot grow in the subsoil, so the land is abandoned. Often, the vegetation natural to the area cannot grow in the subsoil. As a result, new forms of vegetation colonize the area and change the entire flora of the ecosystem.

Succession of a barren area almost always begins with grasses. Next, the low shrubs move into the area, followed by high shrubs. Eventually there is a shrub-tree mixture. The young trees grow and shut out the sunlight from the forest floor. Many of the shrubs are not able to survive and soon disappear from the community. The low-tree community matures into a high-tree forest.

Questions:

1. In terms of succession, why are fires important to certain biomes? Fires help to maintain certain biomes, such as the prairie.
2. How could the succession of a forest be affected by lumbering practices? Lumbering can turn back the land to an earlier stage of succession.
3. How can overgrazing reverse the succession of a grassland ecosystem? The land becomes barren, and different grasses colonize the area.

Essay — Chapter 34

Name ____________ Date ____________

The Succession of Mount St. Helens

On May 18, 1980, Mount St. Helens exploded. The powerful jolt caused an extremely large portion of the mountain's north face to slide away. Hot gases, steam, and gritty ash rocketed out. Trees toppled or were torn from their trunks, leaving ragged stumps. The top layer of soil was stripped away. The hot gases burned everything they contacted.

Millions of flying insects died from the heat and fell from the sky. The blast also killed an estimated 11 million fish, one million birds, 5000 deer, 200 black bears, and 1500 Roosevelt elk. Millions of metric tons of ash smothered the scorched terrain.

Ever since 1980, life has been creeping back into the landscape. In 1983, Congress created the Mount St. Helens National Volcanic Monument. The monument will remain unplanted and will serve as a location where succession can be studied.

Some of the life at Mount St. Helens was not destroyed by the volcanic eruption. Many organisms living in the soil at the time of the blast escaped the hot ash that covered the slopes. Plants that were buried in the snow also survived. Those plants whose roots survived the explosion were some of the first to spring up. The shoots of fireweed and bracken ferns were observed poking through the ash only 10 days after the blast.

Insects were the first animals to come into the area. Daily, insects were carried to Mount St. Helens on wind currents. Spiders spun parachute webs that they used to sail into the very center of the devastated area. The quick return of the insects surprised some ecologists because many thought that plants would have to become well-established first. But, some insects seem to do well without plants. For example, the ground beetle survived high up on the barren mountain, feeding strictly on airborne insects.

In addition to the insects, wind currents also carried new seeds and spores into the area. Rain and its runoff attacked the ash covering, digging gullies where new seeds and spores could sprout. Pocket gophers and earthworms tilled the soil from beneath the ash, giving still more places for the seeds and spores to sprout.

Spirit Lake and many other freshwater lakes were devastated by the blast. Meta Lake was more fortunate. It was covered by a thick layer of ice and snow at the time of the eruption. As a result, most of the aquatic organisms living in the lake survived. Trout and crayfish are two types of animals that have been observed inhabiting the lake.

It did not take long for mammals and birds to migrate to Mount St. Helens. Elk and deer now graze there. Birds feed on insects, seeds of flowers, and grasses. Squirrels and mice forage for food. Tracks of black bears, beavers, and bobcats have been found along a few clear-running streams in which salmon have been observed spawning.

Eight years after the blast, Mount St. Helens is teeming with life. Virtually every species that lived in the region before the eruption has returned. Some of the young evergreens that were wrapped in protective snow on the day of the blast are now over 3 meters tall. Succession is well underway. Mount St. Helens is healing. However, ecologists estimate that it may be several centuries before the area returns to its original state.

Questions:

1. What were the first animals to reappear at Mount St. Helens? insects
2. Pocket gophers are usually considered more of an enemy to plants than an ally because they eat plants and damage them when burrowing. In the succession of Mount St. Helens, how are the gophers considered helpful? The gophers bring up the soil from beneath the ash, thus making soil available.
3. What forms of life would you expect to find in Meta Lake besides trout and crayfish? Answers will vary. Students may say snails, water plants, and other kinds of fish.
4. It is not unusual for snowfall to last on Mount St. Helens until May. If the volcano had erupted in July instead of May, how might the succession be different than that now observed? Answers will vary. The initial stages of succession might have been slower.

Investigation Worksheet — Chapter 34

Name ____________ Date ____________

Problem: How do biomes of North America differ? (text page 734)

Data and Observations:

TABLE 34-1. KEY TO NORTH AMERICAN BIOMES

Biome	Color	Average Temperature	Average Precipitation	Major Plant Forms	Major Animal Forms
Tundra	black	−11.5	.57	lichens, shrubs, moss	mice, moles, lemmings, hares, polar bears, reindeer
Taiga	blue	2.0	3.0	spruce, firs	moose, caribou, weasels, mink
Temperate forest	red	15.9	9.2	deciduous trees such as oak, maple	insects, birds, squirrels, bears
Grassland	green	12.5	7.2	grass	antelopes, rabbits, gophers, ground-nesting birds
Chaparral	brown	15.2	3.1		
Desert	yellow	9.3	1.3	cacti, peyote	jackrabbit, kangaroo rat, horned toad
Tropical forest	orange	24.6	21.8	lianas, bromeliads, no dominant tree species	tree frogs, arthropods, arboreal animals

Questions and Conclusion:

1. Define: (a) biome (b) climatogram (c) precipitation. (a) communities having the same major life forms and climate (b) a graph that depicts monthly temperature and precipitation (c) rainfall
2. Using your climatograms, describe how the pattern of precipitation differs during the seasons in a (a) chaparral versus a desert (b) grassland versus a chaparral. (a) Precipitation in the chaparral is greater, but there is no rainfall from June through August. (b) Highest rainfall in a grassland biome is during the summer months, while in a chaparral rainfall is its lowest during this time.
3. Make an estimate as to the length of the growing season for plants in (a) tundra (b) taiga (c) chaparral (d) tropical forest (e) grassland. (a) 3 months (b) 7 months (c) 9 months (d) 12 months (e) 10 months

Investigation Worksheet — Chapter 34

Name ______________________ Date ______________________

4. Which biome appears to have the: (a) highest annual average precipitation (b) lowest annual average precipitation (c) highest annual average temperature (d) lowest annual average temperature (e) largest area in North America (f) smallest area in North America? (a) rain forest (b) tundra (c) tropical forest (d) tundra (e) taiga (f) chaparral
5. The map of North America is marked off in degrees of latitude. In general, (a) how do the biomes change in regard to annual precipitation and temperature as one moves farther north in latitude (b) how do these changes affect the type of plant life present? (a) Both decrease. (b) The type of plant life will differ in a biome depending on availability of moisture and length of growing season.
6. (a) What biome do you live in? (b) Based on your climatograms and your completed map of North America, describe the average annual precipitation, high and low months of precipitation, average annual temperature, high and low months of temperature, and expected type of vegetation present in the biome where you live. (a) Answers will vary. (b) Answers will vary.

Conclusion: How do biomes of North America differ? They differ in average annual temperature and precipitation; plant and animal life forms present.

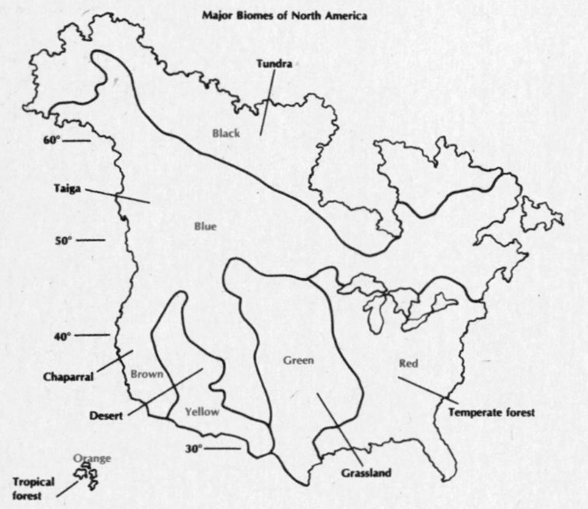

Essay — Chapter 35

Name ______________________ Date ______________________

The Effects of DDT

Dichloro-diphenyl-trichloroethane, or DDT, was synthesized in 1874 by a German chemist. Its importance, however, was not recognized until 1939. That year Paul Müller, a research chemist in Switzerland, tested various chemicals for their insecticidal properties. He discovered the effectiveness of DDT. In 1941, the Swiss used DDT to successfully combat the Colorado potato beetle, and in 1943, the United States also confirmed DDT's effectiveness. In 1948 Müller received the Nobel Prize for his discovery.

DDT is highly toxic to insects and low in toxicity to mammals, especially humans. During World War II, DDT was used to control mosquitoes. It was sprayed on the walls of tropical houses to control insects and insect-borne diseases such as malaria and yellow fever. It was used to control the cotton boll weevil and to improve agricultural and forestry yields.

The miracle of DDT was short-lived. When exposed to pesticides, such as DDT, insect populations build up an immunity. Because DDT lowered the population of the pests, it also indirectly lowered the populations of insect predators. Immunity and lack of predators allowed the pest population to make a rapid comeback. DDT is a broad-spectrum pesticide that persists in the general environment. Its broad toxicity assured that it would affect many organisms other than insects, such as crabs and fish. Its persistence assured that repeated use would enable DDT to accumulate in the environment. In 1945, these dangers were cited by biologists Clarence Cottam and Elmer Higgins of the U.S. Fish and Wildlife Service. Despite this warning, DDT was still used.

By the 1960s, studies showed that DDT was accumulating in the soils of forests in Maine and New Brunswick. Mountain lakes were contaminated with DDT. Penguins and seals in Antarctica had DDT residues in their bodies. Virtually every organism on Earth contained measurable quantities of DDT.

Since living systems obtain energy, water, and nutrients from their environment, they also may accumulate persistent toxins, such as DDT. The accumulation of DDT within the food chain of a marsh was well documented. The water contained concentrations of DDT residues of less than 0.001 ppm, or parts per million. Plankton contained residues between 0.01 and 0.1 ppm; fish contained a few ppm. Birds, especially carnivorous and scavenging birds, contained 10–100 ppm of DDT residues.

Perhaps the most observable effects of DDT on carnivorous birds were seen in the peregrine falcon, the osprey, and the bald eagle. Ospreys feed on fish. DDT residues in the fish caused the birds to produce soft-shelled eggs that were easily broken in the nest. As a result, there were few or no offspring. Within a few years, the osprey population declined. The peregrine falcon and the bald eagle faced similar fates.

The problems associated with broad-spectrum toxins such as DDT were presented in a book written by Rachel Carson. The book, *Silent Spring*, was published in 1962 and focused attention on the effects of pesticides on the environment. A young lawyer, Victor Yannacone, obtained an injunction against the use of DDT. The case was heard in court and in 1974, the Environmental Protection Agency banned the use of DDT in the United States.

Questions:

1. Why was DDT used so widely at first? It did not seem to be toxic to animals or humans and was effective in controlling insects.
2. What are some problems associated with DDT? Answers will vary. Students may say the pests build up a resistance to it; it is not effective as a long-term solution; it leads to dangerous accumulation in the food chain; it persists in the environment.
3. How did DDT help spur the environmental movement? Answers will vary. Students may say that it caused many citizens to become aware of and concerned about the effects of chemicals.

Investigation Worksheet — Chapter 35

Name ______________________ Date ______________________

Problem: What evidence is there that the greenhouse effect is occurring? (text page 750)

Data and Observations:

FIGURE 35–11.

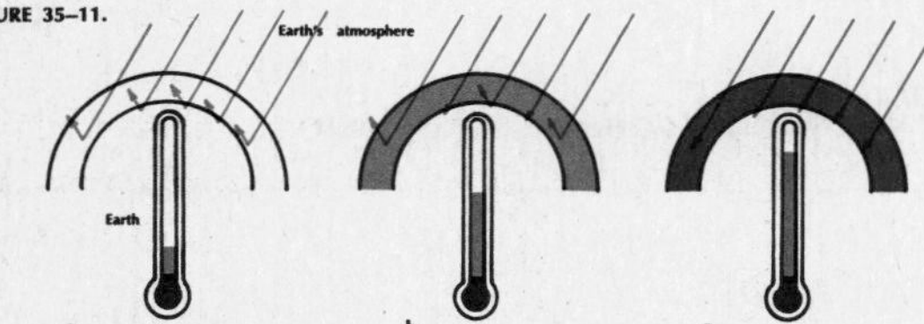

Questions and Conclusion:

1. Explain how: (a) Earth's temperature is affected by the amount of infrared radiation absorbed (b) Earth's temperature is affected by the amount of carbon dioxide present in the atmosphere. (a) The more infrared radiation absorbed, the higher the temperature. (b) Temperature rises in proportion to the amount of carbon dioxide present.
2. (a) Explain how your graphs support your answer to question 1(b). (b) Does the trend seen in years past seem to continue into the year 2000? (c) What is the expected average temperature change by the year 2000? (d) What is the expected change of carbon dioxide in ppm by the year 2000? (a) The graphs show that as carbon dioxide levels increased, so did the temperatures. (b) yes (c) It will rise by 0.8° C. (d) 352 ppm
3. There are several causes for increased carbon dioxide levels in our atmosphere. One is the burning of fossil fuels. A second cause is the continued destruction of forests for agricultural use. (a) What are fossil fuels? (b) List several ways in which the burning of fossil fuels may be lessened. (c) Explain how destruction of forests can increase the amount of carbon dioxide in the atmosphere. (d) List several ways to reduce the destruction of forests. (a) coal, oil, gasoline, natural gas (b) replace them with nuclear fuel, solar heat, and wind; restrict the use of automobiles (c) Decreased photosynthesis will result in more carbon dioxide present in the air. (d) conservation of forests, reforestation, more efficient use of current agricultural lands
4. Predict several outcomes if Earth's average temperature were to rise even a few degrees because of the greenhouse effect. Ice at the polar caps would melt, resulting in a rise in ocean levels and flooding of coastal areas.

Conclusion: What evidence is there that the greenhouse effect is occurring? Earth's atmosphere is warming due to the increase of carbon dioxide gas.

Safety Symbols

The *Biology: Living Systems* Program uses several safety symbols to alert you to possible laboratory dangers. These safety symbols are explained below. Be sure that you understand each symbol before you begin an investigation.

	DISPOSAL ALERT This symbol appears when care must be taken to dispose of materials properly.		ANIMAL SAFETY This symbol appears whenever live animals are studied and the safety of the animals and the student must be ensured.
	BIOLOGICAL SAFETY This symbol appears when there is danger involving bacteria, fungi, or protists.		RADIOACTIVE SAFETY This symbol appears when radioactive materials are used.
	OPEN FLAME ALERT This symbol appears when use of an open flame could cause a fire or an explosion.		CLOTHING PROTECTION SAFETY This symbol appears when substances used could stain or burn clothing.
	THERMAL SAFETY This symbol appears as a reminder to use caution when handling hot objects.		FIRE SAFETY This symbol appears when care should be taken around open flames.
	SHARP OBJECT SAFETY This symbol appears when a danger of cuts or puncture caused by the use of sharp objects exists.		EXPLOSION SAFETY This symbol appears when the misuse of chemicals could cause an explosion.
	FUME SAFETY This symbol appears when chemicals or chemical reactions could cause dangerous fumes.		EYE SAFETY This symbol appears when a danger to the eyes exists. Safety goggles should be worn when this symbol appears.
	ELECTRICAL SAFETY This symbol appears when care should be taken when using electrical equipment.		POISON SAFETY This symbol appears when poisonous substances are used.
	PLANT SAFETY This symbol appears when poisonous plants or plants with thorns are handled.		CHEMICAL SAFETY This symbol appears when chemicals used can cause burns or are poisonous if absorbed through the skin.